MEN AT WAR

Here are twenty-six of the best war stories of all time, selected by Ernest Hemingway, winner of the Nobel Prize for Literature.

Among the authors represented in *Men at War* are William Faulkner, T. E. Lawrence, Winston Churchill, Tolstoy, C. S. Forester, Rudyard Kipling, and many others.

There is much great reading in this book and one of the finest things in it is Hemingway's introduction. In his personal statement about war and men, he tells how and why he gathered together this outstanding collection of stories. It is Hemingway's definitive effort to show what war and death and heroism mean to men in terms of the great military writing of all time.

EDITOR'S NOTE

The editor wishes to thank Colonel Charles Sweeny, Lt.-Col. John W. Thomason, and Maxwell E. Perkins for the invaluable aid and advice they have given in the editing of this book

PUBLISHER'S NOTE

Acknowledgments are due to William Kozlenko for the plan from which this book was developed, and for the suggestion of a number of stories; also to Edmund Fuller, Fred C. Rodewald, Albert Seadler and the many others whose suggestions and contributions helped to make this book.

Men at War

Edited with an introduction by
ERNEST HEMINGWAY

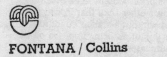
FONTANA / Collins

This shortened version of the Crown Publishers' Edition
was first published in Fontana Books December 1966
Second Impression February 1969
Third Impression November 1972

This collection © Fontana Books 1966
Printed in Great Britain
Collins Clear-Type Press London and Glasgow

TO
JOHN, PATRICK AND
GREGORY HEMINGWAY

CONTENTS

CONTENTS

Introduction*

BY

ERNEST HEMINGWAY

Edited for the 1966 Fontana edition

THIS book will not tell you how to die. Some cheer-leaders of war can always get out a pamphlet telling the best way to go through that small but necessary business at the end. PM may have published it already in a special Sunday issue with pictures. They might even have it bound up as a companion piece to the issue I read in November 1941 entitled "How We Can Lick Japan in Sixty Days."

No. This book will not tell you how to die. This book will tell you, though, how all men from the earliest times we know have fought and died. So when you have read it you will know that there are no worse things to be gone through than men have been through before.

The editor of this anthology, who took part and was wounded in the last war to end war, hates war and hates all the politicians whose mismanagement, gullibility, cupidity, selfishness and ambition brought on this present war and made it inevitable. But once we have a war there is only one thing to do. It must be won. For defeat brings worse things than any that can ever happen in a war.

When you go to war as a boy you have a great illusion of immortality. Other people get killed; not you. It can happen to other people; but not to you. Then when you are badly wounded the first time you lose that illusion and you know it can happen to you. After being severely wounded two weeks before my nineteenth birthday I had a bad time until I figured it out that nothing could happen to me that had not happened to all men before me. Whatever I had to do men had always done. If they had done it then I could do it too and the best thing was not to worry about it.

I was very ignorant at nineteen and had read little and I remember the sudden happiness and the feeling of having a permanent protecting talisman when a young British officer I met when in the hospital first wrote out for me, so that I could remember them, these lines:

* written in 1942.

7

"*By my troth, I care not: a man can die but once; we owe God a death . . . and let it go which way it will, he that dies this year is quit for the next.*"

That is probably the best thing that is written in this book and, with nothing else, a man can get along all right on that. But I would have given anything for a book like this which showed what all the other men that we are a part of had gone through and how it had been with them.

The material has not been grouped chronologically but is rather placed under certain arbitrary heads and divisions. These divisions were made by probably the most intelligent writer on the metaphysics of war that ever lived, General Karl von Clausewitz. There could have been more divisions; just as the book could have been twice as long.

In the last war there was no really good true war book during the entire four years of the war. The only true writing that came through during the war was in poetry. One reason for this is that poets are not arrested as quickly as prose writers would be if they wrote critically since the latter's meaning, if they are good writers, is too uncomfortably clear. The last war, during the years 1915, 1916, 1917, was the most colossal, murderous, mismanaged butchery that has ever taken place on earth. Any writer who said otherwise lied. So the writers either wrote propaganda, shut up, or fought. Of those who fought many died and we shall never know who were the fine writers who would have come out of the war who died in it instead.

But after the war the good and true books finally started to come out. They were mostly all by writers who had never written or published anything before the war. The writers who were established before the war had nearly all sold out to write propaganda during it and most of them never recovered their honesty afterwards. All of their reputations steadily slumped because a writer should be of as great probity and honesty as a priest of God. He is either honest or not, as a woman is either chaste or not, and after one piece of dishonest writing he is never the same again.

A writer's job is to tell the truth. His standard of fidelity to the truth should be so high that his invention, out of his experience, should produce a truer account than anything factual can be. For facts can be observed badly; but when a good writer is creating something, he has time and scope to make it of an absolute truth. If, during a war, conditions are such that a writer cannot publish the truth because its publication would do harm to the State he should write and

8

not publish. If he cannot make a living without publishing he can work at something else. But if he ever writes something which he knows in his inner self is not true, for no matter what patriotic motives, then he is finished. After the war the people will have none of him because he, whose obligation is to tell them truth, has lied to them. And he will never be at peace with himself because he has deserted his one complete obligation.

Sometimes this loss of his good name will not show during his lifetime because such critics, as have also sold out in wartime, will keep his reputation bolstered up along with their own, so long as they are functioning. But when such a writer dies, or a new generation of critics comes, the whole thing collapses.

In selecting the material for this book I found nothing that was useable in the books which were published during the last war. The nearest thing to useable material was an account of a trench raid by Arthur Guy Empey who wrote that glorified mug's-eye view of trench warfare called " Over the Top." But it was such a pitiful piece of bravado writing beside the solid magnificence of Private Frank Richards's writing that it was like comparing the Brooklyn Dodger fan who jumps on the field and slugs an umpire with the beautiful professional austerity of Arky Vaughan, the Brooklyn third baseman. Read Frank Richards, who also wrote that neglected masterpiece, " Old Soldier Sahib," for the finest account of the last war by a professional soldier serving in the ranks that has ever been written.

To clean away the scent of Private Peat that still lingers in the corners of our lecture halls and sweetens our library shelves this book publishes a part of " Her Privates We " originally published, unexpurgated, in a limited edition in England as, " The Middle Parts of Fortune." It is the finest and noblest book of men in war that I have ever read. I read it over once each year to remember how things really were so that I will never lie to myself nor to anyone else about them.

As they get further and further away from a war they have taken part in all men have a tendency to make it more as they wish it had been rather than how it really was. So each year in July, the anniversary of the month when I got the big wound, I read " The Middle Parts of Fortune " and it all comes back again as though it were not yesterday, nor long ago, but as though it were this morning before daylight and you were waiting there, dry-mouthed, for it to start.

9

The only good war book to come out during the last war was "Under Fire" by Henri Barbusse. He was the first one to show us, the boys who went from school or college to the last war, that you could protest, in anything besides poetry, the gigantic useless slaughter and lack of even elemental intelligence in generality that characterised the Allied conduct of that war from 1915 through 1917. His whole book was a protest and an attitude. The attitude was that he hated it. But when you came to read it over to try to take something permanent and representative from it the book did not stand up.

Its greatest quality was his courage in writing it when he did. But the writers who came after him wrote better and truer than he did. They had learned to tell the truth without screaming. Screaming, necessary though it may be to attract attention at the time, reads badly in later years.

I would have liked to include something from "Three Soldiers" by John Dos Passos which, written under the influence of Barbusse, was the first attempt at a realistic book about the war written by an American. But in spite of its great merit, like Barbusse, as a pioneering book, on re-reading it did not stand up. Try to read it yourself and you will see what I mean. The dialogue rings false and the actual combat is completely unconvincing. There are books like that which are as exciting as a fine new play when they come out and, when you return to them after years, are as dead as the scenery of that play if you should happen on it in a storage house.

It has always been a problem to know why certain writing dates and goes bad in this manner. I think it is probably due, as much as anything, to the improper use of slang due to a defective ear. There are certain words which are a permanent, but usually unpublishable part of the language. They are how men have talked actually, when under stress, for hundreds of years. But to substitute slang expressions for these words, slang being a language which becomes a dead language at least every three years, makes a defect in writing which causes it to die as fast as the slang expressions die. It is the "Twenty-three skiddo" and "Ish ka bibble" school of American writing. Its pall, and the lack of all clarity in the combat scenes, is what makes the Dos Passos book unreadable to-day. But the writing of it was as valuable a pioneering feat in American letters as some minor Lewis or Clark's expedition into the Northwest.

There was no real literature of our Civil War, excepting the forgotten "Miss Ravenall's Conversion" by J. W. De Forest, until Stephen Crane wrote "The Red Badge of Courage." Crane wrote it before he had ever seen any war. But he had read the contemporary accounts, had heard the old soldiers, they were not so old then, talk, and above all he had seen Matthew Brady's wonderful photographs. Creating his story out of this material he wrote that great boy's dream of war that was to be truer to how war is than any war the boy who wrote it would ever live to see. It is one of the finest books of our literature because it is all as much of one piece as a great poem is.

If you want to find out how perfect a piece of writing is try to cut it for the purpose of making a selection for an anthology. I do not mean how good a thing is. There is no better writing on war than there is in Tolstoy but it is so huge and overwhelming that any amount of fights and battles can be chopped out of it and maintain all their truth and vigour and you feel no crime in the cutting. Actually "War and Peace" would be greatly improved by cutting; not by cutting the action, but by removing some of the parts where Tolstoy tampered with the truth to make it fit his conclusions. The Crane book, though, could not be cut at all. I am sure he cut it all himself as he wrote it to the exact measure of the poem it is.

Tolstoy carries the contempt of the man of common sense who has been a soldier for most generalship to such a length that it reaches true absurdity. Most generalship is as bad as he believes it to be but he took one of the few really great generals of the world and, inspired by a mystic nationalism, tried to show that this general, Napoleon, did not truly intervene in the direction of his battles but was simply a puppet at the mercy of forces completely beyond his control. Yet when he was writing of the Russians Tolstoy showed in the greatest and truest detail how the operations were directed. His hatred and contempt for Napoleon makes the only weakness in that great book of men at war.

I love "War and Peace" for the wonderful, penetrating and true descriptions of war and of people but I have never believed in the great Count's thinking. I wish there could have been someone in his confidence with authority to remove his heaviest and worst thinking and keep him simply inventing truly. He could invent more with more insight and truth than anyone who ever lived. But his ponderous and Messianic thinking was no better than many another evangelical professor of history and I learned from him to distrust my own

Thinking with a capital T and to try to write as truly, as straightly, as objectively and as humbly as possible.

The account of Bagration's rearguard action is the finest and best understood relation of such an action that I have ever read and it gives an understanding, by presenting things on a small enough scale to be completely comprehended, of what a battle is that no one has ever bettered. I prefer it to the account of Borodino, magnificent though that is. Then, too, from Tolstoy is the wonderful account of young Petya's first action and his death published here in the selection that has been titled, badly enough, for it is about much more than that and it has been presented from the viewpoint of an aristocrat, " The People's War." It has all the happiness, and freshness and nobility of a boy's first encounter with the business of war and it is as true as " The Red Badge of Courage " is true although the two boys had little in common except their youth and that they were first facing that thing which no one knows about who has not done it.

They represent, too, the difference between a first cavalry action and the first action of a foot soldier. A man with a horse is never as alone as a man on foot, for a horse will take you where you cannot make your own legs go. Just as a mechanised force, not by virtue of their armour, but by the fact that they move mechanically, will advance into situations where you could put neither men nor animals; neither get them up there nor hold them there.

After mechanised troops have had enough experience, so that they appreciate accurately the degree of danger involved in their movements, then the same limits in what they will do are reached. It has been one of the great advantages, in the tank warfare in Northern Africa, which the Germans have held that their Commander-in-Chief has always been up with the tanks to see that his orders have been carried out rather than to assume they would be carried out simply because they had been given. He could thus make decisions on the spot and change orders which had become impossible of execution. He was there in person to see that they were obeyed.

In the civil war in Spain the tanks of both sides in early 1937 were completely vulnerable to the effective Russian anti-tank gun, which was employed on the Republican side, and to the even better German anti-tank weapon which was being first used then by the Franco troops, and there were never enough tanks to use them in proper force so that their possibilities had to be always be deduced rather than proven.

There we learned much about the mentality of men in armoured vehicles functioning under the worst possible conditions for their morale.

I have seen a French tank company commander turn up at five o'clock in the morning for an attack so drunk he could not stand, having tried, with brandy, to bolster himself up to have nerve enough to make the attack which he was convinced, from careful study of the ground the day before, was hopeless in the force with which it had to be made. He never got his tanks up to the starting point and was shot, quite properly, that afternoon with only one week more to go on the time he had enlisted for. He had been a good officer at the start, but the necessity to do things in insufficient force and the constant improvement of the German anti-tank guns had, coupled with the approach of the end of his term of enlistment, made him worthless and dangerous.

We learned later that the attack had been a complete surprise. The anti-tank guns which had been in that sector had been removed to another part of the front where the attack had been expected and the French officer could have completed his enlistment with a victorious action. But it was a relief to everyone when he was shot because the amount of fear he was carrying around with him was dangerous, disgusting, and embarrassing. In the next action, a week later, when his tanks were used, very sound elements of infantry were detailed to keep close behind the disgraced tanks with anti-tank grenades and blow them up if they did not keep moving as ordered.

The moral of this digression is, as stated above, that a horse will carry a man in his first action where his legs might not go; and a mechanised vehicle will carry him further than a horse will go; but finally no mechanised vehicle is any better than the heart of the man who handles the controls. So learn about the human heart and the human mind in war from this book. There is much about them in here.

The best account of actual human beings behaving during a world shaking event is Stendhal's picture of young Fabrizio at the battle of Waterloo. That account is more like war and less like the nonsense written about it than any other writing could possibly be. Once you have read it you will have been at the battle of Waterloo and nothing can ever take that experience from you. You will have to read Victor Hugo's account of the same battle, which is a fine, bold, majestic painting of the whole tragedy, to find out what you saw there as you rode with the boy; but you will have actually seen the field of Waterloo already whether you understand it or not. You will have seen a small piece of war as closely and as clearly with Stendhal as any man has ever written of it. It is the classic account of a routed army and beside it all of Zola's piled on detail in his "Debacle" is as dead and unconvincing as a steel engraving. Stendhal served with Napoleon and saw some of the greatest battles of the world. But all he ever wrote about war is the one long passage from "Le Chartreuse de Parme" which is included, complete, in this book.

It was at Waterloo that General Cambronne, when called on to surrender, was supposed to have said, "The Old Guard dies but never surrenders!" What Cambronne actually said was, "Merde!" which the French, when they do not wish to pronounce it, still refer to as, "the word of Cambronne." It corresponds to our four letter word for manure. All the difference between the noble and the earthly accounts of war is contained in the variance between these two quotations. The whole essence of how men speak in actual war is in Stendhal.

This war is only a continuation of the last war. France was not beaten in 1940. France was beaten in 1917. Singapore was not really lost in 1942. It was lost at Gallipoli and on the Somme and in the mud of Passchendaele. Austria was not destroyed in 1938. Austria was destroyed in the battle of Vittorio-Veneto at the end of October in 1918. It was really lost and gone when it failed to beat Italy after Caporetto in the great Austrian victory offensive of the 15th of June, 1918.

All of history is of one piece and it is ourselves, who bore the least weight of casualties in 1917 and 1918, who have to bear the most to defeat Germany this time. Once a nation has entered into a policy of foreign wars, there is no withdrawing. If you do not go to them then they will come to you. It was April 1917 that ended our isolation—it was not Pearl Harbour.

But there will be no lasting peace, nor any possibility of a just peace, until *all lands* where the people are ruled, exploited and governed by any government whatsoever against their consent are given their freedom. This premise has implications which have no place in this introduction.

There is no space to comment on each of the selections in

this book. You will discover for yourself the fascination and lucidity of Sir Charles Oman, the great commentator and historian of the art of war in the Middle Ages. You have in "The Battle of Hastings" the account of the last great effort to use the Teutonic infantry tactics which had once ruled Europe against the rising tide of the feudal cavalry, which was to be the dominant arm for the next two hundred and fifty years until it, in turn, succumbed to the English longbow at Crecy.

Since war is made up of all the elements under which certain selections are listed in this book and since all the selections deal with war, many of them would fit as well under one head as under another. Especially, since war is the province of chance, are there many other stories that could be classified under that fifth division of material.

For a wonderful narrative of the part chance plays in our history, read, "The Stolen Railroad Train," by Marquis James. For excitement and for a great story which should do much to make us appreciate and understand our British allies, read, "Turn About," by William Faulkner.

Charles Nordhoff and James Norman Hall's account of an all day air fight is as different from modern war in the air as the battle of Cannae is from a Commando raid; but you can appreciate the element of chance when you realise that but for the lucky appearance of a French Spad pilot, we would never have had the "Mutiny on the Bounty" trilogy. That is, if it is autobiographical. If it isn't, read it anyway.

If you like the Marbot extract in this book, you must read more of him. It is worth learning French to read the three volumes of his memoirs alone. None of the four great young cavalry leaders of Napoleon left memoirs. Colbert was killed by a sniper in Spain, Sainte-Croix was hit by a shell from an English gunboat in the same Peninsular campaign; Lasalle was killed at Wagram when the battle was all but over, and Montbrun died at Borodino. You know about the life they led and their battles, though, from reading Marbot. That he should have lived to write the book is a miracle.

When reading the memoirs of fighting soldiers, I am always reminded of the story of old Marshal Lefebvre who was entertaining a boyhood friend who could not conceal his envy of the Marshal-Duke's elaborate residence in Paris. "So you are jealous, eh?" the Marshal peered at him. "Eh bien, come out to the garden and I'll have twenty shots at you at thirty paces. If I miss you, then you can have the house and grounds and all that's in it. I was shot at a thousand times from as close range as that before I got this house."

This introduction is written by a man, who, having three sons to whom he is responsible in some ways for having brought them into this unspeakably balled-up world, does not feel in any way detached or impersonal about the entire present mess we live in. Therefore, be pleased to regard this introduction as absolutely personal rather than impersonal writing.

This book has been edited in order that those three boys, as they grow to the age where they can appreciate it and use it and will need it, can have the book that will contain truth about war as near as we can come by it, which was lacking to me when I needed it most. It will not replace experience. But it can prepare for and supplement experience. It can serve as a corrective after experience.

This year, the mother of the oldest boy, who is eighteen, had asked me to have a talk with him about the war in case he should be worried about it in any way. So when we were driving back in the car from the airfield where he had just flown in to spend the few days of vacation that were all he would get before the summer term started at college, I said, "Mother thought you might be worried a little about the war and going to it and all."

"No, Papa," he said. "Don't you worry about that. I'm not worried at all."

"The one thing I really know," I told him, "is that worrying doesn't do any good about anything."

"Don't you worry," he said. "I'm not worried."

That was the end of that conversation. No, worrying does no good. Neither for children nor for their parents. A good soldier does not worry. He knows that nothing happens until it actually happens and you live your life up until then. Danger only exists at the moment of danger. To live properly in war, the individual eliminates all such things as potential danger. Then a thing is only bad when it is bad. It is neither bad before nor after. Cowardice, as distinguished from panic, is almost simply a lack of ability to suspend the functioning of the imagination. Learning to suspend your imagination and live completely in the very second of the present minute with no before and no after is the greatest gift a soldier can acquire. It, naturally, is the opposite of all those gifts a writer should have. That is what makes good writing by good soldiers such a rare thing and why it is so prized when we have it.

You never know how people will react to war. Take self-inflicted wounds. In one famous International Brigade which fought at the battle of Guadalajara so valiantly and well that they made history there in that eight-day battle, there were thirty-seven self-inflicted wounds in the first afternoon the Brigade was in action. That was panic. There is a sure cure for self-inflicted wounds; much more efficacious than court-martial and execution when the offence is proven as was practised in the world war.

It was discovered in the snow and mud of the plateau above Brihuega with that March wind blowing against the constant rolling roar of automatic weapon fire and it consists of loading all the self-inflicted wounded into a truck; taking away their coats and blankets so their comrades in the lines can have that much more warmth; and driving them back to the town of Guadalajara where all the men's wounds were dressed, and then returning the bandaged men to their sections in the line.

After that treatment there were no more self-inflicted wounds in that Brigade except head wounds. Any man who would rather shoot himself in the head than run the chance that the enemy might eventually do that same thing can be, and is, written off as a hopeless coward and listed under, " Died of Wounds and Other Causes."

There was much trouble with self-inflicted wounds in Italy during the last war. The men became very skilful at it and often a pair would team up to shoot each other, usually wrapping sandbags around the arm or leg, to avoid any evidence of a close discharge of the rifle. Others would hold copper coins in their armpits to get a yellow cast of complexion and simulate jaundice. Others deliberately contracted venereal disease in order to leave the lines. There were doctors in Milan who did a thriving trade in injecting paraffin under the kneecaps of their clients to induce lameness. Mussolini himself was wounded superficially in the legs and backside by the premature explosion of an Italian trench mortar in the early years of the war and never returned to the front. I have often thought that all his martial bombast and desire for military glory was a defence mechanism, formed against his own knowledge of how frightened he had been in the world war and the ignominious exit he had made from it at the first opportunity.

17

Against the type of cowardice, or more often panic and stupidity, that produces self-inflicted wounds, I will always remember one marvellous story of the deprecation the truly brave man can feel for them. Evan Shipman, one of my oldest friends, a fine poet and good prose writer, had gone to France in order to drive an ambulance on the Loyalist side in the Spanish Civil War. Our State Department had refused to validate his passport for Spain, so he took the smuggler's route over the Pyrenees border between France and Spain with a group of recruits for the International Brigades. They were all caught by the French gendarmerie and sentenced to a jail term in Toulouse.

Being jailed made Evan so indignant that he determined, instead of driving an ambulance, that he would enlist in the infantry of the Brigades. After coming out of jail he successfully entered Spain by another route and in a short time was at the front, and in the battle of Brunete, one of the fiercest fought of all that war. He fought all through the battle with exemplary courage, staying with the Franco-Belge battalion to whom he had been attached as an interpreter and a runner, and fighting in the fine stand they made against orders which prevented a rout at the very most critical time, and on the last day was severely wounded.

I did not see him for some months and when I did he was pale, ragged, limping and profoundly cheerful.

" Tell me about when you were wounded," I said by the time we had settled down to a drink.

"Why, Hem, it was absolutely nothing. It was nothing at all. I never felt a thing."

"What do you mean, you didn't feel a thing?" The machine gun bullet had gone through his thigh from one side to the other.

"Why, it was really nothing. You see I was unconscious at the time."

" Yes?"

" You see the planes had just caught us in the open and bombed us and I was unconscious at the time. So I didn't feel a thing when they came down and machine gunned us. Really, Hem, it was absolutely nothing. I've hardly even thought of it as a wound. It was almost like having an anæsthetic beforehand."

He turned his drink around in his hand and then said, " Hem, I can never thank you enough for having brought me over here. I was very upset that you might be worried about me. I want you to know that being in Spain is the happiest time I have ever had in my life. Please believe me, Hem. You really must believe me absolutely."

You can set that against all the self-inflicted wound cases. Evan Shipman is a private now in an Armoured unit of the U.S. Army. He was turned down innumerable times by medical examiners, but finally built up enough weight to get a doctor to pass him. He wrote me from where his unit is stationed, "I picked up a copy of 'The Red Badge of Courage,' here in the library and it seems even better than when I first read it."

There is no space now to recommend all the other things you should absolutely read in this book. If I did not think they were all good they would not be in.

This collection of stories, accounts, and narratives is an attempt to give a true picture of men at war. It is not a propaganda book. It seeks to instruct and inform rather than to influence anyone's opinion. Its only and absolute standard for inclusion has been the soundness and truth of the material.

I have seen much war in my lifetime and I hate it profoundly. But there are worse things than war; and all of them come with defeat. The more you hate war, the more you know that once you are forced into it, for whatever reason it may be, you have to win it. You have to win it and get rid of the people that made it and see that, this time, it never comes to us again. We who took part in the last war to end wars are not going to be fooled again. This war is going to be fought until that objective is achieved; if it takes a hundred years if necessary, and no matter whom we have to fight to gain that objective in the end.

WAR IS PART OF THE INTERCOURSE OF THE HUMAN RACE

We say, therefore, War belongs not to the province of Arts or Sciences, but to the province of social life. It is a conflict of great interests which is settled by bloodshed and only in that is it different from others. It would be better, instead of comparing it with Art, to liken it to business competition, which is also a conflict of human interests and activities and it is still more like State politics, which again, on its part, may be looked upon as a kind of business competition on a great scale. Besides, State politics is the womb in which War is developed, in which its outlines lie hidden in a rudimentary state, like the qualities of living creatures in their embryos.

THE BATTLE OF HASTINGS, 1066 A.D.

Charles Oman

As the last great example of an endeavour to use the old infantry tactics of the Teutonic races against the now fully-developed cavalry of feudalism, we have to describe the battle of Hastings, a field which has been fought over by modern critics almost as fiercely as by the armies of Harold Goldwineson and William the Bastard.

About the political and military antecedents of the engagement we have no need to speak at length. Suffice it to say that the final defeat of the old English thegnhood was immediately preceded by its most striking victory. In the summer of 1066 the newly-chosen King Harold was forced to watch two enemies at once. The Norman Duke William had openly protested against the election that had taken place in January, and was known to be gathering a great army and fleet at St. Valery. Harold knew him well, and judged him a most formidable enemy; he had called out the available naval strength of his realm, and a strong squadron was waiting all through June, July, and August, ranging between the Isle of Wight and Dover, ready to dispute the passage of the

From: *History of the Art of War in the Middle Ages,* by Charles Oman.

Channel. At the same time the earls and sheriffs had been warned to have the land forces of the realm ready for mobilisation, and the king with his housecarles lay by the coast in Sussex waiting for news. Duke William came not, for many a week; his host took long to gather, and when his ships were ready, August turned out a month of persistent storm and northerly winds, unsuited for the sailing of a great armament.

Meanwhile there was danger from the North also. King Harold's rebel brother, Earl Tostig, had been hovering off the coast with a small squadron, and had made a descent on the Humber in May, only to be driven away by the Northumbrian Earl Edwin. But Tostig had leagued himself with Harald Hardrada, the warlike and greedy King of Norway, and a Norse invasion was a possibility, though it seemed a less immediate danger than the Norman threat to the South Coast. September had arrived before either of the perils materialised.

By a most unlucky chance the crisis came just when the English fleet had run out of provisions, after keeping the sea for three months. On September 8, Harold ordered it round to London to revictual, and to refit, for it had suffered in the hard weather. It was to resume its cruising as soon as possible. Seven days later came the news that a Norwegian fleet of three hundred sail had appeared off the Yorkshire coast, and had ravaged Cleveland and taken Scarborough. Harold was compelled to commit the guard of the Channel to the winds, which had hitherto served him well, and to fly north with his housecarles to face Hardrada's invasion. On his way he got the disastrous message that the two Earls Edwin of Northumbria and Morkar of Mercia had been beaten in a pitched battle at Fulford, in front of York (September 20), and that the city was treating for surrender. Pressing on with all possible speed, the English king arrived at York in time to prevent this disaster, and the same afternoon he brought the Norsemen to action at Stamford Bridge on the Derwent, seven miles from the city. Here he inflicted on them an absolutely crushing defeat—Hardrada was slain, so was the rebel Earl Tostig, and the invading host was so nearly exterminated that the survivors fled on only twenty-four ships, though they had brought three hundred into the Humber.

The details of the fight are absolutely lost—we cannot unfortunately accept one word of the spirited narrative of the *Heimskringla,* for all the statements in it that can be tested are obviously incorrect. Harold *may* have offered his rebel brother pardon and an earldom, and have promised his Norse ally no more than the famous " seven feet of English earth, since his stature is greater than that of other men." The Vikings *may* have fought for long hours in their shieldring, and have failed at evening only, when their king had been slain by a chance arrow. But we cannot trust a saga which says that Morkar was King Harold Godwineson's brother, and fell at Fulford; that Earl Waltheof (then a child) took part in the fight, and that the English army was mostly composed of cavalry and archers. The whole tale of the *Heimskringla* reads like a version of the battle of Hastings transported to Stamford Bridge by some incredible error. The one detail about it recorded in the Anglo-Saxon Chronicle, namely, that the fighting included a desperate defence of the bridge against the pursuing English, does *not* appear in the Norse narrative at all. We can only be sure that both sides must have fought on foot in the old fashion of Viking and Englishman, " hewing at each other across the war-linden " till the beaten army was well-nigh annihilated.

Meanwhile, on September 28—two days after Stamford Bridge—William of Normandy had landed at Pevensey, unhindered either by the English fleet, which was refitting at London, or by the king's army, which had gone north to repel the Norwegians. The invaders began to waste the land, and met with little resistance, since the king and his chosen warriors were absent. Only at Romney, as we are told, did the landsfolk stand to their arms and beat off the raiders.

Meanwhile the news of William's landing was rapidly brought to Harold at York, and reached him—as we are told—at the very moment when he was celebrating by a banquet his victory over the Northmen. The king received the message on October 1 or October 2 : he immediately hurried southward to London with all the speed that he could make. The victorious army of Stamford Bridge was with him, and the North Country levies of Edwin and Morkar were directed to follow as fast as they were able. Harold reached London on the 7th or 8th of October, and stayed there a few days to gather in the fyrd of the neighbouring shires of the South Midlands. On the 11th he marched forth from the city to face Duke William, though his army was still incomplete. The slack or treacherous earls of the North had not yet brought up their contingents, and the men of the western shires had not been granted time enough to reach the mustering place. But Harold's heart had been stirred by the reports of the cruel ravaging of Kent and Sussex by the Normans, and he was resolved to put his cause to the arbitrament of battle as quickly as possible, though the delay of a few days would perhaps have doubled his army. A rapid march of two days brought him to the outskirts of the Andredsweald, within touch of the district on which William had for the last fortnight been exercising his cruelty.

Harold took up his position at the point where the road from London to Hastings first leaves the woods, and comes forth into the open land of the coast. The chosen ground was the lonely hill above the marshy bottom of Senlac, on which the ruins of Battle Abbey stand, but then marked to the chronicler only by "the hoar apple tree" on its ridge, just as Ashdown had been marked two centuries before by its aged thorn.

The Senlac position consists of a hill some 1100 yards long and 150 yards broad, joined to the main bulk of the Wealden Hills by a sort of narrow isthmus with steep descents on either side. The road from London to Hastings crosses the isthmus, bisects the hill at its highest point, and then sinks down into the valley, to climb again the opposite ridge of Telham Hill. The latter is considerably the higher of the two, reaching 441 feet above the sea-level, while Harold's hill is but 275 at its summit. The English hill has a fairly gentle slope towards the south, the side which looked towards the enemy, but on the north the fall on either side of the isthmus is so steep as to be almost precipitous. The summit of the position, where it is crossed by the road, is the highest point. Here it was that King Harold fixed his two banners, the Dragon of Wessex, and his own standard of the Fighting Man.

The position was very probably one that had served before for some army of an older century, for we learn from the best authorities that there lay about it, especially on its rear, ancient banks and ditches, in some places scarped to a precipitous slope. Perhaps it may have been the camp of some part of Alfred's army in 893-894, when, posted in the east end of the Andredsweald, between the Danish fleet which had come ashore at Lymne and the other host which had camped at Middleton, he endeavoured from his central position to restrain their ravages in Kent and Sussex. No place indeed could have been more suited for a force observing newly-landed foes. It covers the only road from London which then pierced the Andredsweald, and was so close to its edge that the defenders could seek shelter in the impenetrable woods if they wished to avoid a battle.

The hill above the Senlac bottom, therefore, being the obvious position to take, for an army whose tactics compelled it to stand upon the defensive, Harold determined to offer battle there. We need not believe the authorities who tell us that the King had been thinking of delivering a night attack upon the Normans, if he should chance to find them scattered abroad on their plundering, or keeping an inefficient lookout. It was most unlikely that he should dream of groping in the dark through eight miles of rolling ground, to assault a camp whose position and arrangements must have been unknown. His army had marched hard from London, had apparently only reached Senlac at nightfall, and must have been tired out. Moreover, Harold knew William's capacities as a general, and could not have thought it likely that he would be caught unprepared. It must have seemed to him a much more possible event that the Norman might refuse to attack the strong Senlac position, and offer battle in the open and nearer the sea. It was probably in anticipation of some such chance that Harold ordered his fleet, which had run back into the mouth of the Thames in very poor order some four weeks back, to refit itself and sail round the North Foreland, to threaten the Norman vessels now drawn ashore under the cover of a wooden castle at Hastings. He can scarcely have thought it likely that William would retire over seas on the news of his approach, so the bringing up of the fleet must have been intended either to cut off the Norman retreat in the event of a great English victory on land, or to so molest the invader's stranded vessels that he would be forced to return to the shore in order to defend them.

The English position is said by one narrator of the battle to have been entrenched. According to Wace, the latest and most diffuse of our authorities, Harold ordered his men to rear a fence of plaited woodwork from the timber of the forest which lay close at their backs. But the earlier chroniclers, without exception, speak only of the shield-wall of the English, of their dense mass covering the crest of the hill, and of relics of ancient fortifications, the *antiquus agger* and *frequentia fossarum*, and *fovea magna* mentioned above. There is nothing inconceivable in the idea of Harold's having used the old Danish device of palisading a camp, save that he had arrived only on the preceding night, and that his army was weary. In the morning hours of October 14 little could have been done, though between daybreak and the arrival of the Norman host there were certainly three long hours. But it is difficult to suppose that if any serious entrenching had been carried out, the earlier Norman narrators of the fight would have refrained from mentioning it, since the more formidable the obstacles opposed to him, the more notable and creditable would have been the triumph of their duke. And the Bayeux Tapestry, which (despite all destructive criticism) remains a primary authority for the battle, appears to show no traces of any breastwork covering the English front. Probably Wace, writing from oral tradition ninety years after the battle, had heard something of the *frequentia fossarum* mentioned by William of Poictiers, and the *agger* described by Orderic, and translated them into new entrenchments, which he described as works of the best military type of his day.

From end to end of the crest of the hill the English host was ranged in one great solid mass. Probably its line extended from the high road, which crosses the summit nearer to its eastern than to its western side, for some 200 yards to the left, as far as the head of the small steep combe (with a rivulet at its bottom) which lies 200 yards to the due east of the modern parish church; while on the other, or western, side of the high road, the battle-front was much longer, running from the road as far as the upper banks of the other ravine (with a forked brook flowing out of it from two sources) which forms the western flank of the hill. From the road to this ravine there must have been a front of 800 or 850 yards. Harold's two standards were, as we know, set up on the spot which was afterwards marked by the high altar of Battle Abbey. His standing-place must therefore have been in the left-centre rather than in the absolute middle-front of the line. But the spot was dictated by the lie of the ground—here is the actual highest point of the hill, 275 feet above sea-level, while the greater part of the position is along the 250 feet contour. It was the obvious place for the planting of standards to be visible all around, and a commander standing by them could look down from a slight vantage-ground on the whole front of his host.

In this array, the English centre being slightly curved forward, its flank slightly curved back, the army looked to the Normans more like a circular mass than a deployed line. Although the Northumbrian and West-country levies were still missing, the army must have numbered many thousands, for the fyrd of south and central England was present in full force, and stirred to great wrath by the ravages of the Normans. It is impossible to guess at the strength of the host: the figures of the chroniclers, which sometimes swell up to hundreds of thousands, are wholly useless. As the position was about 1100 yards long, and the space required by a single warrior swinging his axe or hurling his javelin was some three feet, the front rank must have been at least some eleven hundred or twelve hundred strong. The hilltop was completely covered by the English, whose spear-shafts appeared to the Norman like a wood, so that they cannot have been a mere thin line: if they were some eight or ten deep, the total must have reached ten or eleven thousand men. Of these the smaller part must have been composed of the fully-armed warriors, the king's housecarles, the thegnhood, and the wealthier and better-equipped freemen, the class owning some five hides of land. The rudely-armed levies of the fyrd must have constituted the great bulk of the army: they bore, as the Bayeux Tapestry shows, the most miscellaneous arms—swords, javelins, clubs, axes, a few bows, and probably even rude instruments of husbandry turned to warlike uses. Their only defensive armour was the round or kite-shaped shield: body and head were clothed only in the tunic and cap of everyday wear.

In their battle array we know that the well-armed housecarles—perhaps two thousand chosen and veteran troops—were grouped in the centre around the king and the royal standards. The fyrd, divided no doubt according to its shires, was ranged on either flank. Presumably the thegns and other fully-armed men formed its front ranks, while the peasantry stood behind and backed them up, though at first only able to hurl their weapons at the advancing foe over the heads of their more fully-equipped fellows.

We must now turn to the Normans. Duke William had undertaken his expedition not as the mere feudal head of the barons of Normandy, but rather as the managing director of a great joint-stock company for the conquest of England, in which not only his own subjects, but hundreds of adventurers, poor and rich, from all parts of western Europe had taken shares. At the assembly of Lillebonne the Norman baronage had refused in their corporate capacity to undertake the vindication of their duke's claims on England. But all, or nearly all, of them had consented to serve under him as volunteers, bringing not merely their usual feudal contingent, but as many men as they could get together. In return they were to receive the spoils of the island kingdom if the enterprise went well. On similar terms William had accepted offers of help from all quarters: knights and sergeants flocked in, ready, " some for land and some for pence," to back his claim. It seems that, though the native Normans were the core of the invading army, yet the strangers considerably outnumbered them on the muster-rolls. Great nobles like Eustace Count of Boulogne, the Breton Count Alan Fergant, and Haimar of

Thouars were ready to risk their lives and resources on the chance of an ample profit. French, Bretons, Flemings, Angevins, knights from the more distant regions of Aquitaine and Lotharingia, even—if Guy of Amiens speaks truly—stray fighting men from among the Norman conquerors of Naples and Sicily, joined the host.

Many months had been spent in the building of a fleet at the mouth of the Dive. Its numbers, exaggerated to absurd figures by many chroniclers, may possibly have reached the six hundred and ninety-six vessels given to the duke by the most moderate estimate. What was the total of the warriors which it carried is as uncertain as its own numbers. If any analogies may be drawn from contemporary hosts, the cavalry must have formed a very heavy proportion of the whole. In continental armies the foot-soldiery were so despised that an experienced general devoted all his attention to increasing the numbers of his horse. If we guess that there may have been three thousand or even four thousand mounted men, and eight thousand or nine thousand foot-soldiers, we are going as far as probability carries us, and must confess that our estimate is wholly arbitrary. The most modest figure given by the chroniclers is sixty thousand fighting men; but, considering their utter inability to realise the meaning of high numbers, we are dealing liberally with them if we allow a fifth of that estimate.

After landing at Pevensey on September 28, William had moved to Hastings and built a wooden castle there for the protection of his fleet. It was then in his power to have moved on London unopposed, for Harold was only starting on his march from York. But the duke had resolved to fight near his base, and spent the fortnight which was at his disposal in the systematic harrying of Kent and Sussex. When his scouts told him that Harold was at hand, and had pitched his camp by Senlac hill, he saw that his purpose was attained; he would be able to fight at his own chosen moment, and at only a few miles' distance from his ships. At daybreak on the morning of October 14, William bade his host get in array, and marched over the eight miles of rolling ground which separate Hastings and Senlac. When they reached the summit of the hill at Telham, the English position came in sight, on the opposite hill, not much more than a mile away.

On seeing the hour of conflict at hand, the duke and his knights drew on their mail-shirts, which, to avoid fatigue, they had not yet assumed, and the host was arrayed in battle order. The form which William had chosen was that of three parallel corps, each containing infantry and cavalry. The centre was composed of the native contingents of Normandy; the left mainly of Bretons and men from Maine and Anjou; the right, of French and Flemings. But there seem to have been some Normans in the flanking divisions also. The duke himself, as was natural, took command in the centre, the wings fell respectively to the Breton Count Alan Fergant and to Eustace of Boulogne: with the latter was associated Roger of Montgomery, a great Norman baron.

In each division there were three lines: the first was composed of bowmen mixed with arbalesters: the second was composed of foot-soldiery armed not with missile weapons but with pike and sword. Most of them seem to have worn mail-shirts, unlike the infantry of the English fyrd. In the rear was the really important section of the army, the mailed knights. We may presume that William intended to harass and thin the English masses with his archery, to attack them seriously with his heavy infantry, who might perhaps succeed in getting to close quarters and engaging the enemy hand to hand; but evidently the crushing blow was to be given by the great force of horsemen who formed the third line of each division.

The Normans deployed on the slopes of Telham, and then began their advance over the rough valley which separated them from the English position.

When they came within range, the archery opened upon the English, and not without effect; at first there must have been little reply to the showers of arrows, since Harold had but very few bowmen in his ranks. The shield-wall, moreover, can have given but a partial protection, though it no doubt served its purpose to some extent. When, however, the Normans advanced farther up the slope, they were received with a furious discharge of missiles of every kind, javelins, lances, taper-axes, and even—if William of Poictiers is to be trusted—rude weapons more appropriate to the neolithic age than to the eleventh century, great stones bound to wooden handles and launched in the same manner that was used for the casting-axe. The archers were apparently swept back by the storm of missiles, but the heavy armed foot pushed up to the front of the English line and got to hand-to-hand fighting with Harold's men. They could, however, make not the least impression on the defenders, and were perhaps already recoiling when William ordered up his cavalry. The horsemen rode up the slope already strewn with corpses, and dashed into the fight. Foremost among them was a minstrel name Taillefer, who galloped forward cheering on his comrades, and playing like a *jongleur* with his sword, which he kept casting into the air and then catching again. He burst right through the shield-wall and into the English line, where he was slain after cutting down several opponents. Behind him came the whole Norman knighthood, chanting their battle-song, and pressing their horses up the slope as hard as they could ride. The foot-soldiery dropped back—through the intervals between the three divisions, as we may suppose—and the duke's cavalry dashed against the long front of the shield-wall, whose front rank men they may have swept down by their mere impetus. Into the English mass, however, they could not break: there was a fearful crash, and a wild interchange of blows, but the line did not yield at any point. Nay, more, the assailants were ere long abashed by the fierce resistance that they met; the English axes cut through shield and mail, lopping off limbs and felling even horses to the ground. Never had the continental horsemen met such infantry before. After a space the Bretons and Angevins of the left wing felt their hearts fail, and recoiled down the hill in wild disorder, many men unhorsed and overthrown in the marshy bottom at the foot of the slope. All along the line the onset wavered, and the greater part of the host gave back, though the centre and right did not fly in wild disorder like the Bretons. A rumour ran along the front that the duke had fallen, and William had to bare his head and to ride down the ranks, crying that he lived, and would yet win the day, before he could check the retreat of his warriors. His brother Odo aided him to rally the waverers, and the greater part of the host was soon restored to order.

As it chanced, the rout of the Norman left wing was destined to bring nothing but profit to William. A great mass of the shire-levies on the English right, when they saw the Bretons flying, came pouring after them down the hill. They had forgotten that their sole chance of victory lay in keeping their front firm till the whole strength of the assailant should be exhausted. It was mad to pursue when two thirds of the hostile army was intact, and its spirit still unbroken. Seeing the tumultuous crowd rushing after the flying Bretons, William wheeled his centre and threw it upon the flank of the pursuers. Caught in disorder, with their ranks broken and scattered, the rash peasantry were ridden down in a few moments. Their light shields, swords, and javelins availed them nothing against the rush of the Norman horse, and the whole horde, to the number of several thousands, were cut to pieces. The great bulk of the English host, however, had not followed the routed Bretons, and the duke saw that his day's work was but begun. Forming up his disordered squadrons, he ordered a second general attack on the line. Then followed an encounter even more fierce than the first. It would appear that the fortune of the Normans was somewhat better in this than in the earlier struggle: one or two temporary breaches were made in the English mass, probably in the places where it had been weakened by the rash onset of the shire-levies an hour before. Gyrth and Leofwine, Harold's two brothers, fell in the forefront of the fight, the former by William's own hand, if we may trust one good contemporary authority. Yet, on the whole, the duke had got little profit by his assault: the English had suffered severe loss, but their long line of shields and axes still crowned the slope, and their cries of " Out! out!" and " Holy Cross!" still rang forth in undaunted tones.

A sudden inspiration then came to William, suggested by the disaster which had befallen the English right in the first conflict. He determined to try the expedient of a feigned flight, a stratagem not unknown to Bretons and Normans of earlier ages. By his orders a considerable portion of the assailants suddenly wheeled about and retired in seeming disorder. The English thought, with more excuse on this occasion than on the last, that the enemy was indeed routed, and for the second time a great body of them broke the line and rushed after the retreating squadrons. When they were well on their way down the slope, William repeated his former procedure. The intact portion of his host fell upon the flanks of the pursuers, while those who had simulated flight faced about and attacked them in front. The result was again a foregone conclusion: the disordered men of the fyrd were hewn to pieces, and few or none of them escaped back to their comrades on the height. But the slaughter in this period of the fight did not fall wholly on the English; a part of the Norman troops who had carried out the false flight suffered some loss by falling into a deep ditch,—perhaps the remains of old entrenchments, perhaps the " rhine " which drained the Senlac bottom, —and were there smothered or trodden down by the comrades who rode over them. But the loss at this point must have been insignificant compared with that of the English.

Harold's host was now much thinned and somewhat shaken, but, in spite of the disasters which had befallen them, they drew together their thinned ranks, and continued the fight. The struggle was still destined to endure for many hours, for the most daring onsets of the Norman chivalry could not yet burst into the serried mass around the standards. The bands which had been cut to pieces were mere shire-levies, and the well-armed housecarles had refused to break their ranks, and still formed a solid core for the remainder of the host.

The fourth act of the battle consisted of a series of vigorous assaults by the duke's horsemen, alternating with volleys of arrows poured in during the intervals between the charges. The Saxon mass was subjected to exactly the same trial which befell the British squares in the battle of Waterloo—incessant charges by a gallant cavalry mixed with a destructive hail of missiles. Nothing could be more maddening than such an ordeal to the infantry-soldier, rooted to the spot by the necessities of his formation. The situation was frightful : the ranks were filled with wounded men unable to retire to the rear through the dense mass of their comrades, unable even to sink to the ground for the hideous press. The enemy was now attacking on both flanks : shields and mail had been riven : the supply of missile spears had given out : the English could but stand passive, waiting for the night or for the utter exhaustion of the enemy. The cavalry onsets must have been almost a relief compared with the desperate waiting between the acts, while the arrow-shower kept beating in on the thinning host. We have indications that, in spite of the disasters of the noon, some of the English made yet a third sally to beat off the archery. Individuals worked to frenzy by the weary standing still, seem to have occasionally burst out of the line to swing axe or sword freely in the open and meet a certain death. But the mass held firm—" a strange manner of battle," says William of Poictiers, " where the one side works by constant motion and ceaseless charges, while the other can but endure passively as it stands fixed to the sod. The Norman arrow and sword worked on : in the English ranks the only movement was the dropping of the dead : the living stood motionless." Desperate as was their plight, the English still held out till evening; though William himself led charge after charge against them, and had three horses killed beneath him, they could not be scattered while their king still survived and their standards still stood upright. It was finally the arrow rather than the sword that settled the day : the duke is said to have bade his archers shoot not point-blank, but with a high trajectory, so that the shafts fell all over the English host, and not merely on its front ranks. One of these chance shafts struck Harold in the eye and gave him a mortal wound. The arrow-shower, combined with the news of the king's fall, at last broke up the English host : after a hundred ineffective charges, a band of Norman knights burst into the midst of the mass, hewed Harold to pieces as he lay wounded at the foot of his banners, and cut down both the Dragon of Wessex and the Fighting Man.

The remnants of the English were now at last constrained to give ground: the few thousands—it may rather have been the few hundreds—who still clung to the crest of the blood-stained hill turned their backs to the foe and sought shelter in the friendly forest in their rear. Some fled on foot through the trees, some seized the horses of the thegns and housecarles from the camp and rode off upon them. But even in retreat they took some vengeance on the conquerors. The Normans, following in disorder, swept down the steep slope at the back of the hill, scarped like a glacis and impassable for horsemen,—the back defence, as we have conjectured, of some ancient camp of other days. Many of the knights, in the confused evening light, plunged down this trap, lost their footing, and lay floundering, man and horse, in the ravine at the bottom. Turning back, the last of the English swept down on them and cut them to pieces before resuming their flight. The Normans thought for a moment that succours had arrived to join the English—and, indeed, Edwin and Morkar's Northern levies were long overdue. The duke himself had to rally them, and to silence the fainthearted counsels of Eustace of Boulogne, who bade him draw back when the victory was won. When the Normans came on more cautiously, following, no doubt, the line of the isthmus and not plunging down the slopes, the last of the English melted away into the forest and disappeared. The hard day's work was done.

The stationary tactics of the phalanx of axemen had failed decisively before William's combination of archers and cavalry, in spite of the fact that the ground had been favourable to the defensive. The exhibition of desperate courage on the part of the English had only served to increase the number of the slain. Of all the chiefs of the army, only Esegar the Staller and Leofric, Abbot of Bourne, are recorded to have escaped, and both of them were dangerously wounded. The king and his brothers, the stubborn housecarles, and the whole thegnhood of Southern England had perished on the field. The English loss was never calculated; practically it amounted to the entire army. Nor is it possible to guess that of the Normans: one chronicle gives twelve thousand,—the figure is absurd, and the authority is not a good or a trustworthy one for English history. But whatever was the relative slaughter on the two sides, the lesson of the battle was unmistakable. The best of infantry, armed only with weapons for close fight and destitute of cavalry support, were absolutely helpless before a capable general who knew how to combine the horseman and the archer. The knights, if unsupported by the bowmen, might have surged for ever against the impregnable shield-wall. The archers, unsupported by the knights, could easily have been driven off the field by a general charge. United by the skilful hand of William, they were invincible.

THE CAVALRY CHARGE AT OMDURMAN

Winston Churchill

Long before the dawn we were astir, and by five o'clock the
21st Lancers were drawn up mounted outside the zeriba. My
squadron-leader Major Finn, an Australian by birth, had
promised me some days before that he would give me "a show"
when the time came. I was afraid that he would count my
mission to Lord Kitchener the day before as quittance; but
I was now called out from my troop to advance with a patrol
and reconnoitre the ridge between the rocky peak of Jebel
Surgham and the river. Other patrols from our squadron
and from the Egyptian cavalry were also sent hurrying forward
in the darkness. I took six men and a corporal. We trotted
fast over the plain and soon began to breast the unknown slopes
of the ridge. There is nothing like the dawn. The quarter
of an hour before the curtain is lifted upon an unknowable
situation is an intense experience of war. Was the ridge held by
the enemy or not? Were we riding through the gloom into
thousands of ferocious savages? Every step might be deadly;
yet there was no time for overmuch precaution. The regiment
was coming on behind us, and dawn was breaking. It was
already half light as we climbed the slope. What should we
find at the summit? For cool, tense excitement I commend
such moments.

Now we are near the top of the ridge. I make one man
follow a hundred yards behind, so that whatever happens, he
may tell the tale. There is no sound but our own clatter. We
have reached the crest line. We rein in our horses. Every
minute the horizon extends; we can already see 200 yards.
Now we can see perhaps a quarter of a mile. All is quiet;
no life but our own breathes among the rocks and sand
hummocks of the ridge. No ambuscade, no occupation in
force! The farther plain is bare below us: we can now
see more than half a mile.

So they have all decamped! Just what we said! All bolted off
to Kordofan; no battle! But wait! The dawn is growing
fast. Veil after veil is lifted from the landscape. What is
this shimmering in the distant plain? Nay—it is lighter now

From: *A Roving Commission.* Copyright 1930, 1939 by
Scribners.

—what are these dark markings beneath the shimmer? *They are there!* These enormous black smears are thousands of men; the shimmering is the glinting of their weapons. It is now daylight. I slip off my horse; I write in my field service notebook " The Dervish army is still in position a mile and a half south-west of Jebel Surgham." I send this message by the corporal direct as ordered to the Commander-in-Chief. I mark it XXX. In the words of the drill book " with all despatch " or as one would say " Hell for leather."

A glorious sunrise is taking place behind us; but we are admiring something else. It is already light enough to use field-glasses. The dark masses are changing their values. They are already becoming lighter than the plain; they are fawn-coloured. Now they are a kind of white, while the plain is dun. In front of us is a vast array four or five miles long. It fills the horizon till it is blocked out on our right by the serrated silhouette of Surgham Peak. This is an hour to live. We mount again, and suddenly new impressions strike the eye and mind. These masses are not stationary. They are advancing, and they are advancing fast. A tide is coming in. But what is this sound which we hear: a deadened roar coming up to us in waves? They are cheering for God, his Prophet and his holy Khalifa. They think they are going to win. We shall see about that presently. Still I must admit that we check our horses and hang upon the crest of the ridge for a few moments before advancing down its slopes.

But now it is broad morning and the slanting sun adds brilliant colour to the scene. The masses have defined themselves into swarms of men, in ordered ranks bright with glittering weapons, and above them dance a multitude of gorgeous flags. We see for ourselves what the Crusaders saw. We must see more of it. I trot briskly forward to somewhere near the sandhills where the 21st Lancers had halted the day before. Here we are scarcely 400 yards away from the great masses. We halt again and I make four troopers fire upon them, while the other two hold their horses. The enemy come on like the sea. A crackle of musketry breaks out on our front and to our left. Dust spurts rise among the sandhills. This is no place for Christians. We scamper off; and luckily no man nor horse is hurt. We climb back on to the ridge, and almost at this moment there returns the corporal on a panting horse. He comes direct from Kitchener with an order signed by the Chief of Staff. " Remain as long as possible, and report how the masses of attack are moving." Talk of Fun! Where will you beat this! On horseback, at daybreak, within shot of an advancing army, seeing everything, and corresponding direct with Headquarters.

So we remained on the ridge for nearly half an hour and I watched close up a scene which few have witnessed. All the masses except one passed for a time out of our view beyond the peak of Surgham on our right. But one, a division of certainly 6,000 men moved directly over the shoulder of the ridge. Already they were climbing its forward slopes. From where we sat on our horses we could see both sides. There was our army ranked and massed by the river. There were the gunboats lying expectant in the stream. There were all the batteries ready to open. And meanwhile on the other side, this large oblong gay-coloured crowd in fairly good order climbed swiftly up to the crest of exposure. We were about 2,500 yards from our own batteries, but little more than 200 from the approaching target. I called these Dervishes " The White Flags." They reminded me of the armies in the Bayeux Tapestries, because of their rows of white and yellow standards held upright. Meanwhile the Dervish centre far out in the plain had come within range, and one after another the British and Egyptian batteries opened upon it. My eyes were rivetted by a nearer scene. At the top of the hill " The White Flags " paused to rearrange their ranks and drew out a broad and solid parade along the crest. Then the cannonade turned upon them. Two or three batteries and all the gunboats, at least thirty guns, opened an intense fire. Their shells shrieked towards us and burst in scores over the heads and among the masses of the White Flag-men. We were so close, as we sat spellbound on our horses, that we almost shared their perils. I saw the full blast of Death strike this human wall. Down went their standards by dozens and their men by hundreds. Wide gaps and shapeless heaps appeared in their array. One saw them jumping and tumbling under the shrapnel bursts; but none turned back. Line after line they all streamed over the shoulder and advanced towards our zeriba, opening a heavy rifle fire which wreathed them in smoke.

Hitherto no one had taken any notice of us; but I now saw Baggara horsemen in twos and threes riding across the plain on our left towards the ridge. One of these patrols of three men came within pistol range. They were dark, cowled figures, like monks on horseback—ugly, sinister brutes with long spears. I fired a few shots at them from the saddle, and they sheered off. I thought we could edge back towards the Nile and so watch both sides while keeping out of harm's way. But now arrived a positive order from Major Finn, whom I had perforce left out of my correspondence with the Commander-in-Chief, saying "Come back at once into the zeriba as the infantry are about to open fire." We should in fact have been safer on the ridge, for we only just got into the infantry lines before the rifle-storm began.

It is not my purpose in this record of personal impressions to give a general account of the Battle of Omdurman. The story has been told so often and in such exact military detail that everyone who is interested in the subject is no doubt well acquainted with what took place. I shall only summarise the course of the battle so far as may be necessary to explain my own experiences.

The whole of the Khalifa's army, nearly 60,000 strong, advanced in battle order from their encampment of the night before, topped the swell of ground which hid the two armies from one another, and then rolled down the gently-sloping amphitheatre in the arena of which, backed upon the Nile, Kitchener's 20,000 troops were drawn up shoulder to shoulder to receive them. Ancient and modern confronted one another. The weapons, the methods and the fanaticism of the Middle Ages were brought by an extraordinary anachronism into dire collision with the organisation and inventions of the nineteenth century. The result was not surprising. As the successors of the Saracens descended the long smooth slopes which led to the river and their enemy, they encountered the rifle fire of two and a half divisions of trained infantry, drawn up two deep and in close order and supported by at least 70 guns on the river bank and in the gunboats, all firing with undisturbed efficiency. Under this fire the whole attack withered and came to a standstill, with a loss of perhaps six or seven thousand men, at least 700 yards away from the British-Egyptian line. The Dervish army, however, possessed nearly 20,000 rifles of various kinds, from the most antiquated to the most modern, and when the spearmen could get no farther, these riflemen lay down on the plain and began a ragged, unaimed but considerable fusillade at the dark line of the thorn-fence zeriba. Now for the first time they began to inflict losses on their antagonists, and in the short space that this lasted perhaps two hundred casualties occurred among the British and Egyptian troops.

Seeing that the attack had been repulsed with great slaughter and that he was nearer to the city of Omdurman than the Dervish army, Kitchener immediately wheeled his five brigades into his usual echelon formation, and with his left flank on the river proceeded to march south towards the city, intending thereby to cut off what he considered to be the remnants of the Dervish army from their capital, their base, their food, their water, their home, and to drive them out into the vast deserts which stared on every side. But the Dervishes were by no means defeated. The whole of their left, having overshot the mark, had not even been under fire. The Khalifa's reserve of perhaps 15,000 men was still intact. All these swarms now advanced with undaunted courage to attack the British and Egyptian forces, which were no longer drawn up in a prepared position, but marching freely over the desert. This second shock was far more critical than the first. The charging Dervishes succeeded everywhere in coming to within a hundred or two hundred yards of the troops, and the rear brigade of Soudanese, attacked from two directions, was only saved from destruction by the skill and firmness of its commander, General Hector Macdonald. However, discipline and machinery triumphed over the most desperate valour, and after an enormous carnage, certainly exceeding 20,000 men, who strewed the ground in heaps and swathes "like snowdrifts," the whole mass of the Dervishes dissolved into fragments and into particles and streamed away into the fantastic mirages of the desert.

The Egyptian cavalry and the camel corps had been protecting the right flank of the zeriba when it was attacked, and the 21st Lancers were the only horsemen on the left flank nearest to Omdurman. Immediately after the first attack had been repulsed we were ordered to leave the zeriba, ascertain what enemy forces, if any, stood between Kitchener and the city, and if possible drive these forces back and clear the way for the advancing army. Of course as a regimental officer one knows very little of what is taking place over the whole field of battle. We waited by our horses during the first attack close down by the river's edge, sheltered by the steep Nile bank from the bullets which whistled overhead. As soon as the fire began to slacken and it was said on all sides that the attack had been repulsed, a General arrived with his staff at a gallop with instant orders to mount and advance. In two minutes the four squadrons were mounted and trotting out of the zeriba in a southerly direction. We ascended again the slopes of Jebel Surgham which had played its part in the first stages of the action, and from its ridges soon saw before us the whole plain of Omdurman with the vast mud city, its minarets and domes, spread before us six or seven miles away. After various halts and reconnoitrings we found ourselves walking forward in what is called " column of troops." There are four troops in a squadron and four squadrons in a regiment. Each of these troops now followed the other. I commanded the second troop from the rear, comprising between twenty and twenty-five Lancers.

Everyone expected that we were going to make a charge. That was the one idea that had been in all minds since we had started from Cairo. Of course there would be a charge. In those days, before the Boer War, British cavalry had been taught little else. Here was clearly the occasion for a charge. But against what body of enemy, over what ground, in which direction or with what purpose, were matters hidden from the rank and file. We continued to pace forward over the hard sand, peering into the mirage-twisted plain in a high state of suppressed excitement. Presently I noticed, 300 yards away on our flank and parallel to the line on which we were advancing, a long row of blue-black objects, two or three yards apart. I thought there were about a hundred and fifty. Then I became sure that these were men—enemy men—squatting on the ground. Almost at the same moment the trumpet sounded " Trot," and the whole long column of cavalry began to jingle and clatter across the front of these crouching figures. We were in the lull of the battle and there was perfect silence. Forthwith from every blue-black blob came a white puff of smoke, and a loud volley of musketry broke the odd stillness. Such a target at such a distance could scarcely be missed, and all along the column here and there horses bounded and a few men fell.

The intentions of our Colonel had no doubt been to move round the flank of the body of Dervishes he had now located, and who, concealed in a fold of the ground behind their riflemen, were invisible to us, and then to attack them from a more advantageous quarter; but once the fire was opened and losses began to grow, he must have judged it inexpedient to prolong his procession across the open plain. The trumpet sounded " Right wheel into line," and all the sixteen troops swung round towards the blue-black riflemen. Almost immediately the regiment broke into a gallop, and the 21st Lancers were committed to their first charge in war!

I propose to describe exactly what happened to me: what I saw and what I felt. I recalled it to my mind so frequently after the event that the impression is as clear and vivid as it was a quarter of a century ago. The troop I commanded was, when we wheeled into line, the second from the right of the regiment. I was riding a handy, sure-footed, grey Arab polo pony. Before we wheeled and began to gallop, the officers had been marching with drawn swords. On account of my shoulder I had always decided that if I were involved in hand-to-hand fighting, I must use a pistol and not a sword. I had purchased in London a Mauser automatic pistol, then the newest and latest design. I had practised carefully with this during our march and journey up the river. This then was the weapon with which I determined to fight. I had first of all to return my sword into its scabbard, which is not the easiest thing to do at a gallop. I had then to draw my pistol from its wooden holster and bring it to full cock. This dual opera-tion took an appreciable time, and until it was finished, apart from a few glances to my left to see what effect the fire was producing, I did not look up at the general scene.

Then I saw immediately before me, and now only half the length of a polo ground away, the row of crouching blue figures firing frantically, wreathed in white smoke. On my right and left my neighbouring troop leaders made a good line. Immediately behind was a long dancing row of lances crouched for the charge. We were going at a fast but steady gallop. There was too much trampling and rifle fire to hear any bullets. After this glance to the right and left and at my troop, I looked again towards the enemy. The scene appeared to be suddenly transformed. The blue-black men were still firing, but behind them there now came into view a depression like a shallow sunken road. This was crowded and crammed with men rising up from the ground where they had hidden. Bright flags appeared as if by magic, and I saw arriving from nowhere Emirs on horseback among and around the mass of the enemy. The Dervishes appeared to be ten or twelve deep at the thickest, a great grey mass gleaming with steel, filling the dry water-course. In the same twinkling of an eye I saw also that our right overlapped their left, that my troop would just strike the edge of their array, and that the troop on my right would charge into air. My subaltern comrade on the right, Wormald of the 7th Hussars, could see the situation too; and we both increased our speed to the very fastest gallop and curved inwards like the horns of the moon. One really had not time to be frightened or to think of anything else but these par-ticular necessary actions which I have described. They com-pletely occupied mind and senses.

The collision was now very near. I saw immediately before me, not ten yards away, the two blue men who lay in my path. They were perhaps a couple of yards apart. I rode at the interval between them. They both fired. I passed through the smoke conscious that I was unhurt. The trooper immediately behind me was killed at this place and at this moment, whether by these shots or not I do not know. I checked my pony as the ground began to fall away beneath his feet. The clever animal dropped like a cat four or five feet down on to the sandy bed of the watercourse, and in this sandy bed I found myself surrounded by what seemed to be dozens of men. They were not thickly packed enough at this point for me to experience any actual collision with them. Whereas Grenfell's troop, next but one on my left, was brought to a complete standstill and suffered very heavy losses, we seemed to push our way through as one has sometimes seen mounted police-men break up a crowd. In less time than it takes to relate, my pony had scrambled up the other side of the ditch. I looked round.

Once again I was on the hard, crisp desert, my horse at a trot. I had the impression of scattered Dervishes running to and fro in all directions. Straight before me a man threw himself on the ground. The reader must remember that I had been trained as a cavalry soldier to believe that if ever cavalry broke into a mass of infantry, the latter would be at their mercy. My first idea therefore was that the man was terrified. But simultaneously I saw the gleam of his curved sword as he drew it back for a hamstringing cut. I had room and time enough to turn my pony out of his reach, and leaning over on the off side I fired two shots into him at about three yards. As I straightened myself in the saddle, I saw before me another figure with uplifted sword. I raised my pistol and fired. So close were we that the pistol itself actually struck him. Man and sword disappeared below and behind me. On my left, ten yards away, was an Arab horseman in a bright-coloured tunic and steel helmet, with chain-mail hang-ings. I fired at him. He turned aside. I pulled my horse into a walk and looked around.

In one respect a cavalry charge is very like ordinary life. So long as you are all right, firmly in your saddle, your horse in hand, and well armed, lots of enemies will give you a wide berth. But as soon as you have lost a stirrup, have a rein cut, have dropped your weapon, are wounded, or your horse is wounded, then is the moment when from all quarters enemies rush upon you. Such was the fate of not a few of my comrades in the troops immediately on my left. Brought to an actual standstill in the enemy's mass, clutched at from every side, stabbed at and hacked at by spear and sword, they were dragged from their horses and cut to pieces by the infuriated foe. But this I did not at the time see or understand. My impressions continued to be sanguine. I thought we were masters of the situation, riding the enemy down, scattering them and killing them. I pulled my horse up and looked about me. There was a mass of Dervishes about forty or fifty yards away on my left. They were huddling and clumping themselves together, rallying for mutual protection. They seemed wild with excitement, dancing about on their feet, shaking their spears up and down. The whole scene seemed to flicker. I have an impression, but it is too fleeting to define, of brown-clad Lancers mixed up here and there with this surging mob. The scattered individuals in my immediate neighbourhood made no attempt to molest me. Where was my troop? Where were the other troops of the squadron? Within a hundred yards of me I could not see a single officer or man. I looked back at the Dervish mass. I saw two or three riflemen crouching and aiming their rifles at me from the fringe of it. Then for the first time that morning I experienced a sudden sensation of fear. I felt myself absolutely alone. I thought these riflemen would hit me and the rest devour me like wolves. What a fool I was to loiter like this in the midst of the enemy! I crouched over the saddle, spurred my horse into a gallop and drew clear of the *mêlée*. Two or three hundred yards away I found my troop already faced about and partly formed up.

The other three troops of the squadron were reforming close by. Suddenly in the midst of the troop up sprang a Dervish. How he got there I do not know. He must have leaped out of some scrub or hole. All the troopers turned upon him thrusting with their lances: but he darted to and fro causing for the moment a frantic commotion. Wounded several times, he staggered towards me raising his spear. I shot him at less than a yard. He fell on the sand, and lay there dead. How easy to kill a man! But I did not worry about it. I found I had fired the whole magazine of my Mauser pistol, so I put in a new clip of ten cartridges before thinking of anything else.

I was still prepossessed with the idea that we had inflicted great slaughter on the enemy and had scarcely suffered at all ourselves. Three or four men were missing from my troop. Six men and nine or ten horses were bleeding from spear thrusts or sword cuts. We all expected to be ordered immediately to charge back again. The men were ready, though they all looked serious. Several asked to be allowed to throw away their lances and draw their swords. I asked my second sergeant if he had enjoyed himself. His answer was " Well, I don't exactly say I enjoyed it, Sir; but I think I'll get more used to it next time." At this the whole troop laughed.

But now from the direction of the enemy there came a succession of grisly apparitions; horses spouting blood, struggling on three legs, men staggering on foot, men bleeding from terrible wounds, fish-hook spears stuck right through them, arms and faces cut to pieces, bowels protruding, men gasping, crying, collapsing, expiring. Our first task was to succour these; and meanwhile the blood of our leaders cooled. They remembered for the first time that we had carbines. Everything was still in great confusion. But trumpets were sounded and orders shouted, and we all moved off at a trot towards the flank of the enemy. Arrived at a position from which we could enfilade and rake the watercourse, two squadrons were dismounted and in a few minutes with their fire at three hundred yards compelled the Dervishes to retreat. We therefore remained in possession of the field. Within twenty minutes of the time when we had first wheeled into line and began our charge, we were halted and breakfasting in the very watercourse that had so nearly proved our undoing. There one could see the futility of the much vaunted *Arme Blanche*. The Dervishes had carried off their wounded, and the corpses of thirty or forty enemy were all that could be counted on the ground. Among these lay the bodies of over twenty Lancers, so hacked and mutilated as to be mostly unrecognisable. In all out of 310 officers and men the regiment had lost in the space of about two or three minutes five officers and sixty-five men killed and wounded, and 120 horses—nearly a quarter of its strength.

Such were my fortunes in this celebrated episode. It is very rarely that cavalry and infantry, while still both unshaken, are intermingled as the result of an actual collision. Either the infantry keep their heads and shoot the cavalry down, or they break into confusion and are cut down or speared as they run. But the two or three thousand Dervishes who faced the 21st Lancers in the watercourse at Omdurman were not in the least shaken by the stress of battle or afraid of cavalry. Their fire was not good enough to stop the charge, but they had no doubt faced horsemen many a time in the wars with Abyssinia. They were familiar with the ordeal of the charge. It was the kind of fighting they thoroughly understood. Moreover, the fight was with equal weapons, for the British too fought with sword and lance as in the days of old.

A white gunboat seeing our first advance had hurried up the river in the hopes of being of assistance. From the crow's nest, its commander, Beatty, watched the whole event with breathless interest. Many years passed before I met this officer or knew that he had witnessed our gallop. When we met I was First Lord of the Admiralty and he the youngest Admiral in the Royal Navy. "What did it look like?" I asked him. "What was your prevailing impression?" "It looked," said Admiral Beatty, "like plum duff: brown currants scattered about in a great deal of suet." With this striking, if somewhat homely, description my account of this adventure may fittingly close.

THE INVADERS

Richard Hillary

We retired early to bed and slept until, at two o'clock in the morning, a gillie banged on the door. Colin got up, took from the gillie's hand a telegram, opened it, and read it. It said: SQUADRON MOVING SOUTH STOP CAR WILL FETCH YOU AT EIGHT OCLOCK DENHOLM. For us, the war began that night.

At ten o'clock we were back at Turnhouse. The rest of the Squadron were all set to leave; we were to move down to Hornchurch, an airdrome twelve miles east of London on the Thames Estuary. Four machines would not be serviceable until the evening and Broody Benson, Pip Cardell, Colin, and I were to fly them down. We took off at four o'clock, some five hours after the others, Broody leading, Pip and I to each side, and Colin in the box, map reading. Twenty-four of us flew south that 10th day of August 1941: of those twenty-four eight were to fly back.

We landed at Hornchurch at about seven o'clock to receive our first shock. Instead of one section there were four Squadrons at readiness; 603 Squadron were already in action. They started coming in about half an hour after we landed, smoke stains along the leading edges of the wings showing that all the guns had been fired. They had acquitted themselves well although caught at a disadvantage of height.

" You don't have to look for them," said Brian. " You have to look for a way out."

From this flight Don MacDonald did not return.

At this time the Germans were sending over comparatively few bombers. They were making a determined attempt to wipe out our entire Fighter Force and from dawn till dusk the sky was filled with Messerschmitt 109s and 110s.

Half a dozen of us always slept at the Dispersal Hut to be ready for a surprise enemy attack at dawn. This entailed being up by 4:30, and by 5:00 o'clock having our machines warmed up and the oxygen, sights, and ammunition tested. The first Hun attack usually came over about breakfast time and from then until 8:00 o'clock at night we were almost continuously in the air. We ate when we could, baked beans and bacon and eggs being sent over from the Mess.

From: *Falling Through Space,* by Richard Hillary. Reynal & Hitchcock, New York.

On the morning after our arrival I walked over with Peter Howes and Broody. Howes was at Hornchurch with another Squadron and worried because he had as yet shot nothing down. Every evening when we came into the Mess he would ask us how many we had got and then go over miserably to his room. His Squadron had had a number of losses and was due for relief. If ever a man needed it, it was Howes. Broody, on the other hand, was in a high state of excitement, his sharp eager face grinning from ear to ear. We left Howes at his Dispersal Hut and walked over to where our machines were being warmed up. The voice of the controller came unhurried over the loud speaker, telling us to take off, and in a few seconds we were running for our machines. I climbed into the cockpit of my plane and felt an empty sensation of suspense in the pit of my stomach. For one second time seemed to stand still and I stared blankly in front of me. I knew that morning I was to kill for the first time. That I might be killed or in any way injured did not occur to me. Later, when we were losing pilots regularly, I did consider it in an abstract way when on the ground; but once in the air, never. I knew it could not happen to me. I suppose every pilot knows that, knows it cannot happen to him; even when he is taking off for the last time, when he will not return, he knows that he cannot be killed. I wondered idly what he was like, this man I would kill. Was he young, was he fat, would he die with the Fuehrer's name on his lips, or would he die alone, in that last moment conscious of himself as a man? I would never know. Then I was being strapped in, my mind automatically checking the controls, and we were off.

We ran into them at 18,000 feet, twenty yellow-nosed Messerschmitt 109s, about five hundred feet above us. Our Squadron strength was eight, and as they came down on us we went into line astern and turned head on to them. Brian Carberry, who was leading the Section dropped the nose of his machine, and I could almost feel the leading Nazi pilot push forward on his stick to bring his guns to bear. At the same moment Brian hauled hard back on his own control stick and led us over them in a steep climbing turn to the left. In two vital seconds they lost their advantage. I saw Brian let go a burst of fire at the leading plane, saw the pilot put his machine into a half roll, and knew that he was mine. Automatically, I kicked the rudder to the left to get him at right angles, turned the gun button to " Fire," and let go in a four-second burst with full deflection. He came right through

47

my sights and I saw the tracers from all eight guns thud home. For a second he seemed to hang motionless; then a jet of red flame shot upwards and he spun to the ground.

For the next few minutes I was too busy looking after myself to think of anything, but when, after a short while, they turned and made off over the Channel, and we were ordered to our base, my mind began to work again.

It had happened.

My first emotion was one of satisfaction, satisfaction at a job adequately done, at the final logical conclusion of months of specialised training. And then I had a feeling of the essential rightness of it all. He was dead and I was alive; it could so easily have been the other way round; and that would somehow have been right too. I realised in that moment just how lucky a fighter pilot is. He has none of the personalised emotions of the soldier, handed a rifle and bayonet and told to charge. He does not even have to share the dangerous emotions of the bomber pilot who night after night must experience that childhood longing for smashing things. The fighter pilot's emotions are those of the duelist—cool, precise, impersonal. He is privileged to kill well. For if one must either kill or be killed, as now one must, it should, I feel, be done with dignity. Death should be given the setting it deserves; it should never be a pettiness; and for the fighter pilot it never can be.

From this flight Broody Benson did not return.

During that August-September period we were always so outnumbered that it was practically impossible, unless we were lucky enough to have the advantage of height, to deliver more than one Squadron attack. After a few seconds we always broke up, and the sky was a smoke trail of individual dogfights. The result was that the Squadron would come home individually, machines landing one after the other at intervals of about two minutes. After an hour, Uncle George would make a check-up on who was missing. Often there would be a telephone call from some pilot to say that he had made a forced landing at some other airdrome, or in a field. But the telephone wasn't always so welcome. It would be a rescue squad announcing the number of a crashed machine; then Uncle George would check it, and cross another name off the list. At that time, the losing of pilots was somehow extremely impersonal; nobody, I think, felt any great emotion—there simply wasn't time for it.

After the hard lesson of the first two days, we became more canny and determined not to let ourselves be caught from above. We would fly on the reciprocal of the course given us by the controller until we got to 15,000 feet, and then fly back again, climbing all the time. By this means we usually saw the Huns coming in below us, and were in a perfect position to deliver a Squadron attack. If caught at a disadvantage, they would never stay to fight, but always turned straight back for the Channel. We arranged a system whereby two planes always flew together—thus if one should follow a plane down the other stayed 500 feet or so above, to protect him from attack in the rear.

Often, machines would come back to their base just long enough for the ground staff, who worked with beautiful speed, to refuel them and put in a new oxygen bottle and more ammunition before taking off again. Uncle George was shot down several times but always turned up unhurt; once we thought Rusty was gone for good, but he was back leading his flight the next day; one sergeant pilot in " A " Flight was shot down four times, but he seemed to bear a charmed life.

The sun and the great height at which we flew often made it extremely difficult to pick out the enemy machines, but it was here that Shep's experience on the moors of Scotland proved invaluable. He led the guard section and always saw the Huns long before anyone else. For me the sun presented a major problem. We had dark lenses on our glasses, but I, as I have mentioned before, never wore mine. They gave me a feeling of claustrophobia. With spots on the windscreen, spots before the eyes, and a couple of spots which might be Messerschmitts, blind spots on my goggles seemed too much of a good thing; I always slipped them up on to my forehead before going into action. For this and for not wearing gloves, I paid a stiff price.

I remember once going practically to France before shooting down a 109. There were two of them, flying at sea-level and headed for the French Coast. Raspberry was flying beside me and caught one halfway across. I got right up close behind the second one and gave it a series of short bursts. It darted about in front, like a startled rabbit, and finally plunged into the sea about three miles off the French Coast.

On another occasion, I was stupid enough actually to fly over France: the sky appeared to be perfectly clear but for one returning Messerschmitt, flying very high. I had been trying to catch him for about ten minutes and was determined that he should not get away.

Eventually I caught him inland from Calais and was just about to open fire when I saw a squadron of twelve Messerschmitts coming in on my right. I was extremely frightened, but turned in towards them and opened fire at the leader. I could see his tracer going past underneath me, and then I saw his hood fly off, and the next moment they were past. I didn't wait to see any more, but made off for home, pursued for half the distance by eleven very determined Germans. I landed a good hour after everyone else to find Uncle George just finishing his check up.

From this flight Larry Cunningham did not return.

After about a week of Hornchurch, I woke late one morning to the noise of machines running up on the airdrome. It irritated me: I had a headache.

Having been on every flight the previous day, the morning was mine to do with as I pleased. I got up slowly, gazed dispassionately at my tongue in the mirror, and wandered over to the Mess for breakfast. It must have been getting on for twelve o'clock when I came out on to the airdrome to find the usual August heat haze forming a dull pall over everything. I started to walk across the airdrome to the Dispersal Point on the far side. There were only two machines on the ground so I concluded that the squadron was already up. Then I heard a shout, and our ground crew drew up in a lorry beside me. Sergeant Ross leaned out:

"Want a lift, sir? We're going round."

"No thanks, Sergeant. I'm going to cut across."

This was forbidden for obvious reasons, but I felt like that.

"O.K., sir. See you round there."

The lorry trundled off down the road in a cloud of dust. I walked on across the landing ground. At that moment I heard the voice of the controller.

"Large enemy bombing formation approaching Hornchurch. All personnel not engaged in active duty take cover immediately."

I looked up. They were still not visible. At the Dispersal Point I saw Bubble and Pip Cardell make a dash for the shelter. Three Spitfires just landed, turned about and came past me with a roar to take off down wind. Our lorry was still trundling along the road, maybe half way round, and seemed suddenly an awfully long way from the Dispersal Point.

I looked up again, and this time I saw them—about a dozen slugs, shining in the bright sun and coming straight on. At the rising scream of the first bomb I instinctively shrugged up my shoulders and ducked my head. Out of the corner of my eye I saw the three Spitfires. One moment they were about twenty feet up in close formation; the next, catapulted apart as though on elastic. The leader went over on his back and plowed along the runway with a rending crash of tearing fabric; number 2 put a wing in and spun round on his airscrew, while the plane on the left was blasted wingless into the next field. I remember thinking stupidly, " That's the shortest flight he's ever taken," and then my feet were nearly knocked from under me, my mouth was full of dirt, and Bubble, gesticulating like a madman from the shelter entrance was yelling: " Run, you bloody fool, run!" I ran. Suddenly awakened to the lunacy of my behaviour, I covered the distance to that shelter as if impelled by a rocket and shot through the entrance while once again the ground rose up and hit me, and my head smashed hard against one of the pillars. I subsided on a heap of rubble and massaged it.

" Who's here?" I asked, peering through the gloom.

" Cardell and I and three of our ground crew," said Bubble, " and, by the Grace of God, you!"

I could see by his mouth that he was still talking but a sudden concentration of the scream and crump of falling bombs made it impossible to hear him.

The air was thick with dust and the shelter shook and heaved at each explosion, yet somehow held firm. For about three minutes the bedlam continued, and then suddenly ceased. In the utter silence which followed nobody moved. None of us wished to be the first to look on the devastation which we felt must be outside. Then Bubble spoke. " Praise God!" he said. " I'm not a civilian. Of all the bloody frightening things I've ever done, sitting in that shelter was the worst. Me for the air from now on!"

It broke the tension and we scrambled out of the entrance. The runways were certainly in something of a mess. Gaping holes and great gobbets of earth were everywhere. Right in front of us a bomb had landed by my Spitfire, covering it with a shower of grit and rubble.

I turned to the aircraftsman standing beside me. " Will you get hold of Sergeant Ross and tell him to have a crew give her an inspection."

He jerked his head toward one corner of the airdrome: " I think I'd better collect the crew myself, sir. Sergeant Ross won't be doing any more inspections."

I followed his glance and saw the lorry, the roof about twenty yards away, lying grotesquely on its side. I climbed into the cockpit, and, feeling faintly sick, tested out the switches. Bubble poked his head over the side.

"Let's go over to the Mess and see what's up: all our machines will be landing down at the reserve landing field anyway."

I climbed out and walked over to find the three Spitfire pilots celebrating in the bar, quite unharmed but for a few superficial scratches, in spite of being machine-gunned by the bombers. "Operations" was undamaged: no hangar had been touched and the Officers' Mess had two windows broken.

The station commander ordered every available man and woman on to the job of repairing the airdrome surface and by four o'clock there was not a hole to be seen. Several unexploded bombs were marked off, and two lines of yellow flags were laid down to mark the runways. At five o'clock our squadron, taking off for a "flap" from the reserve field, landed safely on its home base. Thus, apart from four men killed in the lorry and a network of holes on the landing surface, there was nothing to show for ten minutes' really accurate bombing from 12,000 feet, in which several dozen sticks of bombs had been dropped. It was striking proof of the inefficacy of their attempts to wipe out our advance fighter airdromes.

Brian had a bullet through his foot, and as my machine was still out of commission, I took his place in readiness for the next show. I had had enough of the ground for one day.

Six o'clock came and went, and no call. We started to play poker and I was winning. It was agreed that we should stop at seven: should there be a "flap" between then, the game was off. I gazed anxiously at the clock. I am always unlucky at cards, but when the hands pointed to 6:55 I really began to feel my luck was on the change. But sure enough at that moment came the voice of the controller: "603 Squadron take off and patrol base: further instructions in the air."

We made a dash for our machines and within two minutes were off the ground. Twice we circled the airdrome to allow all twelve planes to get in formation. We were flying in four sections of three: red section leading, blue and green to right and left, and the three remaining planes forming a guard section above and behind us.

I was flying No. 2 in the blue section.

Over the radio came the voice of the controller: "Hullo Red Leader." And then the instructions and their acknowledgment by the leader.

As always, for the first few minutes we flew on the reciprocal of the course given until we reached 15,000 feet. We then turned about and flew on 110° in an all-out climb, thus coming out of the sun and gaining height all the way.

During the climb Uncle George was in constant touch with the ground. We were to intercept about 20 enemy fighters at 25,000 feet. I glanced across at Stapme and saw his mouth moving. That meant he was singing again. He would sometimes do this with his radio set on " send," with the result that mingled with our instructions from the ground we would hear a raucous rendering of " Night and Day." And then quite clearly over the radio I heard the Germans excitedly calling to each other. This was a not infrequent occurrence and it made one feel that they were right behind, although often they were some distance away. I switched my set to " send " and called out " Halts Maul!" and as many other choice pieces of German invective as I could remember. To my delight I heard one of them answer: " You feelthy Englishmen, we will teach you how to speak to a German." I am aware that this sounds a tall story, but several others in the Squadron were listening out and heard the whole thing.

I looked down. It was a completely cloudless sky and way below lay the English countryside, stretching lazily into the distance, a quite extraordinary picture of green and purple in the setting sun.

I took a glance at my altimeter. We were at 28,000 feet. At that moment Shep yelled " Tallyho " and dropped down in front of Uncle George in a slow dive in the direction of the approaching planes. Uncle George saw them at once.

" O.K. Lie astern."

I drew in behind Stapme and took a look at them. They were about 2,000 feet below us, which was a pleasant change, but they must have spotted us at the same moment, for they were forming a protective circle, one behind the other, which is a defence formation hard to break.

" Echelon starboard," came Uncle George's voice.

We spread out fanwise to the right.

" Going down!"

One after the other we peeled off in a power dive. I picked out one machine and switched my gun button to " Fire." At 300 yards I had him in my sights. At 200 I opened up in a long four-second burst and saw the tracer going into his nose. Then I was pulling out, so hard that I could feel my eyes dropping through my neck. Coming round in a slow climbing turn I saw that we had broken them up. The sky was now a mass of individual dog fights. Several of them had already been knocked down. One, I hoped, was mine, but on pulling up I had not been able to see the result. To my left I saw Peter Pease make a head-on attack on a Messerschmitt. They were headed straight for each other and it looked as though the fire of both was striking home. Then at the last moment the Messerschmitt pulled up taking Peter's fire full in the belly. It rolled on to its back, yellow flames pouring from the cockpit, and vanished.

The next few minutes were typical. First the sky a bedlam of machines; then suddenly silence and not a plane to be seen. I noticed then that I was very tired and very hot. The sweat was running down my face in rivulets. But this was no time for vague reflections. Flying around the sky on one's own at that time was not a healthy course of action.

I still had some ammunition left. Having no desire to return to the airdrome until it had all been used to some good purpose, I took a look around the sky for some friendly fighters. About a mile away over Dungeness I saw a formation of about forty Hurricanes on patrol at 20,000 feet. Feeling that there was safety in numbers, I set off in their direction. When about 200 yards from the rear machine, I looked down and saw 5,000 feet below another formation of fifty machines flying in the same direction. Flying stepped up like this was an old trick of the Huns, and I was glad to see we were adopting the same tactics. But as though hit by a douche of cold water, I suddenly woke up. There were far more machines flying together than we could ever muster over one spot. I took another look at the rear machine in my formation, and sure enough, there was the Swastika on its tail. Yet they all seemed quite oblivious to my presence. I had the sun behind me and a glorious opportunity. Closing in to 150 yards I let go a three-second burst into the rear machine. It flicked onto its back and spun out of sight. Feeling like an irresponsible schoolboy who has perpetrated some crime which must inevitably be found out, I glanced round me. Still nobody seemed disturbed. I suppose I could have repeated the performance on the next machine, but I felt that it was inadvisable to tempt Providence too far. I did a quick half roll and made off home, where I found to my irritation that Raspberry, as usual, had three planes down to my one.

There was to be a concert on the Station that night, but as I had to be up at five the next morning for Dawn Patrol, I had a quick dinner and two beers, and went to bed, feeling not unsatisfied with the day.

Perhaps the most amusing though painful experience which

I had was when I was shot down acting as arse-end Charlie to a Squadron of Hurricanes. Arse-end Charlie is the man who weaves backwards and forwards above and behind the Squadron to protect them from attack from the rear. There had been the usual dog fights over the South Coast, and the Squadron had broken up. Having only fired one snap burst, I climbed up in search of friendly Spitfires, but found instead a squadron of Hurricanes flying round the sky at 18,000 feet in sections of stepped-up three, but with no rear guard. So I joined on. I learned within a few seconds the truth of the old warning, "Beware of the Hun in the Sun." I was making pleasant little sweeps from side to side, and peering earnestly into my mirror when, from out of the sun and dead astern, bullets started appearing along my port wing. There is an appalling tendency to sit and watch this happen without taking any action, as though mesmerised by a snake; but I managed to pull myself together and go into a spin, at the same time attempting to call up the Hurricanes and warn them, but I found that my radio had been shot away. At first there appeared to be little damage done and I started to climb again, but black smoke began pouring out of the engine and there was an unpleasant smell of escaping glycol. I thought I had better get home while I could; but as the windscreen was soon covered with oil I realised that I couldn't make it and decided instead to put down at Lympne, where there was an airdrome. Then I realised that I wasn't going to make Lympne either—I was going at full boost and only clocking 90 miles per hour, so I decided that I had better put down in the nearest field before I stalled and spun in. I chose a cornfield and put the machine down on its belly. Fortunately nothing caught fire, and I had just climbed out and switched off the petrol, when to my amazement I saw an ambulance coming through the gate. This I thought was real service, until the corporal and two orderlies who climbed out started cantering away in the opposite direction, their necks craned up to the heavens. I looked up and about 50 yards away a parachute, and suspended on the air, his legs dangling vaguely, Colin. He was a little burned about his face and hands but quite cheerful.

We were at once surrounded by a bevy of officers and discovered that we had landed practically in the back garden of a Brigade cocktail party. A salvage crew from Lympne took charge of my machine, a doctor took charge of Colin, and the rest took charge of me, handing me double whiskies for the nerves at a laudable rate. I was put up that night by the

Brigadier, who thought I was suffering from a rather severe shock, largely because by dinner time I was so pie-eyed that I didn't dare open my mouth but answered all his questions with a glassy stare. The next day I went up to London by train, a somewhat incongruous figure, carrying a helmet and parachute. The prospect of a long and tedious journey by tube to Hornchurch did not appeal to me, so I called up the Air Ministry and demanded a car and a WAAF. I was put on to the good lady in charge of transport, a sergeant, who protested apologetically that she must have the authorisation of a Wing Commander. I told her forcibly that at this moment I was considerably more important than any Wing Commander, painted a vivid picture of the complete disorganisation of Fighter Command in the event of my not being back at Hornchurch within an hour, and clinched the argument by telling her that my parachute was a military secret which must on no account be seen in a train. By the afternoon I was flying again.

That evening there was a terrific attack on Hornchurch and for the first time since coming south, I saw some bombers. There were twelve Dornier 215s flying in close formation at about 12,000 feet, and headed back for France. I was on my way back to the airdrome when I first sighted them about 5,000 feet below me. I dived straight down in a quarter head-on attack. It seemed quite impossible to miss, and I pressed the button. Nothing happened, I had already fired all my ammunition. I could not turn back, so I put both my arms over my head and went straight through the formation, never thinking I'd get out of it unscratched. I landed on the airdrome with the machine riddled with bullets, but quite serviceable.

From this flight Bubble Waterson did not return.

And so August drew to a close with no slackening of pressure in the enemy offensive. Yet the Squadron showed no signs of strain, and I personally was content. This was what I had waited for, waited for nearly a year; and I was not disappointed. If I felt anything, it was a sensation of relief. We had little time to think, and each day brought new action. No one thought of the future: sufficient unto the day was the emotion thereof. At night one switched off one's mind like an electric light.

It was one week after Bubble went that I fell through space into the North Sea.

THE PEOPLE'S WAR

Count Leo Tolstoy

The battle of Borodino with the occupation of Moscow and the flight of the French, that followed without any more battles, is one of the most instructive phenomena in history.

All historians are agreed that the external activity of states and peoples in their conflicts finds expression in wars; that the political power of states and peoples is increased or diminished as the immediate result of success or defeat in war.

Strange are the historical accounts that tell us how some king or emperor, quarrelling with another king or emperor, levies an army, fights a battle with the army of his foe, gains a victory, kills three, five, or ten thousand men, and consequently subdues a state and a whole people consisting of several millions; and incomprehensible it seems that the defeat of any army, one hundredth of the whole strength of a people, should force that people to submit. Yet all the facts of history (so far as we know it) confirm the truth of the statement, that the successes or defeats of a nation's army are the causes or, at least, the invariable symptoms of the increase or diminution of the power of a nation. An army gains a victory, and immediately the claims of the conquering people are increased to the detriment of the conquered. An army is defeated, and at once the people loses its rights in proportion to the magnitude of the defeat; and if its army is utterly defeated, the people is completely conquered. So (according to history) it has been from the most ancient times up to the present. All Napoleon's earlier wars serve as illustrations of the rule. As the Austrian armies were defeated, Austria was deprived of her rights, and the rights and power of France were increased. The victories of the French at Jena and at Auerstadt destroyed the independent existence of Prussia.

But suddenly in 1812, the French gained a victory before Moscow. Moscow was taken, and in consequence of that, with no subsequent battles, not Russia, but the French army of six hundred thousand, and then Napoleonic France itself ceased to exist. To strain the facts to fit the rules of history, to maintain that the field of Borodino was left in the hands of the Russians, or that after the evacuation of Moscow, there were battles that destroyed Napoleon's army—is impossible.

From: *War and Peace.*

After the victory of the French at Borodino, there was no general engagement, nor even a skirmish of any great importance, yet the French army ceased to exist. What is the meaning of it? If it had been an example from the history of China, we could have said it was not an historical fact (the resource of historians, when anything will not fit in with their rules). If it had occurred in a conflict on a small scale, in which only small numbers of soldiers had taken part, we might have looked upon it as an exception. But all this took place before the eyes of our fathers, for whom it was a question of life and death for their country; and the war was on a larger scale than any wars we know of.

The sequel of the campaign of 1812—from Borodino to the final expulsion of the French—has proved that victories are not always a cause nor even an invariable sign of conquest; it has proved that the force that decides the fate of peoples does not lie in military leaders nor even in armies and battles, but in something else.

The French historians, who describe the position of the French troops before they marched out of Moscow, assert that everything was in good order in the Grande Armée, except the cavalry, the artillery and the transport, and that there was no forage for the horses and cattle. There was no remedy for this defect, because the peasants of the surrounding country burned their hay rather than let the French have it.

Victory did not bring forth its usual results, because the peasants, Karp and Vlas, by no means persons of heroic feelings (after the French evacuation, they hurried with their carts to pillage Moscow), and the immense multitude of others like them burnt their hay rather than bring it to Moscow, however high the prices offered them.

Let us imagine two men, who have come out to fight a duel with swords in accordance with all the rules of the art of swordsmanship. The fencing has lasted for some time. All at once one of the combatants, feeling that he is wounded, grasping that it is no joking matter, but a question of life and death, flings away his sword, and snatching up the first cudgel that comes handy, begins to brandish that. But let us imagine that the combatant, who has so sensibly made use of the best and simplest means for the attainment of his object, should be inspired by the traditions of chivalry to try and disguise the real cause of the conflict and should persist in declaring that he had been victor in the duel in accordance with all the rules of swordsmanship. One can imagine what confusion and obscurity would arise from his description of the duel!

The duellist, who insisted on the conflict being fought in accordance with the principles of the fencer's art, stands for the French; his opponent, who flung away his sword and snatched up a cudgel, did like the Russians; and the attempted description of the duel in accordance with the rules of swordsmanship has been given us by the historians of the war.

From the time of the burning of Smolensk a war began which did not follow any of the old traditions of warfare. The burning of towns and villages, the retreat after every battle, the blow dealt at Borodino and followed by retreat, the burning of Moscow, the capture of marauders, the seizing of transports, —the whole of the irregular warfare was a departure from the rules.

Napoleon was aware of it, and from the time when he stood waiting in Moscow in the correct pose of the victorious fencer, and instead of his opponent's sword, saw the bludgeon raised against him, he never ceased complaining to Kutuzov and to the Emperor Alexander that the war was being conducted contrary to all the rules of war. (As though any rules existed for the slaughter of men!)

In spite of the complaints of the French that they did not keep to the rules, in spite of the fact that the Russians in the highest positions felt it somehow shameful to be fighting with a cudgel, and wanted to take up the correct position *en quarte* or *en tierce*, to make a skilful thrust, *en prime* and so on, the cudgel of the people's war was raised in all its menacing and majestic power; and troubling itself about no question of any one's tastes or rules, about no fine distinctions, with stupid simplicity, with perfect consistency, it rose and fell and belaboured the French till the whole invading army had been driven out.

And happy the people that will not, as the French did in 1813, saluting according to the rules, gracefully and cautiously offer the sword hilt to the magnanimous conqueror. Happy the people who, in the moment of trial, asks no questions how others would act by the recognised rules in such cases, but with ease and directness picks up the first cudgel that comes handy and deals blows with it, till resentment and revenge give way to contempt and pity.

One of the most conspicuous and advantageous departures from the so-called rules of warfare is the independent action of men acting separately against men huddled together in a mass. Such independent activity is always seen in a war that assumes a national character. In this kind of warfare, instead of forming in a crowd to attack a crowd, men disperse in small groups, attack singly and at once fly, when attacked by superior forces, and then attack again, when an opportunity presents itself. Such were the methods of the guerillas in Spain; of the mountain tribes in the Caucasus, and of the Russians in 1812.

War of this kind has been called partisan warfare on the supposition that this name defined its special significance. But this kind of warfare does not follow any rules of war, but is in direct contradiction to a well-known rule of tactics, regarded as infallible. That rule lays it down that the attacking party must concentrate his forces in order to be stronger than his opponent at the moment of conflict.

Partisan warfare (always successful, as history testifies) acts in direct contradiction of this rule.

The so-called "partisan" warfare had begun with the enemy's entrance into Smolensk. Before the irregular warfare was officially recognised by our government many thousands of the enemy's soldiers—straggling, marauding, or foraging parties—had been slain by Cossacks and peasants, who killed these men as instinctively as dogs set upon a stray mad dog. Denis Davydov was the first to feel with his Russian instinct the value of this terrible cudgel which belaboured the French, and asked no questions about the etiquette of the military art; and to him belongs the credit of the first step towards the recognition of this method of warfare.

The first detachment of irregulars—Davydov's—was formed on 24th August, and others soon followed. In the latter stages of the campaign these detachments became more and more numerous.

The irregulars destroyed the Grande Armée piecemeal. They swept up the fallen leaves that were dropping of themselves from the withered tree, and sometimes they shook the tree itself. By October, when the French were fleeing to Smolensk, there were hundreds of these companies, differing widely from one another in number and in character. Some were detachments that followed all the usual routine of an army, with infantry, artillery, staff-officers, and all the conveniences of life. Some consisted only of Cossacks, mounted men. Others were small bands of men, on foot and also mounted. Some consisted of peasants, or of landowners and their serfs, and remained unknown. There was a deacon at the head of such a band, who took several hundred prisoners in a month. There was the village elder's wife, Vassilisa, who killed hundreds of the French.

The latter part of October was the time when this guerilla warfare reached its height. That period of this warfare, in which the irregulars were themselves amazed at their own audacity, were every moment in dread of being surrounded and captured by the French, and never unsaddling, hardly dismounting, hid in the woods, in momentary expectation of pursuit, was already over. The irregular warfare had by now taken definite shape; it had become clear to all the irregulars what they could, and what they could not, accomplish with the French. By now it was only the commanders of detachments marching with staff-officers according to the rules at a distance from the French who considered much impossible. The small bands of irregulars who had been at work a long while, and were at close quarters with the French, found it possible to attempt what the leaders of large companies did not dare to think of doing. The Cossacks and the peasants, who crept in among the French, thought everything possible now.

On the 22nd of October, Denisov, who was a leader of a band of irregulars, was eagerly engaged in a typical operation of this irregular warfare. From early morning he had been with his men moving about the woods that bordered the high road, watching a big convoy of cavalry baggage and Russian prisoners that had dropped behind the other French troops, and under strong escort—as he learned from his scouts and from prisoners—was making its way to Smolensk. Not only Denisov and Dolohov (who was also a leader of a small band acting in the same district) were aware of the presence of this convoy. Some generals in command of some larger detachments, with staff-officers, also knew of this convoy, and, as Denisov said, their mouths were watering for it. Two of these generals—one a Pole, the other a German—had almost at the same time sent to Denisov an invitation to join their respective detachments in attacking the convoy.

"No, friend, I wasn't born yesterday!" said Denisov, on reading these documents; and he wrote to the German that in spite of his ardent desire to serve under so brilliant and renowned a general, he must deprive himself of that happiness because he was already under the command of the Polish general. To the Pole he wrote the same thing, informing him that he was already serving under the command of the German.

Having thus disposed of that difficulty, Denisov, without communicating on the subject to the higher authorities, intended with Dolohov to attack and carry off this transport with his own small force. The transport was, on the 22nd of October, going from the village of Mikulino to the village of Shamshevo. On the left side of the road between Mikulino and Shamshevo there were great woods, which in places bordered on the road, and in places were a verst or more from the road. Denisov, with a small party of followers, had been the whole day riding about in these woods, sometimes plunging into their centre, and sometimes coming out at the edge, but never losing sight of the moving French. In the morning, not far from Mikulino, where the wood ran close to the road, the Cossacks of Denisov's party had pounced on two French waggonloads of saddles, stuck in the mud, and had carried them off into the wood. From that time right on to evening, they had been watching the movements of the French without attacking them. They wanted to avoid frightening them, and to let them go quietly on to Shamshevo, and then, joining Dolohov (who was to come that evening to a trysting-place in the wood, a verst from Shamshevo, to concert measures with them), from two sides to fall at dawn like an avalanche of snow on their heads, and to overcome and capture all of them at a blow.

Six Cossacks had been left behind, two versts from Mikulino, where the wood bordered the road. They were to bring word at once as soon as any fresh columns of French came into sight.

In front of Shamshevo, Dolohov was in the same way to watch the road to know at what distance there were other French troops. With the transport there was supposed to be fifteen hundred men. Denisov had two hundred men, and Dolohov might have as many more. But superiority in numbers was no obstacle to Denisov. There was only one thing that he still needed to know, and that was what troops these were; and for that object Denisov needed to take a "tongue" (that is some man belonging to that column of the enemy). The attack on the wagons in the morning was all done with such haste that they killed all the French soldiers in charge of the wagons, and captured alive only a little drummer-boy, who had straggled away from his own regiment, and could tell them nothing certain about the troops forming the column.

To make another descent upon them, Denisov thought, would be to risk alarming the whole column, and so he sent on ahead to Shamshevo a peasant, Tihon Shtcherbatov, to try if he could capture at least one of the French quartermasters from the vanguard.

It was a warm, rainy, autumn day. The sky and the horizon were all of the uniform tint of muddy water. Sometimes a mist seemed to be falling, and sometimes there was a sudden downpour of heavy, slanting rain.

Denisov, in a long cape and a high fur cap, both streaming with water, was riding a thin, pinched-looking, thoroughbred horse. With his head aslant, and his ears pricked up, like his horse, he was frowning at the driving rain, and anxiously looking before him. His face, which had grown thin, and was covered with a thick, short, black beard, looked wrathful.

Beside Denisov, wearing also a long cape and a high cap, and mounted on a sleek, sturdy Don horse, rode the esaul, or hetman of the Cossacks—Denisov's partner in his enterprises.

The esaul, Lovaisky, a thin man, also in a cape, and a high cap, was a long creature, flat as a board, with a pale face, flaxen hair, narrow, light eyes, and an expression of calm self-confidence both in his face and his attitude. Though it was impossible to say what constituted the peculiarity of horse and rider, at the first glance at the esaul and at Denisov, it was evident that Denisov was both wet and uncomfortable; that Denisov was a man sitting on a horse; while the esaul seemed as comfortable and calm as always, and seemed not a man sitting on a horse, but a man forming one whole with a horse—a single being enlarged by the strength of two.

A little ahead of them walked a peasant-guide, soaked through and through in his grey full coat and white cap.

A little behind, on a thin, delicate Kirghiz pony, with a flowing tail and mane, and a mouth flecked with blood, rode a young officer in a blue French military coat. Beside him rode an hussar, with a boy in a tattered French uniform and blue cap, perched upon his horse behind him. The boy held on to the hussar with hands red with cold, and kept moving his bare feet, trying to warm them, and lifting his eyebrows, gazed about him wonderingly. This was the French drummer, who had been taken in the morning.

Along the narrow, muddy, cut-up forest-track there came hussars in knots of three and four at a time, and then Cossacks; some in capes, some in French cloaks; others with horse-cloths pulled over their heads. The horses, chestnut and bay, all looked black from the soaking rain. Their necks looked strangely thin with their drenched manes, and steam rose in clouds from them. Clothes, saddles, and bridles, all were sticky and swollen with the wet, like the earth and the fallen leaves with which the track was strewn. The men sat huddled up, trying not to move, so as to keep warm the water that had already reached their skins, and not to let any fresh stream of cold rain trickle in anywhere under their seat, or at their knees or necks. In the midst of the file of Cossacks two wagons, drawn by French horses, and Cossack saddle-horses hitched on in front, rumbled over stumps and branches, and splashed through the ruts full of water.

Denisov's horse, in avoiding a puddle in the track, knocked his rider's knee against a tree.

"Ah, devil!" Denisov cried angrily; and showing his teeth, he struck his horse three times with his whip, splashing himself and his comrades with mud. Denisov was out of humour, both from the rain and hunger (no one had eaten anything since morning); and, most of all, from having no news of Dolohov, and from no French prisoner having been caught to give him information.

"We shall never have such another chance to fall on the transport as to-day. To attack them alone would be risky, and to put it off to another day—some one of the bigger leaders will carry the booty off from under our noses," thought Denisov, continually looking ahead, and fancying he saw the messenger from Dolohov he expected.

Coming out into a clearing from which he could get a view to some distance on the right, Denisov stopped.

"There's some one coming," he said.

The esaul looked in the direction Denisov was pointing to.

"There are two men coming—an officer and a Cossack. Only I wouldn't be *prepositive* that is the colonel himself," said the esaul, who loved to use words that were unfamiliar to the Cossacks. The two figures, riding downhill, disappeared from sight, and came into view again a few minutes later. The foremost was an officer, dishevelled looking, and soaked through, with his trousers tucked up above his knees; he was lashing his horse into a weary gallop. Behind him a Cossack trotted along, standing up in his stirrups. This officer, a quite young boy, with a broad, rosy face and keen, merry eyes, galloped up to Denisov, and handed him a sopping packet.

"From the general," he said. "I must apologise for its not being quite dry. . . ."

Denisov, frowning, took the packet and broke it open.

"Why, they kept telling us it was so dangerous," said the officer, turning to the esaul while Denisov was reading the letter. "But Komarov"—and he indicated the Cossack—"and

I were prepared. We have both two pistol . . . But what's this?" he asked, seeing the French drummer-boy. "A prisoner? You have had a battle already? May I talk to him?"

"Rostov! Petya!" Denisov cried at that moment, running through the packet that had been given him. "Why, how was it you didn't say who you were?" and Denisov, turning with a smile, held out his hand to the officer. This officer was Petya Rostov.

Petya had been all the way preparing himself to behave with Denisov as a grown-up person and an officer should do, making no reference to their previous acquaintance. But as soon as Denisov smiled at him, Petya beamed at once, blushed with delight, and forgetting all the formal demeanour he had been intending to preserve, he began telling him how he had ridden by the French, and how glad he was he had been given this commission, and how he had already been in a battle at Vyazma, and how a certain hussar had distinguished himself in it.

"Well, I am glad to see you," Denisov interrupted him, and his face looked anxious again.

"Mihail Feoklititch," he said to the esaul, "this is from the German again, you know. He" (Petya) "is in his suite." And Denisov told the esaul that the letter, which had just been brought, repeated the German general's request that they would join him in attacking the transport. "If we don't catch them by to-morrow, he'll snatch them from under our noses," he concluded.

While Denisov was talking to the esaul, Petya, disconcerted by Denisov's cold tone, and imagining that that tone might be due to the condition of his trousers, furtively pulled them down under his cloak, trying to do so unobserved, and to maintain as martial an air as possible.

"Will your honour have any instructions to give me?" he said to Denisov, putting his hand to the peak of his cap, and going back to the comedy of adjutant and general, which he had prepared himself to perform, "or should I remain with your honour?"

"Instructions? . . ." said Denisov absently. "Well, can you stay till to-morrow?"

"Ah, please . . . May I stay with you?" cried Petya.

"Well, what were your instructions from your general—to go back at once?" asked Denisov.

Petya blushed.

"Oh, he gave me no instructions. I think I may?" he said interrogatively.

"All right, then," said Denisov. And turning to his followers, he directed a party of them to go to the hut in the wood, which they had fixed on as a resting-place, and the officer on the Kirghiz horse (this officer performed the duties of an adjutant) to go and look for Dolohov, to find out where he was, and whether he were coming in the evening.

Denisov himself, with the esaul and Petya, intended to ride to the edge of the wood near Shamshevo to have a look at the position of the French, where their attack next day was to take place.

"Come, my man," he said to their peasant guide, "take us to Shamshevo."

Denisov, Petya, and the esaul, accompanied by a few Cossacks and the hussars with the prisoner turned to the left and crossed a ravine towards the edge of the wood.

On leaving Moscow, Petya had parted from his parents to join his regiment, and shortly afterwards had been appointed an orderly in attendance on a general who was in command of a large detachment. From the time of securing his commission, and even more since joining a regiment in active service, and taking part in the battle of Vyazma, Petya had been in a continual state of happy excitement at being grown-up, and of intense anxiety not to miss any opportunity of real heroism. He was highly delighted with all he had seen and experienced in the army, but, at the same time, he was always fancying that wherever he was not, there the most real and heroic exploits were at that very moment being performed. And he was in constant haste to be where he was not.

On the 21st of October, when his general expressed a desire to send some one to Denisov's company, Petya had so piteously besought him to send him, that the general could not refuse. But, as he was sending him off, the general recollected Petya's foolhardy behaviour at the battle of Vyazma, when, instead of riding by way of the road to take a message, Petya had galloped across the lines under the fire of the French, and had there fired a couple of pistol-shots. Recalling that prank, the general explicitly forbade Petya's taking part in any enterprise whatever that Denisov might be planning. This was why Petya had blushed and been disconcerted when Denisov asked him if he might stay. From the moment he set off till he reached the edge of the wood, Petya had fully intended to do his duty steadily, and to return at once. But when he saw the French, and saw Tihon, and learned that the attack would certainly take place that night, with the rapid transition from one view to another, characteristic of young people, he made up his mind that his general, for whom he had till that moment had the greatest respect, was a poor stick, and only a German, that Denisov was a hero, and the esaul a hero, and Tihon a hero, and that it would be shameful to leave them at a moment of difficulty.

It was getting dark when Denisov, with Petya and the esaul, reached the forester's hut. In the half-dark they could see saddled horses, Cossacks and hussars, rigging up shanties in the clearing, and building up a glowing fire in a hollow near, where the smoke would not be seen by the French. In the porch of the little hut there was a Cossack with his sleeves tucked up, cutting up a sheep. In the hut, three officers of Denisov's band were setting up a table made up of doors. Petya took off his wet clothes, gave them to be dried, and at once set to work to help the officers in fixing up a dining-table.

In ten minutes the table was ready and covered with a napkin. On the table was set vodka, a flask of rum, white bread, and roast mutton, and salt.

Sitting at the table with the officers, tearing the fat, savoury mutton with greasy fingers, Petya was in a childishly enthusiastic condition of tender love for all men and a consequent belief in the same feeling for himself in others.

" So what do you think, Vassily Fyodorovitch," he said to Denisov, " it won't matter my staying a day with you, will it?" And without waiting for an answer, he answered himself: " Why, I was told to find out, and here I am finding out . . . Only you must let me go into the middle . . . into the real . . . I don't care about rewards . . . But I do want . . ." Petya clenched his teeth and looked about him, tossing his head and waving his arm.

" Into the real, real thing . . ." Denisov said, smiling.

" Only, please, do give me a command of something altogether, so that I really might command," Petya went on. " Why, what would it be to you? Ah, you want a knife?" he said to an officer, who was trying to tear off a piece of mutton. And he gave him his pocket-knife.

The officer praised the knife.

" Please keep it. I have several like it . . ." said Petya, blushing. " Heavens! Why, I was quite forgetting," he cried suddenly. " I have some capital raisins, you know the sort without stones. We have a new canteen-keeper, and he does get first-rate things. I bought ten pounds of them. I'm fond of sweet things. Will you have some?" . . . And Petya ran out to his Cossack in the porch, and brought in some panniers in which there were five pounds of raisins. "Please take some."

"Don't you need a coffee-pot?" he said to the esaul; "I bought a famous one from our canteen-keeper! He has first-rate things. And he's very honest. That's the great thing. I'll be sure and send it you. Or perhaps your flints are worn out; that does happen sometimes. I brought some with me, I have got them here . . ." he pointed to the panniers. "A hundred flints. I bought them very cheap. You must please take as many as you want or all, indeed . . ." And suddenly, dismayed at the thought that he had let his tongue run away with him, Petya stopped short and blushed.

He began trying to think whether he had been guilty of any other blunders. And running through his recollections of the day the image of the French drummer-boy rose before his mind.

"We are enjoying ourselves, but how is he feeling? What have they done with him? Have they given him something to eat? Have they been nasty to him?" he wondered.

But thinking he had said too much about the flints, he was afraid to speak now.

"Could I ask about him?" he wondered. "They'll say: he's a boy himself, so he feels for the boy. I'll let them see to-morrow whether I'm a boy! Shall I feel ashamed if I ask?" Petya wondered. "Oh, well! I don't care," and he said at once, blushing and watching the officers' faces in dread of detecting amusement in them:

"Might I call that boy who was taken prisoner, and give him something to eat . . . perhaps . . ."

"Yes, poor little fellow," said Denisov, who clearly saw nothing to be ashamed of in this reminder. "Fetch him in here. His name is Vincent Bosse. Fetch him in."

"I'll call him in."

"Yes, do. Poor little fellow," repeated Denisov.

Petya was standing at the door as Denisov said this. He slipped in between the officers and went up to Denisov.

"Let me kiss you, dear fellow," he said. "Ah, how jolly it is! How splendid!" And, kissing Denisov, he ran out into the yard.

"Bosse! Vincent!" Petya cried, standing by the door.

"Whom do you want, sir?" said a voice out of the darkness. Petya answered that he wanted the French boy, who had been taken prisoner that day.

"Ah, Vesenny?" said the Cossack.

His name Vincent had already been transformed by the Cossacks into Vesenny, and by the peasants and the soldiers into Visenya. In both names there was a suggestion of the spring—vesna—which seemed to them to harmonise with the figure of the young boy.

"He's warming himself there at the fire. Ay, Visenya! Visenya!" voices called from one to another with laughter in the darkness. "He is a sharp boy," said an hussar standing near Petya. "We gave him a meal not long ago. He was hungry, terribly."

There was a sound of footsteps in the darkness, and the drummer-boy came splashing through the mud with his bare feet towards the door.

"Ah, that's you!" said Petya. "Are you hungry? Don't be afraid, they won't hurt you," he added, shyly and cordially touching his hand. "Come in, come in."

"Thank you," answered the drummer, in a trembling, almost childish voice, and he began wiping the mud off his feet on the threshold. Petya had a great deal he longed to say to the drummer-boy, but he did not dare. He stood by him in the porch, moving uneasily. Then he took his hand in the darkness and squeezed it. "Come in, come in," he repeated, but in a soft whisper.

"Oh, if I could only do something for him!" Petya was saying inwardly, and opening the door he ushered the boy in before him.

When the drummer-boy had come into the hut, Petya sat down at some distance from him, feeling that it would be lowering his dignity to take much notice of him. But he was feeling the money in his pocket and wondering whether it would do to give some to the drummer-boy.

Denisov gave orders for the drummer-boy to be given some vodka and mutton, and to be put into a Russian dress, so that he should not be sent off with the other prisoners, but should stay with the band. Petya's attention was diverted from the boy by the arrival of Dolohov. He had heard a great many stories told in the army of Dolohov's extraordinary gallantry and of his cruelty to the French. And therefore from the moment Dolohov entered the hut Petya could not take his eyes off him, and flinging up his head, he assumed a more and more swaggering air, that he might not be unworthy of associating even with a hero like Dolohov.

Dolohov's appearance struck Petya as strange through its simplicity.

Denisov was dressed in a Cossack coat; he had let his beard grow, and had a holy image of Nikolay, the wonder-worker, on his breast. His whole manner of speaking and all his gestures were suggestive of his peculiar position. Dolohov, on the contrary, though in old days he had worn a Persian dress in Moscow, looked now like the most correct officer of the Guards. He was clean-shaven; he wore the wadded coat of the Guards with a St. George medal on a ribbon, and a plain forage cap, put on straight on his head. He took his wet cloak off in the corner and, without greeting any one, went straight up to Denisov and began at once asking questions about the matter in hand. Denisov told him of the designs the larger detachment had upon the French convoy, of the message Petya had brought, and the answer he had given to both generals. Then he told him all he knew of the position of the French.

"That's so. But we must find out what troops they are, and what are their numbers," said Dolohov; "we must go and have a look at them. We can't rush into the thing without knowing for certain how many there are of them. I like to do things properly. Come, won't one of you gentlemen like to come with me to pay them a call in their camp? I have an extra uniform with me."

"I, I . . . I'll come with you!" cried Petya.

"There's not the slightest need for you to go," said Denisov, addressing Dolohov; "and as for him I wouldn't let him go on any account."

"That's good!" cried Petya; "why shouldn't I go? . . ."

"Why, because there's no reason to."

"Oh, well, excuse me . . . because . . . because . . . I'm going, and that's all. You will take me?" he cried, turning to Dolohov.

"Why not? . . ." Dolohov answered, absently, staring into the face of the French drummer-boy.

"Have you had that youngster long?" he asked Denisov.

"We caught him to-day, but he knows nothing; I have kept him with us."

"Oh, and what do you do with the rest?" said Dolohov.

"What do I do with them? I take a receipt for them, and send them off!" cried Denisov, suddenly flushing. "And I make bold to say that I haven't a single man's life on my con-science. Is there any difficulty in your sending thirty, or three hundred men, under escort, to the town rather than stain—I say so bluntly—one's honour as a soldier?"

"It's all very well for this little count here at sixteen to talk of such refinements," Dolohov said, with a cold sneer; "but it's high time for you to drop all that."

"Why, I am not saying anything, I only say that I am certainly going with you," said Petya shyly.

"But for me and you, mate, it's high time to drop such delicacy," Dolohov went on, apparently deriving peculiar gratification from talking on a subject irritating to Denisov. "Why have you kept this lad," he said, "except because you are sorry for him? Why, we all know how much your receipts are worth. You send off a hundred men and thirty reach the town. They die of hunger or are killed on the way. So isn't it just as well to make short work of them?"

The esaul, screwing up his light-coloured eyes, nodded his head approvingly.

"That's not my affair, no need to discuss it. I don't care to have their lives on my conscience. You say they die. Well, let them. Only not through my doing."

Dolohov laughed.

"Who prevented their taking me twenty times over? But you know if they do catch me—and you too with your chivalrous sentiments—it will just be the same—the nearest aspentree." He paused. "We must be getting to work, though. Send my Cossack here with the pack. I have two French uniforms. Well, are you coming with me?" he asked Petya.

"I? Yes, yes, of course," cried Petya, blushing till the tears came into his eyes, and glancing at Denisov.

While Dolohov had been arguing with Denisov what should be done with prisoners, Petya had again had that feeling of discomfort and nervous hurry; but again he had not time to get a clear idea of what they were talking about. "If that's what is thought by grown-up men, famous leaders, then it must be so, it must be all right," he thought. "And the great thing is, that Denisov shouldn't dare to imagine that I must obey him, that he can order me about. I shall certainly go with Dolohov into the French camp. He can go, and so can I!"

To all Denisov's efforts to dissuade him from going, Petya replied that he too liked doing things properly and not in haphazard fashion, and that he never thought about danger to himself.

"For, you must admit, if we don't know exactly how many men there are there, it might cost the life of hundreds, and it is only we two, and so I very much wish it, and I shall certainly, most certainly go, and don't try to prevent me," he said; " it won't be any use . . ."

Petya and Dolohov, after dressing up in French uniforms and shakoes, rode to the clearing from which Denisov had looked at the French camp, and coming out of the wood, descended into the hollow in the pitch darkness. When they had ridden downhill, Dolohov bade the Cossacks accompanying him to wait there, and set off at a smart trot along the road towards the bridge. Petya, faint with excitement, trotted along beside him.

" If we are caught, I won't be taken alive. I have a pistol," whispered Petya.

" Don't speak Russian," said Dolohov, in a rapid whisper, and at that moment they heard in the dark the challenge : " Who goes there?" and the click of a gun.

The blood rushed into Petya's face, and he clutched at his pistol.

" Uhlans of the Sixth Regiment," said Dolohov, neither hastening nor slackening his horse's pace.

The black figure of a sentinel stood on the bridge.

" The password?"

Dolohov reined in his horse, and advanced at a walking pace.

" Tell me, is Colonel Gerard here?" he said.

" Password?" repeated the sentinel, making no reply and barring their way.

" When an officer makes his round, sentinels don't ask him for the password . . ." cried Dolohov, suddenly losing his temper and riding straight at the sentinel. " I ask you, is the colonel here?"

And not waiting for an answer from the sentinel, who moved aside, Dolohov rode at a walking pace uphill.

Noticing the black outline of a man crossing the road, Dolohov stopped the man, and asked where the colonel and officers were. The man, a soldier with a sack over his shoulder, stopped, came close up to Dolohov's horse, stroking it with his hand, and told them in a simple and friendly way that the colonel and the officers were higher up the hill, on the right, in the courtyard of the farm, as he called the little manor-house.

After going further along the road, from both sides of which they heard French talk round the camp-fires, Dolohov turned into the yard of the manor-house. On reaching the gate, he dismounted and walked towards a big, blazing fire, round which several men were sitting, engaged in loud conversation.

There was something boiling in a cauldron on one side, and a soldier in a peaked cap and blue coat, kneeling in the bright glow of the fire, was stirring it with his ramrod.

"He's a tough customer," said one of the officers, sitting in the shadow on the opposite side of the fire.

"He'll make them run, the rabbits" (a French proverb), said the other, with a laugh.

Both paused, and peered into the darkness at the sound of the steps of Petya and Dolohov approaching with their horses.

"*Bonjour, messieurs!*" Dolohov called loudly and distinctly.

There was a stir among the officers in the shadow, and a tall officer with a long neck came round the fire and went up to Dolohov.

"Is that you, Clément?" said he. "Where the devil . . ." but becoming aware of his mistake, he did not finish, and with a slight frown greeted Dolohov as a stranger, and asked him what he could do for him. Dolohov told him that he and his comrade were trying to catch up their regiment, and asked, addressing the company in general, whether the officers knew anything about the Sixth Regiment. No one could tell them anything about it; and Petya fancied the officers began to look at him and Dolohov with unfriendly and suspicious eyes.

For several seconds no one spoke.

"If you're reckoning on some soup, you have come too late," said a voice from behind the fire, with a smothered laugh.

Dolohov answered that they had had supper, and wanted to push on further that night.

He gave their horses to the soldier who was stirring the pot, and squatted down on his heels beside the officer with the long neck. The latter never took his eyes off Dolohov, and asked him again what regiment did he belong to.

Dolohov appeared not to hear the question. Making no answer, he lighted a short French pipe that he took from his pocket, and asked the officers whether the road ahead of them were safe from Cossacks.

"The brigands are everywhere," answered an officer from behind the fire.

Dolohov said that the Cossacks were only a danger for stragglers like himself and his comrade; "he supposed they would not dare to attack large detachments," he added inquiringly.

No one replied.

"Well, now he will come away," Petya was thinking every moment, as he stood by the fire listening to the talk.

But Dolohov took up the conversation that had dropped,

and proceeded to ask them point-blank how many men there were in their battalion, how many battalions they had, and how many prisoners.

When he asked about the Russian prisoners, Dolohov added: "Nasty business dragging those corpses about with one. It would be better to shoot the vermin," and he broke into such a strange, loud laugh, that Petya fancied the French must see through their disguise at once, and he involuntarily stepped back from the fire.

Dolohov's words and laughter elicited no response, and a French officer whom they had seen (he lay rolled up in a coat), sat up and whispered something to his companion. Dolohov stood up and called to the men who held their horses.

"Will they give us the horses or not?" Petya wondered, unconsciously coming closer to Dolohov.

They did give them the horses. "*Bonjour, messieurs,*" said Dolohov.

Petya tried to say "*Bonsoir,*" but he could not utter a sound. The officers were whispering together. Dolohov was a long while mounting his horse, who would not stand still; then he rode out of the gate at a walking pace. Petya rode beside him, not daring to look round, though he was longing to see whether the French were running after him or not.

When they came out on to the road, Dolohov did not turn back towards the open country, but rode further along it into the village.

At one spot he stood still, listening. "Do you hear?" he said. Petya recognised the sound of voices speaking Russian, and saw round the camp-fire the dark outlines of Russian prisoners. When they reached the bridge again, Petya and Dolohov passed the sentinel, who, without uttering a word, paced gloomily up and down. They came out to the hollow where the Cossacks were waiting for them.

"Well now, good-bye. Tell Denisov, at sunrise, at the first shot," said Dolohov, and he was going on, but Petya clutched at his arm.

"Oh!" he cried, "you are a hero! Oh! how splendid it is! how jolly! How I love you!"

"That's all right," answered Dolohov, but Petya did not let go of him, and in the dark Dolohov made out that he was bending over to him to be kissed. Dolohov kissed him, laughed, and turning his horse's head, vanished into the darkness.

On reaching the hut in the wood, Petya found Denisov in the porch. He was waiting for Petya's return in great uneasiness, anxiety, and vexation with himself for having let him go.

"Thank God!" he cried. "Well, thank God!" he repeated, hearing Petya's ecstatic account. "And, damn you, you have prevented my sleeping!" he added. "Well, thank God; now, go to bed. We can still get a nap before morning."

"Yes . . . no," said Petya. "I'm not sleepy yet. Besides, I know what I am; if once I go to sleep, it will be all up with me. And besides, it's not my habit to sleep before a battle."

Petya sat for a little while in the hut, joyfully recalling the details of his adventure, and vividly imagining what was coming next day. Then, noticing that Denisov had fallen asleep, he got up and went out of doors.

It was still quite dark outside. The rain was over, but the trees were still dripping. Close by the hut could be seen the black outlines of the Cossacks' shanties and the horses tied together. Behind the hut there was a dark blur where two wagons stood with the horses near by, and in the hollow there was a red glow from the dying fire. The Cossacks and the hussars were not all asleep; there mingled with the sound of the falling drops and the munching of the horses, the sound of low voices, that seemed to be whispering.

Petya came out of the porch, looked about him in the darkness, and went up to the wagons. Some one was snoring under the wagons, and saddled horses were standing round them munching oats. In the dark Petya recognised and approached his own mare, whom he called Karabach, though she was in fact of a Little Russian breed.

"Well, Karabach, to-morrow we shall do good service," he said, sniffing her nostrils and kissing her.

"Why, aren't you asleep, sir?" said a Cossack, sitting under the wagon.

"No; but . . . Lihatchev—I believe that's your name, eh? You know I have only just come back. We have been calling on the French." And Petya gave the Cossack a detailed account, not only of his adventure, but also of his reasons for going, and why he thought it better to risk his life than to do things in a haphazard way.

"Well, you must be sleepy; get a little sleep," said the Cossack.

"No, I am used to it," answered Petya. "And how are the flints in your pistols—not worn out? I brought some with me. Don't you want any? Do take some."

The Cossack popped out from under the wagon to take a closer look at Petya.

"For, you see, I like to do everything carefully," said Petya. "Some men, you know, leave things to chance, and don't have things ready, and then they regret it. I don't like that."

"No, to be sure," said the Cossack.

"Oh, and another thing, please, my dear fellow, sharpen my sabre for me; I have blunt . . ." (but Petya could not bring out a lie) . . . "it has never been sharpened. Can you do that?"

"To be sure I can."

Lihatchev stood up, and rummaged in the baggage, and Petya stood and heard the martial sound of steel and whetstone. He clambered on to the wagon, and sat on the edge of it. The Cossack sharpened the sabre below.

"Are the other brave fellows asleep?" said Petya.

"Some are asleep, and some are awake, like us."

"And what about the boy?"

"Vesenny? He's lying yonder in the hay. He's sleeping well after his fright. He was so pleased."

For a long while after that Petya sat quiet, listening to the sounds. There was a sound of footsteps in the darkness, and a dark figure appeared.

"What are you sharpening?" asked a man coming up to the wagon.

"A sabre for the gentleman here."

"That's a good thing," said the man, who seemed to Petya to be a hussar. "Was the cup left with you here?"

"It's yonder by the wheel." The hussar took the cup. "It will soon be daylight," he added, yawning, as he walked off.

Petya must, one would suppose, have known that he was in a wood, with Denisov's band of irregulars, a verst from the road; that he was sitting on a wagon captured from the French; that there were horses fastened to it; that under it was sitting the Cossack Lihatchev sharpening his sabre; that the big black blur on the right was the hut, and the red, bright glow below on the left the dying camp-fire; that the man who had come for the cup was an hussar who was thirsty. But Petya knew nothing of all that, and refused to know it. He was in a fairyland, in which nothing was like the reality. The big patch of shadow might be a hut certainly, but it might be a cave leading down into the very depths of the earth. The red patch might be a fire, but it might be the eye of a huge monster. Perhaps he really was sitting now on a wagon, but very likely he was sitting not on a wagon, but on a fearfully high tower, and if he fell off, he would go on flying to the earth for a whole day, for a whole month—fly and fly for ever and never reach it. Perhaps it was simply the Cossack Lihatchev sitting under the wagon; but very likely it was the kindest, bravest, most wonderful and splendid man in the world whom no one knew of. Perhaps it really was an hussar who had come for water and gone into the hollow; but perhaps he had just vanished, vanished altogether and was no more.

Whatever Petya had seen now, it would not have surprised him. He was in a land of fairy, where everything was possible.

He gazed at the sky. The sky too was an enchanted realm like the earth. It had begun to clear, and the clouds were scudding over the tree-tops, as though unveiling the stars. At times it seemed as though they were swept away, and there were glimpses of clear, black sky between them. At times these black patches looked like storm-clouds. At times the sky seemed to rise high, high overhead, and then again to be dropping down so that one could reach it with the hand.

Petya closed his eyes and began to nod. The branches dripped. There was a low hum of talk and the sound of some one snoring. The horses neighed and scuffled.

"Ozheeg, zheeg, ozheeg, zheeg . . ." hissed the sabre on the whetstone; and all at once Petya seemed to hear harmonious music, an orchestra playing some unfamiliar, solemnly sweet hymn. Petya was as musical by nature as Natasha, and far more so than Nikolay; but he had had no musical training, and never thought about music, so that the melody that came unexpectedly into his mind had a special freshness and charm for him. The music became more and more distinct. The melody grew and passed from one instrument to another. There was being played what is called a fugue, though Petya had not the slightest idea of what was meant by a fugue. Each instrument—one like a violin, others like flutes, but fuller and more melodious than violins and flutes—played its part, and before it had finished the air, melted in with another, beginning almost the same air, and with a third and a fourth; and all mingled into one harmony, and parted again, and again mingled into solemn church music, and then into some brilliant and triumphant song of victory.

"Oh yes, of course I am dreaming," Petya said to himself, nodding forward. "It is only in my ears. Perhaps, though, it's my own music. Come, again. Strike up, my music! Come! . . ."

He closed his eyes. And from various directions the sounds began vibrating as though from a distance, began to strike up, to part, and to mingle again, all joined in the same sweet and solemn hymn. "Ah how exquisite! As much as I want, and as I like it!" Petya said to himself. He tried to conduct this immense orchestra.

"Come, softly, softly, now!" And the sounds obeyed him. "Come, now fuller, livelier! More and more joyful!" And from unknown depths rose the swelling, triumphant sounds. "Now, voices, join in!" Petya commanded. And at first in the distance he heard men's voices, then women's. The voices swelled into rhythmic, triumphant fulness. Petya felt awe and joy as he drank in their marvellous beauty.

With the triumphant march of victory mingled the song of voices, and the drip of the branches and the zheeg, zheeg, zheeg of the sabre on the whetstone; and again the horses neighed and scuffled, not disturbing the harmony, but blending into it. How long it lasted, Petya could not tell; he was enjoying it, and wondering all the while at his own enjoyment, and regretting he had no one to share it with. He was waked by the friendly voice of Lihatchev.

"It's ready, your honour, you can cut the French in two now."

Petya waked up.

"Why, it's light already; it's really getting light," he cried. The horses, unseen before, were visible to the tails now, and through the leafless boughs there could be seen a watery light. Petya shook himself, jumped up, took a rouble out of his pocket, and gave it to Lihatchev, brandished his sabre to try it, and thrust it into the scabbard. The Cossacks were untying the horses and fastening the saddlegirths.

"And here is the commander," said Lihatchev.

Denisov came out of the hut, and calling to Petya, bade him get ready.

Rapidly in the twilight the men picked out their horses, tightened saddlegirths, and formed into parties. Denisov stood by the hut, giving the last orders. The infantry of the detachment moved on along the road, hundreds of feet splashing through the mud. They quickly vanished among the trees in the mist before the dawn. The esaul gave some order to the Cossacks. Petya held his horse by the bridle, eagerly awaiting the word of command to mount. His face glowed from a dip in cold water, and his eyes gleamed. He felt a chill running down his back, and a kind of rapid, rhythmic throbbing all over.

"Well, have you everything ready?" said Denisov. "Give us our horses."

They brought the horses up. Denisov was vexed with the Cossack because the saddlegirths were slack, and swore at him as he mounted his horse. Petya put his foot in the stirrup. The horse, as its habit was, made as though to nip at his leg; but Petya leaped into the saddle, unconscious of his own weight, and looking round at the hussars moving up from behind in the darkness, he rode up to Denisov.

"Vassily Fyodorovitch, you will trust me with some commission? Please . . . for God's sake . . ." he said. Denisov seemed to have forgotten Petya's existence. He looked round at him.

"One thing I beg of you," he said sternly, "to obey me and not to put yourself forward."

All the way Denisov did not say another word to Petya; he rode on in silence. By the time that they reached the edge of the wood, it was perceptibly getting light in the open country. Denisov whispered something to the esaul, and the Cossacks began riding by Petya and Denisov. When they had all passed on Denisov put his spurs to his horse, and rode downhill. Slipping and sinking back on their haunches, the horses slid down into the hollow with their riders. Petya kept beside Denisov. The tremor all over him was growing more intense. It was getting lighter and lighter, but the mist hid objects at a distance. When he had reached the bottom, Denisov looked back and nodded to the Cossack beside him.

"The signal," he said. The Cossack raised his arm, and a shot rang out. At the same moment they heard the tramp of horses galloping in front, shouts from different directions, and more shots.

The instant that he heard the first tramp of hoofs and shouts, Petya gave the rein to his horse, and lashing him on, galloped forward, heedless of Denisov, who shouted to him. It seemed to Petya that it suddenly became broad daylight, as though it were midday, at the moment when he heard the shot. He galloped to the bridge. The Cossacks were galloping along the road in front. At the bridge he jostled against a Cossack who had lagged behind, and he galloped on. In front Petya saw men of some sort—the French he supposed—running across the road from right to left. One slipped in the mud under his horse's legs.

Cossacks were crowding about a hut, doing something. A fearful scream rose out of the middle of the crowd. Petya galloped to this crowd, and the first thing he saw was the white face and trembling lower-jaw of a Frenchman, who had clutched hold of a lance aimed at his breast.

"Hurrah! . . . Mates . . . ours . . ." shouted Petya, and giving the rein to his excited horse, he galloped down the village street.

WAR IS THE PROVINCE OF DANGER, AND THEREFORE COURAGE ABOVE ALL THINGS IS THE FIRST QUALITY OF A WARRIOR

Courage is of two kinds: First, physical courage, or courage in presence of danger to the person; and next, moral courage, or courage before responsibility, whether it be before the judgment seat of external authority or of the inner power, the conscience. We only speak here of the first.

Courage before danger to the person, again, is of two kinds. First it may be indifference to danger, whether it proceeds from the organism of the individual, contempt of death or habit. In any of these kinds it is to be regarded as a permanent condition.

Secondly, courage may proceed from positive motives, such as personal pride, patriotism, enthusiasm of any kind. In this case courage is not so much a normal condition as an impulse. We may conceive that the two kinds act differently. The first kind is more certain, because it has become a second nature, never forsakes the man; the second often leads him farther. In the first there is more of firmness, in the second of boldness. The first leaves the judgment clearer, the second raises its power at times, but often bewilders it. The two combined make up the most perfect kind of courage.

HORATIUS AT THE BRIDGE

Livy

By this time the Tarquins had fled to Lars Porsena, king of Clusium. There, with advice and entreaties, they besought him not to suffer them, who were descended from the Etrurians and of the same blood and name, to live in exile and poverty; and advised him not to let this practice of expelling kings to pass unpunished. Liberty, they declared, had charms enough in itself; and unless kings defended their crowns with as much vigour as the people pursued their liberty, the highest must be reduced to a level with the lowest; there would be

From: *The History of Rome, Book II.*

nothing exalted, nothing distinguished above the rest; hence there must be an end of regal government, the most beautiful institution both among gods and men. Porsena, thinking it would be an honour to the Tuscans that there should be a king at Rome, especially one of the Etrurian nation, marched towards Rome with an army. Never before had such terror seized the Senate, so powerful was the state of Clusium at the time, and so great the renown of Porsena. Nor did they only dread their enemies, but even their own citizens, lest the common people, though excess of fear should, by receiving the Tarquins into the city, accept peace even though purchased with slavery. Many concessions were therefore granted to the people by the Senate during that period. Their attention, in the first place, was directed to the markets, and persons were sent, some to the Volscians, others to Cumæ, to buy up corn. The privilege of selling salt, because it was farmed at a high rate, was also taken into the hands of the government, and withdrawn from private individuals; and the people were freed from port-duties and taxes, in order that the rich, who could bear the burden, should contribute; the poor paid tax enough if they educated their children. This indulgent care of the fathers accordingly kept the whole state in such concord amid the subsequent severities of the siege and famine, that the highest as well as the lowest abhorred the name of king; nor was any individual afterwards so popular by intriguing practices as the whole Senate was by their excellent government.

Some parts of the city seemed secured by the walls, others by the River Tiber. The Sublician Bridge well-nigh afforded a passage to the enemy, had there not been one man, Horatius Cocles (fortunately Rome had on that day such a defender) who, happening to be posted on guard at the bridge, when he saw the Janiculum taken by a sudden assault and the enemy pouring down thence at full speed, and that his own party, in terror and confusion, were abandoning their arms and ranks, laying hold of them one by one, standing in their way and appealing to the faith of gods and men, he declared that their flight would avail them nothing if they deserted their post; if they passed the bridge, there would soon be more of the enemy in the Palatium and Capitol than in the Janiculum. For that reason he charged them to demolish the bridge, by sword, by fire, or by any means whatever; declaring that he would stand the shock of the enemy as far as could be done by one man. He then advanced to the first entrance of the bridge, and being easily distinguished among those who showed their backs in retreating, faced about to engage the foe hand to hand, and by his surprising bravery he terrified the enemy. Two indeed remained with him from a sense of shame: Sp. Lartius and T. Herminius, men eminent for their birth, and renowned for their gallant exploits. With them he for a short time stood the first storm of the danger, and the severest brunt of the battle. But as they who demolished the bridge called upon them to retire, he obliged them also to withdraw to a place of safety on a small portion of the bridge that was still left. Then casting his stern eyes toward the officers of the Etrurians in a threatening manner, he now challenged them singly, and then reproached them, slaves of haughty tyrants who, regardless of their own freedom, came to oppress the liberty of others. They hesitated for a time, looking round one at the other, to begin the fight; shame then put the army in motion, and a shout being raised, they hurled weapons from all sides at their single adversary; and when they all stuck in his upraised shield, and he with no less obstinacy kept possession of the bridge, they endeavoured to thrust him down from it by one push, when the crash of the falling bridge was heard, and at the same time a shout of the Romans raised for joy at having completed their purpose, checked their ardour with sudden panic. Then said Cocles: "Holy Father Tiber, I pray thee, receive these arms, and this thy soldier, in thy propitious stream." Armed as he was, he leaped into the Tiber, and amid showers of darts, swam across safe to his party, having dared an act which is likely to obtain with posterity more fame than credit. The state was grateful for such valour; a statue was erected to him in the comitium, and as much land given to him as he could plough in one day. The zeal of private individuals was also conspicuous among his public honours. For amid the great scarcity, each contributed something, according to his supply, depriving himself of his own support.

THE FIGHT ON THE HILLTOP

Ernest Hemingway

El Sordo was making his fight on a hilltop. He did not like this hill and when he saw it he thought it had the shape of a chancre. But he had had no choice except this hill and he had picked it as far away as he could see it and galloped for it, the automatic rifle heavy on his back, the horse labouring, barrel heaving between his thighs, the sack of grenades swinging against one side, the sack of automatic rifle pans banging against the other, and Joaquín and Ignacio halting and firing, halting and firing to give him time to get the gun in place.

There had still been snow then, the snow that had ruined them, and when his horse was hit so that he wheezed in a slow, jerking, climbing stagger up the last part of the crest, splattering the snow with a bright, pulsing jet, Sordo had hauled him along by the bridle, the reins over his shoulder as he climbed. He climbed as hard as he could with the bullets spatting on the rocks, with the two sacks heavy on his shoulders, and then, holding the horse by the mane, had shot him quickly, expertly, and tenderly just where he had needed him, so that the horse pitched, head forward down to plug a gap between two rocks. He had gotten the gun to firing over the horse's back and he fired two pans, the gun chattering, the empty shells pitching into the snow, the smell of burnt hair from the burnt hide where the hot muzzle rested, him firing at what came up to the hill, forcing them to scatter for cover, while all the time there was a chill in his back from not knowing what was behind him. Once the last of the five men had reached the hilltop the chill went out of his back and he had saved the pans he had left until he would need them.

There were two more horses dead along the slope and three more were dead here on the hilltop. He had only succeeded in stealing three horses last night and one had bolted when they tried to mount him bareback in the corral at the camp when the first shooting had started.

Of the five men who reached the hilltop three were wounded. Sordo was wounded in the calf of his leg and in two places in his left arm. He was very thirsty, his wounds had stiffened, and one of the wounds in his left arm was very painful. He also had a bad headache and as he lay waiting for the planes to come he thought of a joke in Spanish. It was, "*Hay que tomar la muerte como si fuera aspirina*," which means, "You will have to take death as an aspirin." But he did not make the joke aloud. He grinned somewhere inside the pain in his head and inside the nausea that came whenever he moved his arm and looked around at what was left of his band.

The five men were spread out like the points of a five-pointed star. They had dug with their knees and hands and made mounds in front of their heads and shoulders with the dirt and piles of stones. Using this cover, they were linking the individual mounds up with stones and dirt. Joaquín, who was eighteen years old, had a steel helmet that he dug with and he passed dirt in it.

He had gotten this helmet at the blowing up of the train. It had a bullet hole through it and every one had always joked at him for keeping it. But he had hammered the jagged edges of the bullet hole smooth and driven a wooden plug into it and then cut the plug off and smoothed it even with the metal inside the helmet.

When the shooting started he had clapped this helmet on his head so hard it banged his head as though he had been hit with a casserole and, in the last lung-aching, leg-dead, mouth-dry, bullet-spatting, bullet-cracking, bullet-singing run up the final slope of the hill after his horse was killed, the helmet had seemed to weigh a great amount and to ring his bursting forehead with an iron band. But he had kept it. Now he dug with it in a steady, almost machine-like desperation. He had not yet been hit.

"It serves for something finally," Sordo said to him in his deep, throaty voice.

"*Resistir y fortificar es vencer*," Joaquín said, his mouth stiff with the dryness of fear which surpassed the normal thirst of battle. It was one of the slogans of the Communist party and it meant, "Hold out and fortify, and you will win."

Sordo looked away and down the slope at where a cavalryman was sniping from behind a boulder. He was very fond of this boy and he was in no mood for slogans.

"What did you say?"

One of the men turned from the building that he was doing. This man was lying flat on his face, reaching carefully up with his hands to put a rock in place while keeping his chin flat against the ground.

Joaquín repeated the slogan in his dried-up boy's voice without checking his digging for a moment.

"What was the last word?" the man with his chin on the ground asked.

"*Vencer*," the boy said. "Win."

"*Mierda*," the man with his chin on the ground said.

"There is another that applies to here," Joaquín said, bringing them out as though they were talismans, "Pasionaria says it is better to die on your feet than to live on your knees."

"*Mierda* again," the man said and another man said, over his shoulder, "We're on our bellies, not our knees."

"Thou, Communist. Do you know your Pasionaria has a son thy age in Russia since the start of the movement?"

"It's a lie," Joaquín said.

"*Qué va*, it's a lie," the other said. "The dynamiter with the rare name told me. He was of thy party, too. Why should he lie?"

"It's a lie," Joaquín said. "She would not do such a thing as keep a son hidden in Russia out of the war."

"I wish I were in Russia," another of Sordo's men said. "Will not thy Pasionaria send me now from here to Russia, Communist?"

"If thou believest so much in thy Pasionaria, get her to get us off this hill," one of the men who had a bandaged thigh said.

"The fascists will do that," the man with his chin in the dirt said.

"Do not speak thus," Joaquín said to him.

"Wipe the pap of your mother's breast off thy lips and give me a hatful of that dirt," the man with his chin on the ground said. "No one of us will see the sun go down this night."

El Sordo was thinking: It is shaped like a chancre. Or the breast of a young girl with no nipple. Or the top cone of a volcano. You have never seen a volcano, he thought. Nor will you ever see one. And this hill is like a chancre. Let the volcano alone. It's late now for the volcanos.

He looked very carefully around the withers of the dead horse and there was a quick hammering of firing from behind a boulder well down the slope and he heard the bullets from the submachine gun thud into the horse. He crawled along behind the horse and looked out of the angle between the horse's hindquarters and the rock. There were three bodies on the slope just below him where they had fallen when the fascists had rushed the crest under cover of the automatic rifle and submachine gunfire and he and the others had broken down the attack by throwing and rolling down hand grenades. There were other bodies that he could not see on the other sides of the hill crest. There was no dead ground by which attackers could approach the summit and Sordo knew that as long as his ammunition and grenades held out and he had as many as four men they could not get him out of there unless they brought up a trench mortar. He did not know whether they had sent to La Granja for a trench mortar. Perhaps they had not, because surely, soon, the planes would come. It had been four hours since the observation plane had flown over them.

This hill is truly like a chancre, Sordo thought, and we are the very pus of it. But we killed many when they made that stupidness. How could they think that they would take us thus? They have such modern armament that they lose all their sense with overconfidence. He had killed the young officer who had led the assault with a grenade that had gone bouncing and rolling down the slope as they came up it, running, bent half over. In the yellow flash and grey roar of smoke he had seen the officer dive forward to where he lay now like a heavy, broken bundle of old clothing marking the farthest point that the assault had reached. Sordo looked at this body and then, down the hill, at the others.

They are brave but stupid people, he thought. But they have sense enough now not to attack us again until the planes come. Unless, of course, they have a mortar coming. It would be easy with a mortar. The mortar was the normal thing and he knew that they would die as soon as a mortar came up, but when he thought of the planes coming up he felt as naked on that hilltop as though all of his clothing and even his skin had been removed. There is no nakeder thing than I feel, he thought. A flayed rabbit is as well covered as a bear in comparison. But why should they bring planes? They could get us out of here with a trench mortar easily. They are proud of their planes, though, and they will probably bring them. Just as they were so proud of their automatic weapons that they made that stupidness. But undoubtedly they must have sent for a mortar, too.

One of the men fired. Then jerked the bolt and fired again, quickly.

" Save thy cartridges," Sordo said.

" One of the sons of the great whore tried to reach that boulder," the man pointed.

" Did you hit him?" Sordo asked, turning his head with difficulty.

"Nay," the man said. "The fornicator ducked back."

"Who is a whore of whores is Pilar," the man with his chin in the dirt said. "That whore knows we are dying here."

"She could do no good," Sordo said. The man had spoken on the side of his good ear and he had heard him without turning his head. "What could she do?"

"Take these sluts from the rear."

"*Qué va,*" Sordo said. "They are spread around a hillside. How would she come on them? There are a very hundred and fifty of them. Maybe more now."

"But if we hold out until dark," Joaquín said.

"And if Christmas comes on Easter," the man with his chin on the ground said.

"And if thy aunt had *cojones* she would be thy uncle," another said to him. "Send for thy Pasionaria. She alone can help us."

"I do not believe that about the son," Joaquín said. "Or if he is there he is training to be an aviator or something of that sort."

"He is hidden there for safety," the man told him.

"He is studying dialectics. Thy Pasionaria has been there. So have Lister and Modesto and others. The one with the rare name told me."

"That they should go to study and return to aid us," Joaquín said.

"That they should aid us now," another man said. "That all the cruts of Russian sucking swindlers should aid us now." He fired and said, "*Me cago en tal;* I missed him again."

"Save thy cartridges and do not talk so much or thou wilt be very thirsty," Sordo said. "There is no water on this hill."

"Take this," the man said and rolling on his side he pulled a wineskin that he wore slung from his shoulder over his head and handed it to Sordo. "Wash thy mouth out, old one. Thou must have much thirst with thy wounds."

"Let all take it," Sordo said.

"Then I will have some first," the owner said and squirted a long stream into his mouth before he handed the leather bottle around.

"Sordo, when thinkest thou the planes will come?" the man with his chin in the dirt asked.

"Any time," said Sordo. "They should have come before."

"Do you think these sons of the great whore will attack again?"

"Only if the planes do not come."

He did not think there was any need to speak about the mortar. They would know it soon enough when the mortar came.

"God knows they've enough planes with what we saw yesterday."

"Too many," Sordo said.

His head hurt very much and his arm was stiffening so that the pain of moving it was almost unbearable. He looked up at the bright, high blue early summer sky as he raised the leather wine bottle with his good arm. He was fifty-two years old and he was sure this was the last time he would see that sky.

He was not at all afraid of dying but he was angry at being trapped on this hill which was only utilizable as a place to die. If we could have gotten clear, he thought. If we could have made them come up the long valley or if we could have broken loose across the road it would have been all right. But this chancre of a hill. We must use it as well as we can and we have used it very well so far.

If he had known how many men in history have had to use a hill to die on it would not have cheered him any for, in the moment he was passing through, men are not impressed by what has happened to other men in similar circumstances any more than a widow of one day is helped by the knowledge that other loved husbands have died. Whether one has fear of it or not, one's death is difficult to accept. Sordo had accepted it but there was no sweetness in its acceptance even at fifty-two, with three wounds and him surrounded on a hill.

He joked about it to himself but he looked at the sky and at the far mountains and he swallowed the wine and he did not want it. If one must die, he thought, and clearly one must, I can die. But I hate it.

Dying was nothing and he had no picture of it nor fear of it in his mind. But living was a field of grain blowing in the wind on the side of a hill. Living was a hawk in the sky. Living was an earthen jar of water in the dust of the threshing with the grain flailed out and the chaff blowing. Living was a horse between your legs and a carbine under one leg and a hill and a valley and a stream with trees along it and the far side of the valley and the hills beyond.

Sordo passed the wine bottle back and nodded his head in thanks. He leaned forward and patted the dead horse on the shoulder where the muzzle of the automatic rifle had burned the hide. He could still smell the burnt hair. He thought how he had held the horse there, trembling, with the fire around them, whispering and cracking, over and around them like a curtain, and had carefully shot him just at the intersection of the crosslines between the two eyes and the ears. Then as the horse pitched down he had dropped down behind his warm, wet back to get the gun to going as they came up the hill.

" *Eras mucho caballo*," he said, meaning, " Thou wert plenty of horse."

El Sordo lay now on his good side and looked up at the sky. He was lying on a heap of empty cartridge hulls but his head was protected by the rock and his body lay in the lee of the horse. His wounds had stiffened badly and he had much pain and he felt too tired to move.

" What passes with thee, old one?" the man next to him asked.

" Nothing. I am taking a little rest."

" Sleep," the other said. " *They* will wake us when they come."

Just then some one shouted from down the slope.

" Listen, bandits!" the voice came from behind the rocks where the closest automatic rifle was placed. " Surrender now before the planes blow you to pieces."

" What is it he says?" Sordo asked.

Joaquín told him. Sordo rolled to one side and pulled himself up so that he was crouched behind the gun again.

" Maybe the planes aren't coming," he said. " Don't answer them and do not fire. Maybe we can get them to attack again."

" If we should insult them a little?" the man who had spoken to Joaquín about La Pasionaria's son in Russia asked.

" No," Sordo said. " Give me thy big pistol. Who has a big pistol?"

" Here."

" Give it to me." Crouched on his knees he took the big 9 mm. Star and fired one shot into the ground beside the dead horse, waited, then fired again four times at irregular intervals. Then he waited while he counted sixty and then fired a final shot directly into the body of the dead horse. He grinned and handed back the pistol.

" Reload it," he whispered, " and that every one should keep his mouth shut and no one shoot."

" *Bandidos!*" the voice shouted from behind the rocks.

No one spoke on the hill.

"*Bandidos!* Surrender now before we blow thee to little pieces."

"They're biting," Sordo whispered happily.

As he watched, a man showed his head over the top of the rocks. There was no shot from the hilltop and the head went down again. El Sordo waited, watching, but nothing more happened. He turned his head and looked at the others who were all watching down their sectors of the slope. As he looked at them the others shook their heads.

"Let no one move," he whispered.

"Sons of the great whore," the voice came now from behind the rocks again.

"Red swine. Mother rapers. Eaters of the milk of thy fathers."

Sordo grinned. He could just hear the bellowed insults by turning his good ear. This is better than the aspirin, he thought. How many will we get? Can they be that foolish? The voice had stopped again and for three minutes they heard nothing and saw no movement. Then the sniper behind the boulder a hundred yards down the slope exposed himself and fired. The bullet hit a rock and ricocheted with a sharp whine. Then Sordo saw a man, bent double, run from the shelter of the rocks where the automatic rifle was across the open ground to the big boulder behind which the sniper was hidden. He almost dove behind the boulder.

Sordo looked around. They signalled to him that there was no movement on the other slopes. El Sordo grinned happily and shook his head. This is ten times better than the aspirin, he thought, and he waited, as happy as only a hunter can be happy.

Below on the slope the man who had run from the pile of stones to the shelter of the boulder was speaking to the sniper.

"Do you believe it?"

"I don't know," the sniper said.

"It would be logical," the man, who was the officer in command, said. "They are surrounded. They have nothing to expect but to die."

The sniper said nothing.

"What do you think?" the officer asked.

"Nothing," the sniper said.

"Have you seen any movement since the shots?"

"None at all."

The officer looked at his wrist watch. It was ten minutes to three o'clock.

"The planes should have come an hour ago," he said. Just then another officer flopped in behind the boulder. The sniper moved over to make room for him.

"Thou, Paco," the first officer said. "How does it seem to thee?"

The second officer was breathing heavily from his sprint up and across the hillside from the automatic rifle position

"For me it is a trick," he said.

"But if it is not? What a ridicule we make waiting here and laying siege to dead men."

"We have done something worse than ridiculous already," the second officer said. "Look at that slope."

He looked up the slope to where the dead were scattered close to the top. From where he looked the line of the hilltop showed the scattered rocks, the belly, projecting legs, shod hooves jutting out, of Sordo's horse, and the fresh dirt thrown up by the digging.

"What about the mortars?" asked the second officer.

"They should be here in an hour. If not before."

"Then wait for them. There has been enough stupidity already."

"*Bandidos!*" the first officer shouted suddenly, getting to his feet and putting his head well up above the boulder so that the crest of the hill looked much closer as he stood upright. "Red swine! Cowards!"

The second officer looked at the sniper and shook his head. The sniper looked away but his lips tightened.

The first officer stood there, his head all clear of the rock and with his hand on his pistol butt. He cursed and vilified the hilltop. Nothing happened. Then he stepped clear of the boulder and stood there looking up the hill.

"Fire, cowards, if you are alive," he shouted. "Fire on me who has no fear of any Red that ever came out of the belly of the great whore."

This last was quite a long sentence to shout and the officer's face was red and congested as he finished.

The second officer, who was a thin sunburned man with quiet eyes, a thin-lipped mouth and a stubble of beard over his hollow cheeks, shook his head again. It was this officer who was shouting who had ordered the first assault. The young lieutenant who was dead up the slope had been the best friend of this other lieutenant who was named Paco Berrendo and who was listening to the shouting of the captain, who was obviously in a state of exaltation.

92

"Those are the swine who shot my sister and my mother," the captain said. He had a red face and a blond, British-looking moustache and there was something wrong about his eyes. They were a light blue and the lashes were light, too. As you looked at them they seemed to focus slowly. Then "Reds," he shouted, "Cowards!" and commenced cursing again.

He stood absolutely clear now and, sighting carefully, fired his pistol at the only target that the hilltop presented: the dead horse that had belonged to Sordo. The bullet threw up a puff of dirt fifteen yards below the horse. The captain fired again. The bullet hit a rock and sung off.

The captain stood there looking at the hilltop. The Lieutenant Berrendo was looking at the body of the other lieutenant just below the summit. The sniper was looking at the ground under his eyes. Then he looked up at the captain.

"There is no one alive up there," the captain said. "Thou," he said to the sniper, "go up there and see."

The sniper looked down. He said nothing.

"Don't you hear me?" the captain shouted at him.

"Yes, my captain," the sniper said, not looking at him.

"Then get up and go." The captain still had his pistol out. "Do you hear me?"

"Yes, my captain."

"Why don't you go, then?"

"I don't want to, my captain."

"You don't *want* to?" The captain pushed the pistol against the small of the man's back. "You don't *want* to?"

"I am afraid, my captain," the soldier said with dignity.

Lieutenant Berrendo, watching the captain's face and his odd eyes, thought he was going to shoot the man then.

"Captain Mora," he said.

"Lieutenant Berrendo?"

"It is possible the soldier is right."

"That he is right to say he is afraid? That he is right to say he does not *want* to obey an order?"

"No. That he is right that it is a trick."

"They are all dead," the captain said. "Don't you hear me say they are all dead?"

"You mean our comrades on the slope?" Berrendo asked him. "I agree with you."

"Paco," the captain said, "don't be a fool. Do you think you are the only one who cared for Julián? I tell you the Reds are dead. Look!"

93

He stood up, then put both hands on top of the boulder and pulled himself up, kneeling-up awkwardly, then getting on his feet.

"Shoot," he shouted, standing on the grey granite boulder and waved both his arms. "Shoot me! Kill me!"

On the hilltop El Sordo lay behind the dead horse and grinned.

What a people, he thought. He laughed, trying to hold it in because the shaking hurt his arm.

"Reds," came the shout from below. "Red canaille. Shoot me! Kill me!"

Sordo, his chest shaking, barely peered past the horse's crupper and saw the captain on top of the boulder waving his arms. Another officer stood by the boulder. The sniper was standing at the other side. Sordo kept his eye where it was and shook his head happily.

"Shoot me," he said softly to himself. "Kill me!" Then his shoulders shook again. The laughing hurt his arm and each time he laughed his head felt as though it would burst, but the laughter shook him again like a spasm.

Captain Mora got down from the boulder.

"Now do you believe me, Paco?" he questioned Lieutenant Berrendo.

"No," said Lieutenant Berrendo.

"*Cojones!*" the captain said. "Here there is nothing but idiots and cowards."

The sniper had gotten carefully behind the boulder again and Lieutenant Berrendo was squatting beside him.

The captain, standing in the open beside the boulder, commenced to shout filth at the hilltop. There is no language so filthy as Spanish. There are words for all the vile words in English and there are other words and expressions that are used only in countries where blasphemy keeps pace with the austerity of religion. Lieutenant Berrendo was a very devout Catholic. So was the sniper. They were Carlists from Navarra and while both of them cursed and blasphemed when they were angry they regarded it as a sin which they regularly confessed.

As they crouched now behind the boulder watching the captain and listening to what he was shouting, they both disassociated themselves from him and what he was saying. They did not want to have that sort of talk on their consciences on a day in which they might die. Talking thus will not bring luck, the sniper thought. Speaking thus of the *Virgen* is bad luck. This one speaks worse than the Reds.

Julián is dead, Lieutenant Berrendo was thinking. Dead there on the slope on such a day as this is. And this foul mouth stands there bringing more ill fortune with his blasphemies.

Now the captain stopped shouting and turned to Lieutenant Berrendo. His eyes looked stranger than ever.

"Paco," he said, happily, "you and I will go up there."

"Not me."

"What?" The captain had his pistol out again.

I hate these pistol brandishers, Berrendo was thinking. They cannot give an order without jerking a gun out. They probably pull out their pistols when they go to the toilet and order the move they will make.

"I will go if you order me to. But under protest," Lieutenant Berrendo told the captain.

"Then I will go alone," the captain said. "The smell of cowardice is too strong here."

Holding his pistol in his right hand, he strode steadily up the slope. Berrendo and the sniper watched him. He was making no attempt to take any cover and he was looking straight ahead of him at the rocks, the dead horse, and the fresh-dug dirt of the hilltop.

El Sordo lay behind the horse at the corner of the rock, watching the captain come striding up the hill.

Only one, he thought. We got only one. But from his manner of speaking, he is *caza mayor*. Look at him walking. Look what an animal. Look at him stride forward. This one is for me. This one I take with me on the trip. This one coming now makes the same voyage I do. Come on, Comrade Voyager. Come striding. Come right along. Come along to meet it. Come on. Keep on walking. Don't slow up. Come right along. Come as thou art coming. Don't stop and look at those. That's right. Don't even look down. Keep on coming with your eyes forward. Look, he has a moustache. What do you think of that? He runs to a moustache, the Comrade Voyager. He is a captain. Look at his sleeves. I said he was *caza mayor*. He has the face of an *Inglés*. Look. With a red face and blond hair and blue eyes. With no cap on and his moustache is yellow. With blue eyes. With pale blue eyes. With pale blue eyes with something wrong with them. With pale blue eyes that don't focus. Close enough. Too close. Yes, Comrade Voyager. Take it. Comrade Voyager.

He squeezed the trigger of the automatic rifle gently and it pounded back three times against his shoulder with the slippery jolt the recoil of a tripoded automatic weapon gives.

The captain lay on his face on the hillside. His left arm was under him. His right arm that had held the pistol was stretched forward of his head. From all down the slope they were firing on the hill crest again.

Crouched behind the boulder, thinking that now he would have to sprint across that open space under fire, Lieutenant Berrendo heard the deep hoarse voice of Sordo from the hill-top.

"Bandidos!" the voice came. "Bandidos! shoot me! Kill me!"

On the top of the hill El Sordo lay behind the automatic rifle laughing so that his chest ached, so that he thought the top of his head would burst.

"*Bandidos*," he shouted again happily. "Kill me, *bandidos*!" Then he shook his head happily. We have lots of company for the Voyage, he thought.

He was going to try for the other officer with the automatic rifle when he would leave the shelter of the boulder. Sooner or later he would have to leave it. Sordo knew that he could never command from there and he thought he had a very good chance to get him.

Just then the others on the hill heard the first sound of the coming of the planes.

El Sordo did not hear them. He was covering the down-slope edge of the boulder with his automatic rifle and he was thinking: when I see him he will be running already and I will miss him if I am not careful. I could shoot behind him all across that stretch. I should swing the gun with him and ahead of him. Or let him start and then get on him and ahead of him. I will try to pick him up there at the edge of the rock and swing just ahead of him. Then he felt a touch on his shoulder and he turned and saw the grey, fear-drained face of Joaquín and he looked where the boy was pointing and saw the three planes coming.

At this moment Lieutenant Berrendo broke from behind the boulder and, with his head bent and his legs plunging, ran down and across the slope to the shelter of the rocks where the automatic rifle was placed.

Watching the planes, Sordo never saw him go.

"Help me to pull this out," he said to Joaquín and the boy dragged the automatic rifle clear from between the horse and the rock.

The planes were coming on steadily. They were in echelon and each second they grew larger and their noise was greater.

"Lie on your backs to fire at them," Sordo said. "Fire ahead of them as they come."

He was watching them all the time. "*Cabrones! Hijos de puta!*" he said rapidly.

"Ignacio!" he said. "Put the gun on the shoulder of the boy. Thou!" to Joaquín. "Sit there and do not move. Crouch over. More. No. More."

He lay back and sighted with the automatic rifle as the planes came on steadily.

"Thou, Ignacio, hold me the three legs of that tripod." They were dangling down the boy's back and the muzzle of the gun was shaking from the jerking of his body that Joaquín could not control as he crouched with bent head hearing the droning roar of their coming.

Lying flat on his belly and looking up into the sky watching them come, Ignacio gathered the legs of the tripod into his two hands and steadied the gun.

"Keep thy head down," he said to Joaquín. "Keep thy head forward."

"Pasionaria says 'Better to die on thy—'" Joaquín was saying to himself as the drone came nearer them. Then he shifted suddenly into "Hail Mary, full of grace, the Lord is with thee; Blessed art thou among women and Blessed is the fruit of thy womb, Jesus. Holy Mary, Mother of God, pray for us sinners now and at the hour of our death. Amen. Holy Mary, Mother of God," he started, then he remembered quickly as the roar came now unbearably and started an act of contrition racing in it, "Oh my God, I am heartily sorry for having offended thee who art worthy of all my love——"

Then there were the hammering explosions past his ears and the gun barrel hot against his shoulder. It was hammering now again and his ears were deafened by the muzzle blast. Ignacio was pulling down hard on the tripod and the barrel was burning his back. It was hammering now in the roar and he could not remember the act of contrition.

All he could remember was at the hour of our death. Amen. At the hour of our death. Amen. At the hour. At the hour. Amen. The others all were firing. Now and at the hour of our death. Amen.

Then, through the hammering of the gun, there was the whistle of the air splitting apart and then in the red black roar the earth rolled under his knees and then waved up to hit him in the face and then dirt and bits of rock were falling all over and Ignacio was lying on him and the gun was lying on him. But he was not dead because the whistle came again and the earth rolled under him with the roar. Then it came again and the earth lurched under his belly and one side of the hilltop rose into the air and then fell slowly over them where they lay.

The planes came back three times and bombed the hilltop but no one on the hilltop knew it. Then the planes machine-gunned the hilltop and went away. As they dove on the hill for the last time with their machine guns hammering, the first plane pulled up and winged over and then each plane did the same and they moved from echelon to V-formation and went away into the sky in the direction of Segovia.

Keeping a heavy fire on the hilltop, Lieutenant Berrendo pushed a patrol up to one of the bomb craters from where they could throw grenades onto the crest. He was taking no chances of any one being alive and waiting for them in the mess that was up there and he threw four grenades into the confusion of dead horses, broken and split rocks, and torn yellow-stained explosive-stinking earth before he climbed out of the bomb crater and walked over to have a look.

No one was alive on the hilltop except the boy Joaquín, who was unconscious under the dead body of Ignacio. Joaquín was bleeding from the nose and from the ears. He had known nothing and had no feeling since he had suddenly been in the very heart of the thunder and the breath had been wrenched from his body when the one bomb struck so close and Lieutenant Berrendo made the sign of the cross and then shot him in the back of the head, as quickly and as gently, if such an abrupt movement can be gentle, as Sordo had shot the wounded horse.

Lieutenant Berrendo stood on the hilltop and looked down the slope at his own dead and then across the country seeing where they had galloped before Sordo had turned at bay here. He noticed all the dispositions that had been made of the troops and then he ordered the dead men's horses to be brought up and the bodies tied across the saddles so that they might be packed in to La Granja.

"Take that one, too," he said. "The one with his hands on the automatic rifle. That should be Sordo. He is the oldest and it was he with the gun. No. Cut the head off and wrap it in a poncho." He considered a minute. "You might as well take all the heads. And of the others below on the slope and where we first found them. Collect the rifles and pistols and pack that gun on a horse."

Then he walked down to where the lieutenant lay who had been killed in the first assault. He looked down at him but did not touch him.

"*Qué cosa más mala es la guerra*," he said to himself, which meant, "What a bad thing war is."

Then he made the sign of the cross again and as he walked down the hill he said five Our Fathers and five Hail Marys for the repose of the soul of his dead comrade. He did not wish to stay to see his orders being carried out.

AT ALL COSTS

Richard Aldington

"Blast!"

Captain Hanley, commanding "B" Company, stumbled over a broken duckboard and fell forward against the side of the trench. His tilted helmet shielded his face, but the trench wall felt oozy and soggy to his naked hand as he tried to steady himself.

"Mind that hole, Parker."

"Very good, sir."

He felt wet mud soaking through his breeches above the short gum boots, and his right sleeve was wet to the elbow. He fumbled in his gas bag, also wet with slimy mud, to see that the mask goggles were unbroken. O.K., but he swore again with a sort of exasperated groan over the crashing bruise on his right knee.

"Are you 'it, sir?"

"No, I only fell in that mucking hole again. I've told the ser'ant-major umpteen times to get it mended. One of these days the brigadier'll fall into it and then there'll be hell to pay. Help me find my torch. I hope the bloody thing isn't broken." The two men groped in the darkness, fingering the slimy mud and tilted broken duckboards. Suddenly they crashed helmets.

"Sorry, sir."

"All right, sorry."

"Doesn't seem to be 'ere, sir."

"Never mind, we'll look for it in the morning."

They stumbled on cautiously. The trench was very deep (old German communication), very dark, very shell-smashed, very muddy. A black, heavy-clouded night, about an hour before dawn. Occasionally a strange ghostly glow appeared as a distant Very light was fired, and made for them a near dark horizon of tumbled shell-tormented parapet. The trench swerved, and Hanley dimly made out the shape of three crosses —Canadians. Halfway. Fifty yards farther on was another turn, where a piece of corrugated iron revetment had been flung onto the top of the high parapet, where its jagged outline looked like a grotesque heraldic dragon.

It had been an ideal night for gas and would be an ideal

From: *Roads to Glory*, by permission of the Author.

dawn—heavy, windless, foggy—for a surprise attack. Hanley had been up and about the trenches most of the night. Since that rotten gas attack on the Somme, where he lost twenty-three men, he took no risks. Up and down the trenches, warning the N.C.O.s to look out for gas. Now he was on the way to his advance posts. Be there in case of an attack. . . .

Splash, squelch, splodge. Somebody coming towards them.

"Who are you?"

"Mockery."

"Is that the word tonight, Parker?"

"Yessir."

"That you, Hanley?" Voice coming towards them.

"Hullo, Williams. I thought you were in Hurdle Alley?"

"I was, but I thought I'd have a look at these posts. They're a hell of a way from the front line."

"I know. Damn this organisation in depth. Are they all right?"

"Yes. He sent over about forty minnies, Ser'ant Cramp said, but no casualties. He was flipping over some of those flying pineapples when I left."

From their own back areas came an irregular but ceaseless crashing of artillery. Heavy shells shrilled high above them as they swooped at enemy communications and night parties.

"Strafing the old Boche a good bit tonight," said Williams.

"Yes, it's been quite heavy. Might almost be a windup at H.Q."

"Boche are very quiet tonight."

"Yes; well, cheerio. Tell Thompson to keep our breakfast hot; and don't stand down until I get back."

"Right you are, cheerio."

Hanley visited his posts. They were established in a ruined unrepaired German trench at the foot of a long forward slope. This had once been the British front line, but was now held only by scattered observation posts, with the main front line several hundred yards to the rear. The British bombardment increased, and the shrill scream of the passing shells was almost continuous. Very lights and rockets went up from the German lines. Hanley cursed the loss of his torch—damned difficult to get about without it. He came to the first post.

"You there, Ser'ant Tomlinson?"

A figure moved in the darkness.

"Yes, sir."

"Anything to report?"

"No, sir."

"Mr. Williams said there were some minnies and pine-apples."

"Yes, sir, but it's very quiet, sir."

"Um. Any patrols still out?"

"No, sir, all in."

"Very well. Carry on, ser'ant."

"Very good, sir."

Much the same news at the other posts. Hanley returned to Number 1 post, nearest the communication trench, at dawn. The men were standing to. Hanley got on the fire-step in a shell-smashed abandoned bay, and watched with his glasses slung round his neck. The artillery had died down to a couple of batteries, when the first perceptible lightening of the air came. Hanley felt cold in his mud-soaked breeches and tunic. Very gradually, very slowly, the darkness dissipated, as if thin imperceptible veils were being rolled up in a transformation scene. The British wire became visible. In the trembling misty light No Man's Land seemed alive with strange shapes and movements. Hanley pressed cold hands on his hot eyes, puffy with lack of sleep. He looked again. Yes, yes, surely, they were climbing over the parapet and lying down in front. He seized a rifle leaning against the trench, loaded with an S O S rocket bomb. Funny Sergeant Tomlinson and the men were so silent. Perhaps he was imagining things, the same old dawn-mirage movement which had been responsible for so many false alarms. He waited a couple of minutes with closed eyes, and then looked very carefully through his glasses. Silly ass! The men coming over the parapets were the German wire pickets. He put the rifle down, glad the men had not seen him, and went round the traverse to Sergeant Tomlinson and Parker.

"Stand to for another twenty minutes, ser'ant, and then let two men from Number 2 post and two from Number 4 go and get your breakfasts."

"Very good, sir."

On the way back Hanley found his torch—the glass bulb was smashed; like most things in this bloody war, he reflected. Well, they'd passed another dawn without an attack—that was something. He got on a fire-step in the main line and took another look. A cloudy but rainless morning. Not a sign of life in the enemy trenches, scarcely a sound. He gave the order to stand down, and sent Parker to join his section for breakfast.

The company dugout was a large one, built as the head-quarters of a German battalion. It was remarkably lousy. Hanley threw his torch, revolver-belt, and helmet on his wire and sacking bed, and sat down on a box beside a small table laid with four knives and forks on a newspaper. He felt tired, too tired even to enjoy the hot bacon and eggs which formed the infantry officers' best meal of the day. The three subalterns chatted. Hanley pushed away his plate and stood up.

"I'm going to turn in. Tell the signaller to wake me if anything important happens."

"Right-o."

Hanley hung up his revolver and helmet, arranged his pack as a pillow, swung himself still booted and wet onto the bed, and wrapped himself in a blanket. For a few minutes he lay drowsily, listening to the throb of blood in his head and the quiet mutter of the other officers. His eyes still ached even when shut. He drowsed, then half awoke as he remembered that he had not indented for enough ammunition, decided that could wait, and—was dead asleep.

Hanley opened his eyes and lay quite still. Why were they talking so loudly? In a flash he was wide awake and swung up, sitting with his legs over the side of the bed. The colonel. Damn! Being found asleep like that! And, of course, the colonel would not know that he had been up and down the line all night. Damn! Well, never mind. He gave one dab with both hands at his rumpled hair, and stood up.

"Good morning, sir."

"Oh, good morning, Hanley. Williams said you'd been up all night. Sorry to disturb you."

"Quite all right, sir."

A large-scale trench map of their sector was spread on the table, half concealing another small-scale artillery map of the whole district.

"Just sit down for a few minutes, Hanley. I've got important news."

The other officers grouped beside them, gazing at the colonel and listening.

"Very important news," the colonel went on in a slow voice, "and not particularly pleasant, I'm afraid."

He pulled a neat bundle of documents from his pocket, opened one labelled " SECRET AND CONFIDENTIAL " and spread it on the table. They all gazed at it—the inexorable decree of Fate—and then again at the colonel, the agent of that Fate, of all their fates.

"That is a confidential document from Corps Headquarters.

I'll tell you briefly what it is, and you can look it over after-wards. The night before last the division on our left made an identification raid, and captured a prisoner. From this and other information it seems certain that we shall be attacked—tomorrow morning—about an hour before dawn."

Each of the four company officers drew a short imperceptible breath, glanced at each other and then quickly away. Hanley leaned his elbow on the table.

"Yes, sir?"

"It will be a surprise attack, with a very short but violent preliminary bombardment." The colonel spoke very slowly and deliberately, looking down absently at the map, and gently twisting the lowest button of his tunic with the fingers of his right hand. "All reports confirm our information, and the Air Force report great enemy activity behind the lines. You heard the bombardment of their communications last night."

"Yes, sir."

There was complete silence in the dugout, as the colonel paused. A pile of tin plates fell with a clatter in the servants' compartment. None of the officers moved. Hanley noticed how clean the colonel's gas bag was.

"There will probably be twenty to thirty German divisions in the attack, which will be on a sixteen-mile front. We are about in the middle."

"Yes, sir."

The colonel moved on his box. He stretched out all the fingers of his left hand, and tapped rapidly on the table alternately with the stretched little finger and thumb.

"The Canadian Corps and several reserve divisions are being brought up at once to occupy a position about five miles to our rear. They cannot fully man the whole battle line before three tomorrow afternoon. Our duty is to delay the enemy advance until that time or longer. Our positions must be held at all costs, to the last man."

There was a long silence. The colonel ceased drumming with his fingers and looked at them.

"Have you any questions to ask?"

"Yes, sir. Am I to leave my posts out?"

"Two hours before dawn, you will withdraw them to straighten your own line. One section, with a sergeant and a subaltern, will remain at the end of the communication trench. The subaltern will be a volunteer. His duty is to fire a green light when the German attacking line reaches him. The artillery barrage will then shorten to defend your line.

You, Hanley, will have a Very-light pistol loaded with a red light, and you will fire it when the first German jumps into your trench. The object, of course, is to inform the artillery when they must shorten the defensive barrage."

"Yes, sir."

"Any more questions?"

"No, sir, not for the moment."

"You'll arrange with your officers, Hanley, as to which shall volunteer to fire the green light."

"Very good, sir."

"And I want you to come to a conference of company officers with the brigadier at Battalion Headquarters this afternoon."

"Very good, sir. What time?"

"Oh, make it three o'clock."

"Very well, sir."

The colonel rose.

"You know your battle positions, of course; but we'll discuss that this afternoon. Oh, by the bye, I'm sending up green envelopes for everyone in the company this morning. The letters must be sent down by runner at four. Of course, not a word about the attack must be mentioned either to N.C.O.s or men until after the letters have gone."

"Of course, sir."

"And—er—naturally you will not mention the matter yourselves."

"No, sir, of course not."

"All right. Good-bye. Will you come along with me, Hanley? I should like to walk round your main defence line with you."

"Very good, sir."

There was silence in the dugout. They could hear the colonel and Hanley scuffling up the low dugout stairs. Williams tapped a cigarette on his case and bent down to light it at the candle burning on the table. He puffed a mouthful of smoke, with a twist to his lips.

"Well, that's that. Napoo, eh?"

"Looks like it."

"What about a drink?"

"Right-o."

Williams shouted:

"Thomp-sooon."

From the distance came a muffled: "Sir?"

A Tommy appeared in the doorway.

"Bring us a bottle of whisky and the mugs."

"Very good, sir."

All that day Hanley was in a state of dazed hebetude, from which he emerged from time to time. He felt vaguely surprised that everything was so much as usual. There were sentries at their posts, runners going along the trenches, an occasional airplane overhead, a little artillery—just the ordinary routine of trench warfare. And yet within twenty-four hours their trenches would be obliterated, he and thousands with him would be dead, obliterated, unless by some chance, some odd freak, he was made prisoner. He heard repeated over and over again in his head the words: "Position must be held at all costs, position must be held at all costs." He felt suddenly angry. Held at all costs! All jolly fine and large to write from the safety of Montreuil, but what about those who had to make good such dramatic sentiments with their lives? The front was ridiculously denuded of men—why, his own under-strength company held very nearly a battalion front, and had a flank to guard as well. If they fought like madmen and stood to the last man, they might hold up three waves—an hour at most. And they were asked to hold out for nearly twelve hours! Ridiculous, good God, ridiculous!

He found the colonel shaking him by the arm.

"What's the matter with you, Hanley? You don't seem to hear what I'm saying."

"I beg your pardon, sir, I——"

"I think you ought to bring a Lewis gun up to this point. You've got an excellent field of fire here."

"Very good, sir."

Hanley noted the change to be made in his field service message book. They walked on, and the colonel made various other suggestions—so many orders—which Hanley duly noted. The colonel paused at the corner of the communication trench leading to Battalion Headquarters. He waved to the orderlies to stand apart.

"We'll discuss the general plan of defence at the conference this afternoon. Make a note of anything that occurs to you, any information you want, and bring it up."

"Right, sir."

The colonel hesitated a moment.

"It's a very difficult position, Hanley, I know, but we must all do our duty."

"Of course, sir."

" I shall lead the counter-attack of the Reserve Company myself."

" Yes, sir."

" A great deal depends on our putting up a good show."

" Yes, sir."

" I suggest you go round to the dugout and speak to all your men this evening. Put a good face on it, you know. Tell them we are all prepared, and shall easily beat off the attack, and that reinforcements are being hurried up to relieve us. And above all impress upon them that these trenches *must* be held at all costs."

" Very good, sir."

The colonel held out his hand.

" I may not have another opportunity to speak to you in private. Good-bye, and the best of luck. I know you'll do your duty."

" Thank you, sir. Good-bye."

" Good-bye."

When Hanley stooped under the low entrance of the dugout chamber, the three subalterns were seated round the table with flushed cheeks, talking loudly. The whisky bottle was more than half-empty. A sudden spurt of anger shot through him. He strode up to the table and knocked the cork level with the top of the bottle neck with one hard smack of his hand. He spoke harshly:

" What's this nonsense?"

Williams, the eldest of the three subalterns, answered, half-defiantly, half-ashamedly:

" We're only having a drink. Where's the harm?"

" Only a drink! Before lunch! Now, look here, you fellows. The whisky that's left in that bottle is all that's going to be drunk in this mess between now and dawn tomorrow. Understand? One of the damned stupidities of this damned war is that every officer thinks it's the thing to be a boozer. It isn't. The men don't drink. They get a tablespoon of rum a day. Why should we make sots of ourselves? We're responsible for their lives. See? And we're responsible for these trenches. We've got to leave 'em on stretchers or stay here and manure 'em. See? We've got a bloody rotten job ahead of us, a stinking rotten job, and I wish those who ordered it were here to carry out their own damned orders. But they're not. Not bloody likely. But the people at home trust us. We're responsible to them, first and foremost. We took on the job, and we've got to carry it out. And carry it out dead bloody sober. Got me?"

The men were silent, looking sheepishly at the newspaper on the table with its wet rings from mug bottoms. Hanley took an empty mug and tossed some of the whisky from Williams's mug into it.

" Drink up. Here's hell!"

They drank.

Hanley shouted:

" Thomp-sooooon!"

Thompson appeared in the door.

" Take those mugs away."

" Very good, sir."

" How many bottles of whisky have you?"

" Three, sir."

" Bring them here, and a sandbag."

" Very good, sir."

Hanley scribbled a few words in his message book, and tore out the slip. He put the bottles in the sandbag.

" Parker!"

Parker in his turn appeared.

" Sir?"

" Take that sandbag down to Battalion H.Q. Give it to one of the officers, and bring back his signed receipt."

" Very good, sir."

The other officers exchanged glances. Williams, who had his back turned to Hanley, made a grimace of derision. The others frowned at him.

Hanley was busy throughout the day, making arrangements, giving orders, attending the conference—which lasted a long time—and going round to speak to the men. He only had time to write a very brief letter to his wife, enclosing one still briefer to his father. He wrote calmly, almost coldly in his effort to avoid emotion and self-pity. He even managed to squeeze out a joke for each letter. As soon as they were finished the two letters vanished in the open sandbag containing the company mail, and the runner started at once for Headquarters. Somehow it was a relief to have those letters gone. The last links with England, with life, were broken. Finished, done with, almost forgotten. It was easier to carry on now.

But was it? There was that damned business of the volunteer subaltern. Hanley rubbed his clenched fist against his cheek, and found that he had forgotten to shave. He called his servant and told him to bring some hot water in a cigarette tin. Shaving for the last time. Hardly worth it, really. Still, must be done. Morale, and all that.

He shaved carefully. One of the subalterns went out to relieve the officer on duty. One was asleep. Williams was writing a situation report. Hanley bit the back of his hand hard, then shoved both hands in his breeches pockets, looking at Williams's bent head.

"Williams!"

Williams looked up.

"Yes?"

"There's this business of the volunteer to——"

"Oh, that's all settled."

"Settled!"

"Yes. I'm going."

"You're going! But you've only been married two months."

"Yes. That's why I thought I'd like to get it over as quickly as possible."

"But I was going to put your platoon at the end of Hurdle Alley. You might just be able to get back to battalion, you know."

"And feel a swine for the rest of my life—which would be about two hours? Thanks. No, I'd rather get it over, if you don't mind, Hanley."

"Oh, all right."

They were silent. Then Hanley said.

"Well, I'll just go and talk to the men . . . er . . . So long."

"So long."

All working parties were cancelled to give the men as much rest as possible, but there was inevitably a lot of extra work, bringing up ammunition, rations, and water. As soon as dusk fell the whole Reserve Company and some pioneers came up to strengthen the wire. The British artillery was ceaselessly active. Hardly a shot came from the German lines—an ominous sign.

After dinner Hanley lay down to sleep for a few hours. Must be as fresh as possible. He wrapped the blanket up to his chin and shut his eyes. The other three off duty were lying down, too. But Hanley could not sleep. It was all so strange, so strange, and yet so ordinary. Just like any other night, and yet the last night. Inevitably the last night? How could they escape, with orders to hold on at all costs? Half of them would go in the bombardment, which would be terrific. Bombs, bullets, and bayonets would finish off the rest. The dugouts would be wrecked with bombs and high explosive charges. A few of the wounded might be picked up later. A few of the men might escape down Hurdle Alley after the officers were gone. But no, the N.C.O.s could be relied on to hold out to the last. They were done for, napoo. No après la guerre for *them*—bon soir, toodle-oo, good-byeeee. The silly words repeated and repeated in his brain until he hated them. He opened his eyes and gazed at the familiar dugout. His wire bed was at an angle to the others, and he could see the shapes of Williams and the two other officers muffled up silent in their blankets—as still and silent as they would be in twenty-four hours' time. There was the candle burning in the holder roughly bent from a tin biscuit box. The flame was absolutely steady in the airless, earthy smelling dugout. There were the boxes for seats, the table with its maps, tins of cigarettes, chits, and the five mugs beside the whisky bottle for the last parting drink. The bare, murky walls of chalk were damp and clammy-looking with condensed breath. The revolvers, helmets, and gas bags were hung at the bed-heads. He listened to the other men breathing, and felt an absurd regret at leaving the dugout to be smashed. After all, that and other dugouts like it were the only home they had known for months and months. Breaking up the happy home! He became aware that he felt a bit sickish, that he had been feeling like that for several hours, and pretending not to.

He gently drew his wrist from under the blanket and looked at his luminous watch. Eleven thirty-five. He had to be up at two—must get some sleep. With almost a start he noticed that Williams was looking at his own watch in the same stealthy way. So he couldn't sleep either. Poor devil. Profoundly, almost insanely in love with that wife of his. Poor devil. But still, for the matter of that, so was Hanley in love with his wife. His heart seemed to turn in his body, and he felt an acute pain in the muscles above it as he suddenly realised fully that it was all over, that he would never see her again, never feel her mouth pressed to his, never again touch her lovely, friendly body. He clutched his hand over his face until it hurt to prevent himself from groaning. God, what bloody agony! O God, he'd be a mass of dead rotting decay, and she'd still be young and beautiful and alert and desirable, O God, and her life would run on, run on, there'd be all the grief and the sorrowing for her and tears in a cold widowed bed, O God, but the years would run on and she'd still be young and desirable, and somebody else would want her, some youngster, some wangler, and youth and her flesh and life would be clamorous, and her bed would no longer be cold and widowed. O God, God. Something wet ran down his cheek. Not a tear, but the cold clammy sweat from his forehead. God, what agony!

Hanley suddenly sat up. If he was suffering like that, Williams must be suffering, too. Better to get up and pretend to talk than lie and agonise like that. He got out of bed. Williams raised his head:

"What's up. It isn't two, is it?"

The other men looked up, too, showing that neither of them had been asleep. Hanley shivered and rubbed his hands to warm them in the chill dugout.

"No, only five to twelve. But I couldn't sleep. Hope I don't disturb you. Benson must be relieved in a few minutes," he added inconsequently.

The other three rolled out of bed and stood stretching and rubbing their hands.

"Too cold to sleep in this damned damp place," said one of them.

"What about a drink?"

"If you have it now, you can't have it later on," said Hanley. "Better wait until two."

Williams put on his equipment and helmet and went up to relieve Benson. The others sat on the boxes trying to talk. Benson came down.

"Anything on?" asked Hanley casually.

"Lots of lights, ordinary strafing on their side. A hell of a bombardment from our side."

"Perhaps if they see we've got wind of it, they'll postpone the attack?" suggested the youngest officer.

"Rot," said Benson. "They know jolly well that all this part of the line has been denuded to feed the Fifth Army. They'll attack, all right."

They were silent. Hanley looked at his watch. Five past twelve. How damnably slowly the time went; and yet these were their last minutes on earth. He felt something had to be done.

"Let's have a hand at bridge."

"What, tonight, now?"

"Well, why not? It's no good sitting here grumping like owls, and you don't suggest a prayer meeting, do you?"

The last suggestion was met with oaths of a forcible nature. Hanley cleared the table and threw down the cards.

"Cut for deal."

Just before two, Hanley slipped into his breeches pocket the ten francs he had won, and stood up. He put on trench coat and muffler, tried his broken torch for about the twentieth time, then threw it down disgustedly and fitted on his equipment. The subaltern who was to relieve Williams on trench duty was already dressed and waiting. Hanley put on his hat and turned to the others.

"I'll come round and see you after you've taken up battle positions; but if by any chance I don't see you again—cheerio."

"Cheerio."

They found Williams, his runner, and a sergeant waiting in the trench outside the dugout entrance.

"Anything doing?"

"Nothing particular. I went on patrol. Their wire's got gaps cut, with knife-rests in the gaps, all the way along."

"Um."

"Lot of signal rockets, too."

"I see. Our artillery seems to have ceased altogether."

"Saving ammunition for the show."

"Be more sensible to strafe now while the Boche is taking up battle positions."

"Oh, well, that's the staff's job, not ours."

Hanley, Williams, the sergeant, two runners, started for the Outpost Line. The trench was drier, the night not so dark, with faint stars mistily gleaming among light clouds. Weather clearing up—just the Boche's luck again. The five men moved along without talking, absorbed partly in a strange anxious pre-occupation, partly in keeping upright on the slippery trench. Hanley and Williams, of course, knew the full extent of their danger, had faced the ultimate despair, passed beyond revolt or hope. The sergeant still hoped—that he might be wounded and taken prisoner. The two men only knew they were " in for a show." All were dry-mouthed, a little sickish with apprehension, a little awkward in all their movements; the thought of deserting their posts never even occurred to them.

They passed the three Canadian crosses, distinctly outlined on the quiet sky; then the dragon piece of corrugated iron. At the end of the communication trench they found waiting the men from the four posts, under a sergeant. Hanley spoke in low tones—there might be advance patrols lying just outside their wire.

" All your men present, ser'ant?"

" Yes, sir."

" Right. You know your orders. See that each section joins its own platoon, and then report to your own platoon commander. Don't waste time."

" Very good, sir."

The line of men filed past them in the darkness. For the hundredth time Hanley noticed the curious pathos of fatigue in these silent moving figures—the young bodies somehow tired to age and apathy. When they had gone he took Williams a little aside.

" If I were you, I should see that each of you occupies a separate bay. Get in the first bay yourself, then the runner, then the sergeant. They won't dare try to bolt back past you. Besides—er—there's more chance if you're spread out."

" I was wondering what happens if all three of us are knocked out before the Boche actually gets into the trench, and so no green light is fired?"

" Oh, we must risk that. Besides, there are similar volunteer parties on every company front."

" I see."

" I took a compass bearing from the fire-step outside Company H.Q. yesterday, so I shan't miss your light. I expect they'll be on us ten minutes later. Perhaps we'll beat off the first two or three attacks."

" Yes. Perhaps."

They were silent. Then Hanley made an effort.

" Well, good-bye, old man. Best of luck."

" Best of luck, good-bye."

They were too shy and English even to shake hands.

It was past three when Hanley and Parker got back to their own line and found the whole company standing to in battle positions. Hanley kept his signallers on the first floor of the big dugout. He sent off to Battalion Headquarters the code message which meant they were in battle positions and all ready. He took a candle and went down to the lower dugout, where they had spent so many nights. It looked barer and damper than ever, empty except for the bare sacking beds, the boxes, the table.

Outside in the trench the air was moist and fresh. He took two Very pistols, one loaded with green, one with red, and laid them on either side of him on the parapet. Hanley was at the extreme left of the bay, with two riflemen to his right. Twenty yards to his left was the communication trench leading to the outpost line, now blocked with wire and knife-rests, and guarded by a bombing section.

A signaller came up from the dugout with a message. Hanley went down and read it by the light of a candle. He noticed the bowed back and absorbed look of a signaller tapping out a message on a Fullerphone. The message he had received simply reiterated the order that their positions were to be held at all costs. Hanley felt angry, screwed up the piece of paper and stuffed it in his pocket. Damn them, how many more times did they think that order had to be given? He returned to the trench, and resumed his watch.

3.50 A.M. One battery of German guns languishly firing on back areas—pretense that all was as usual.

3.52 A.M. Signal rockets all along the German line. Then silence.

3.55 A.M. Two miles to his right a fierce bombardment, stretching over several miles. The battle had begun.

3.57 A.M. Two miles to his left another bombardment. The British artillery on their own front opened up a defensive barrage.

4 A.M. With a terrific crash, which immediately blotted out the roar of the other bombardments, the German artillery on their own front came into action. Hanley half-recoiled. He had been in several big bombardments, and thought he had experienced the utmost limit of artillery. But this was more tremendous, more hellish, more appalling than anything he had experienced. The trench of the outpost line was one continuous line of red, crashing trench mortars and shells. The communication trench was plastered with five-nines. Shells were falling all along their own line—he heard the sharp cry " Stretcher-bearer " very faintly from somewhere close at hand.

The confusion and horror of a great battle descended on him. The crash of shells, the roar of the guns, the brilliant flashes, the eerie piercing scream of a wounded man, the rattle of the machine-guns, the Lewis guns, the two riflemen beside him madly working the bolts of their rifles and fumbling as with trembling hands they thrust in a fresh clip of cartridges— all somehow perceived, but thrust aside in his intense watch. A green light went up about half a mile to the left, then another a little nearer. Hanley stared more intently in the direction of Williams's post—and found himself saying over and over again without knowing he was saying it: "O God, help him, O God, help him, O God, help him."

Suddenly two green lights appeared, one fired straight up as a signal—probably Williams—the other almost along the ground, as if fired at somebody—probably the runner, wounded or in a panic. Sergeant dead, no doubt—Williams and his runner dead, too, by now. Hanley fired a green light. Two minutes later the British barrage shortened.

Hanley grasped the Very pistol loaded with red. Their turn now.

"Stretcher-bearer, stretcher-bearer!"

Crash! A shell right on their bay.

Hanley staggered and felt a fearful pain in his right knee where a shell splinter had hit him. In the faint light of dawn he saw vaguely that one of the riflemen lay huddled on the fire-step, leaving his rifle still on the parapet; the other man had been blown backwards into the trench, and lay with his feet grimly and ludicrously caught in a torn piece of revetment. His helmet had been knocked from his head.

Faint pops of bombs to his immediate left—they were coming up the communication trench. He peered into the steel-smashed light of dawn, but saw only smoke and the fierce red flash of explosions.

Suddenly, to his left, he saw German helmets coming up the communication trench—they had passed the wire barrier! He looked to his right—a little knot of Germans had got through the wire—a Lewis gun swept them away like flies. He felt the blood running down his leg.

Somebody was standing beside him. A voice, far off, was speaking:

"Bombing attack beaten off, sir."

"Very good, carry on."

"There's only two of us left, sir."

"Carry on."

"Very good, sir."

More Germans on the right; another, longer row coming up the communication trench. Then, suddenly, Germans seemed to spring up in every direction. Hanley fired six shots from his Webley at those in front. He saw others falling hit, or jumping into the trench on either side.

A red light shot up straight in the air. A second later two bombs fell in the bay. A torn, crumped figure collapsed sideways. The Germans reorganised, while the moppers-up did their job.

THE PASS OF THERMOPYLAE

430 B.C.

Charlotte Yonge

*" Stranger, bear this message to the Spartans, that we
lie here obedient to their laws."*[1]

There was trembling in Greece. " The Great King," as the
Greeks called the chief potentate of the East, whose domains
stretched from the Indian Caucasus to the Ægæus, from the
Caspian to the Red Sea, was marshalling his forces against
the little free states that nestled amid the rocks and gulfs of
the Eastern Mediterranean. Already had his might devoured
the cherished colonies of the Greeks on the eastern shore of
the Archipelago, and every traitor to home institutions found
a ready asylum at that despotic court, and tried to revenge his
own wrongs by whispering incitements to invasion. " All
people, nations, and languages," was the commencement of
the decrees of that monarch's court; and it was scarcely
a vain boast, for his satraps ruled over subject kingdoms, and
among his tributary nations he counted the Chaldean, with
his learning and old civilisation, the wise and steadfast Jew,
the skilful Phœnician, the learned Egyptian, the wild freeboot-
ing Arab of the desert, the dark-skinned Ethiopian, and over
all these ruled the keen-witted, active native Persian race,
the conquerors of all the rest, and led by a chosen band proudly
called the Immortal. His many capitals—Babylon the great,
Susa, Persepolis, and the like—were names of dreamy splendour to the Greeks, described now and then by Ionians from
Asia Minor who had carried their tribute to the king's own
feet, or by courtier slaves who had escaped with difficulty
from being all too serviceable at the tyrannic court. And the
lord of this enormous empire was about to launch his count-
less host against the little cluster of states the whole of which
together would hardly equal one province of the huge Asiatic
realm! Moreover, it was a war not only on the men, but on
their gods. The Persians were zealous adorers of the sun
and of fire; they abhorred the idol-worship of the Greeks,
and defiled and plundered every temple that fell in their

From: [1] *Simonides: Epitaph on the tomb of the Spartans who
fell at Thermopylae. The Book of Golden Deeds.*

way. Death and desolation were almost the best that could be looked for at such hands; slavery and torture from cruelly barbarous masters would only too surely be the lot of numbers should their land fall a prey to the conquerors.

True it was that ten years back the former Great King had sent his best troops to be signally defeated upon the coast of Attica; but the losses at Marathon had but stimulated the Persian lust of conquest, and the new King Xerxes was gathering together such myriads of men as should crush down the Greeks and overrun their country by mere force of numbers.

The muster-place was at Sardis, and there Greek spies had seen the multitudes assembling and the state and magnificence of the king's attendants. Envoys had come from him to demand earth and water from each state in Greece, as emblems that land and sea were his; but each state was resolved to be free, and only Thessaly, that which lay first in his path, consented to yield the token of subjugation. A council was held at the Isthmus of Corinth, and attended by deputies from all the states of Greece, to consider of the best means of defence. The ships of the enemy would coast round the shores of the Ægean Sea, the land army would cross the Hellespont on a bridge of boats lashed together, and march southwards into Greece. The only hope of averting the danger lay in defending such passages as, from the nature of the ground, were so narrow that only a few persons could fight hand to hand at once, so that courage would be of more avail than numbers.

The first of these passes was called Tempe, and a body of troops was sent to guard it; but they found that this was useless and impossible, and came back again. The next was at Thermopylæ. Look in your map of the Archipelago, or Ægean Sea, as it was then called, for the great island of Negropont, or by its old name, Eubœa. It looks like a piece broken off from the coast, and to the north is shaped like the head of a bird, with the beak running into a gulf, that would fit over it, upon the mainland, and between the island and the coast is an exceedingly narrow strait. The Persian army would have to march round the edge of the gulf. They could not cut straight across the country, because the ridge of mountains called Œta rose up and barred their way. Indeed, the woods, rocks, and precipices came down so near the seashore that in two places there was only room for one single wheel track between the steeps and the impassable morass that formed the border of the gulf on its south side. These two very narrow places were called the gates of the pass, and were about a mile apart. There was a little more width left in the intervening space; but in this there were a number of springs of warm mineral water, salt and sulphurous, which were used for the sick to bathe in, and thus the place was called Thermopylæ, or the Hot Gates. A wall had once been built across the westernmost of these narrow places, when the Thessalians and Phocians, who lived on either side of it, had been at war with one another; but it had been allowed to go to decay, since the Phocians had found out that there was a very steep, narrow mountain path along the bed of a torrent by which it was possible to cross from one territory to the other without going round this marshy road.

This was therefore an excellent place to defend. The Greek ships were all drawn up on the farther side of Eubœa to prevent the Persian vessels from getting into the strait and landing men beyond the pass, and a division of the army was sent off to guard the Hot Gates. The council at the Isthmus did not know of the mountain pathway, and thought that all would be safe as long as the Persians were kept out of the coast path.

The troops sent for this purpose were from different cities, and amounted to about 4,000, who were to keep the pass against two millions. The leader of them was Leonidas, who had newly become one of the two kings of Sparta, the city that above all in Greece trained its sons to be hardy soldiers, dreading death infinitely less than shame. Leonidas had already made up his mind that the expedition would probably be his death, perhaps because a prophecy had been given at the Temple at Delphi that Sparta should be saved by the death of one of her kings of the race of Hercules. He was allowed by law to take with him 300 men, and these he chose most carefully, not merely for their strength and courage, but selecting those who had sons, so that no family might be altogether destroyed. These Spartans, with their helots or slaves, made up his own share of the numbers, but all the army was under his generalship. It is even said that the 300 celebrated their own funeral rites before they set out, lest they should be deprived of them by the enemy, since, as we have already seen, it was the Greek belief that the spirits of the dead found no rest till their obsequies had been performed. Such preparations did not daunt the spirits of Leonidas and his men; and his wife, Gorgo, was not a woman to be faint-hearted or hold him back. Long before, when she was a very little girl, a word of hers had saved her father from listening to a traitorous message from the King of Persia; and every

Spartan lady was bred up to be able to say to those she best loved that they must come home from battle "with the shield or on it"—either carrying it victoriously or borne upon it as a corpse.

When Leonidas came to Thermopylæ, the Phocians told him of the mountain path through the chestnut woods of Mount Œta, and begged to have the privilege of guarding it on a spot high up on the mountain side, assuring him that it was very hard to find at the other end, and that there was every probability that the enemy would never discover it. He consented, and encamping around the warm springs, caused the broken wall to be repaired and made ready to meet the foe.

The Persian army were seen covering the whole country like locusts, and the hearts of some of the southern Greeks in the pass began to sink. Their homes in the Peloponnesus were comparatively secure: had they not better fall back and reserve themselves to defend the Isthmus of Corinth? But Leonidas, though Sparta was safe below the Isthmus, had no intention of abandoning his northern allies, and kept the other Peloponnesians to their posts, only sending messengers for further help.

Presently a Persian on horseback rode up to reconnoitre the pass. He could not see over the wall, but in front of it and on the ramparts he saw the Spartans, some of them engaged in active sports, and others in combing their long hair. He rode back to the king, and told him what he had seen. Now, Xerxes had in his camp an exiled Spartan prince, named Demaratus who had become a traitor to his country, and was serving as counsellor to the enemy. Xerxes sent for him, and asked whether his countrymen were mad to be thus employed instead of fleeing away; but Demartus made answer that a hard fight was no doubt in preparation, and that it was the custom of the Spartans to array their hair with especial care when they were about to enter upon any great peril. Xerxes would, however, not believe that so petty a force could intend to resist him, and waited four days, probably expecting his fleet to assist him; but as it did not appear, the attack was made.

The Greeks, stronger men and more heavily armed, were far better able to fight to advantage than the Persians with their short spears and wicker shields, and beat them off with great ease. It is said that Xerxes three times leapt off his throne in despair at the sight of his troops being driven backwards; and thus for two days it seemed as easy to force a way through the Spartans as through the rocks themselves. Nay, how could slavish troops, dragged from home to spread the victories of an ambitious king, fight like freemen who felt that their strokes were to defend their homes and children?

But on that evening a wretched man, named Ephialtes, crept into the Persian camp, and offered, for a great sum of money, to show the mountain path that would enable the enemy to take the brave defenders in the rear. A Persian general, named Hydarnes, was sent off at nightfall with a detachment to secure this passage, and was guided through the thick forests that clothed the hillside. In the stillness of the air, at daybreak, the Phocian guards of the path were startled by the crackling of the chestnut leaves under the tread of many feet. They started up, but a shower of arrows was discharged on them, and forgetting all save the present alarm, they fled to a higher part of the mountain, and the enemy, without waiting to pursue them, began to descend.

As day dawned, morning light showed the watchers of the Grecian camp below a glittering and shimmering in the torrent bed where the shaggy forests opened; but it was not the sparkle of water, but the shine of gilded helmets and the gleaming of silvered spears! Moreover, a Cimmerian crept over to the wall from the Persian camp with tidings that the path had been betrayed; that the enemy were climbing it, and would come down beyond the Eastern Gate. Still, the way was rugged and circuitous, the Persians would hardly descend before midday, and there was ample time for the Greeks to escape before they could thus be shut in by the enemy.

There was a short council held over the morning sacrifice. Megistias, the seer, on inspecting the entrails of the slain victim, declared, as well he might, that their appearance boded disaster. Him Leonidas ordered to retire, but he refused, though he sent home his only son. There was no disgrace to an ordinary tone of mind in leaving a post that could not be held, and Leonidas recommended all the allied troops under his command to march away while yet the way was open. As to himself and his Spartans, they had made up their minds to die at their post, and there could be no doubt that the example of such a resolution would do more to save Greece than their best efforts could ever do if they were careful to reserve themselves for another occasion.

All the allies consented to retreat, except the eighty men who came from Mycæne and the 700 Thespians, who declared that they would not desert Leonidas. There were also 400 Thebans who remained; and thus the whole number that stayed with Leonidas to confront two million of enemies were fourteen hundred warriors, besides the helots or attendants on the 300 Spartans, whose number is not known, but there was probably at least one to each. Leonidas had two kinsmen in the camp, like himself claiming the blood of Hercules, and he tried to save them by giving them letters and messages to Sparta; but one answered that " he had come to fight, not to carry letters," and the other that " his deeds would tell all that Sparta wished to know." Another Spartan, named Dienices, when told that the enemy's archers were so numerous that their arrows darkened the sun, replied, " So much the better: we shall fight in the shade." Two of the 300 had been sent to a neighbouring village, suffering severely from a complaint in the eyes. One of them, called Eurytus, put on his armour, and commanded his helot to lead him to his place in the ranks; the other, called Aristodemus, was so overpowered with illness that he allowed himself to be carried away with the retreating allies. It was still early in the day when all were gone, and Leonidas gave the word to his men to take their last meal. " To-night," he said, " we shall sup with Pluto."

Hitherto he had stood on the defensive, and had husbanded the lives of his men; but he now desired to make as great a slaughter as possible, so as to inspire the enemy with dread of the Grecian name. He therefore marched out beyond the wall, without waiting to be attacked, and the battle began. The Persian captains went behind their wretched troops and scourged them on to the fight with whips! Poor wretches! they were driven on to be slaughtered, pierced with the Greek spears, hurled into the sea, or trampled into the mud of the morass; but their inexhaustible numbers told at length. The spears of the Greeks broke under hard service, and their swords alone remained; they began to fall, and Leonidas himself was among the first of the slain. Hotter than ever was the fight over his corpse, and two Persian princes, brothers of Xerxes, were there killed; but at length word was brought that Hydarnes was over the pass, and that the few remaining men were thus enclosed on all sides. The Spartans and Thespians made their way to a little hillock within the wall, resolved to let this be the place of their last stand; but the hearts of the Thebans failed them, and they came towards the Persians holding out their hands in entreaty for mercy. Quarter was given to them, but they were all branded with the king's mark as untrustworthy deserters. The helots probably at this time escaped into the mountains; while the small desperate band stood side by side on the hill still fighting to the last, some with swords, others with daggers, others even with their hands and teeth, till not one living man remained amongst them when the sun went down. There was only a mound of slain, bristled over with arrows.

Twenty thousand Persians had died before that handful of men! Xerxes asked Demaratus if there were many more at Sparta like these, and was told there were 8,000. It must have been with a somewhat failing heart that he invited his courtiers from the fleet to see what he had done to the men who dared to oppose him, and showed them the head and arm of Leonidas set up upon a cross; but he took care that all his own slain, except 1,000, should first be put out of sight. The body of the brave king was buried where he fell, as were those of the other dead. Much envied were they by the unhappy Aristodemus, who found himself called by no name but the " Coward," and was shunned by all his fellow-citizens. No one would give him fire or water, and after a year of misery he redeemed his honour by perishing in the forefront of the battle of Platæa, which was the last blow that drove the Persians ingloriously from Greece.

WAR IS THE PROVINCE OF UNCERTAINTY

Three-fourths of those things upon which action in War must be calculated, are hidden more or less in the clouds of great uncertainty. Here, then, above all, a fine and penetrating mind is called for, to search out the truth by the tact of its judgment.

An average intellect may, at one time, perhaps hit upon this truth by accident; an extraordinary courage, at another, may compensate for the want of this tact; but in the majority of cases the average result will always bring to light the deficient understanding.

HARPER'S FERRY

Leonard Ehrlich

John Brown slipped from the cot. It was still dark; the day would soon come. He dressed silently, with care; Owen, Oliver, and Jeremiah Anderson were asleep about him. He went into the kitchen, closing the door gently. He lit the lamp. Then he got the stove going with a wood fire; set up the huge kettle for coffee that the men would take, and a pot of water for his own tea. He shivered. The ague which had seeped into his body during the secret hunted days in the Kansas swamps, was still strong in his blood. He shivered with it, feeling a flush along his throat; and knew that the day coming boded rain.

He took his Bible from the chest, and went to the window. A dimmest grey began to show in the sky. The Sabbath is here, he thought; and it will be given to His work. It will be hallowed, but not rest from labour. And as he stood there with the book unopened in his hand, he felt a joy sweep over him:

I am not in a dream. I am John Brown here in the kitchen, with a fire going and the smell of coffee in my nostrils. I am John Brown, a man doing the common duties of life, living in this world. But I am more than John Brown. I have no desires that are my own, because I have passed beyond

From: *God's Angry Man*: Copyright 1932. Simon & Schuster.

all desires. I am not in a dream, I smell the coffee, but I am two. I am the clay, yet the self which is He. I exist, yet I do not save in His will. I am not in a dream, the light breaks outside, I hear a crow. It is the Sabbath, the day of our labour.

And almost all things are by the law purged with blood; and without shedding of blood is no remission.

Rain clouded the window in a slow dismal fall; a wind shook it to a devil's tattoo. Owen Brown sat on the porch, with a rifle under his old coat. Inside the men thronged the room, very still. Stevens was reading solemnly in his deep vibrant voice:

"Whereas, Slavery, throughout its entire existence in the United States is none other than a most barbarous, unprovoked and unjustifiable War of one portion of its citizens upon another portion; the only conditions of which are perpetual imprisonment and hopeless servitude or absolute extermination; in utter disregard and violation of those eternal and self-evident truths set forth . . . therefore, we citizens, and the oppressed people, do for the time being ordain and establish the following Provisional Constitution. . . ."

". . . And now, gentlemen," said the old man. "Let me press this one thing on your minds. You all know how dear life is to you, and how dear your lives are to your friends; and in remembering that, consider that the lives of others are dear to them as yours are to you. Do not, therefore, take the life of anyone if you can possibly avoid it. But if it is necessary to take life in order to save your own, then make sure work of it."

The hours moved slowly. The men oiled their rifles, tightened the iron pikes on the wood-shafts; then they waited. The old man sat in the gloom of the kitchen, writing a letter by the lamp-light.

Night came. They ate the meal which their Commander-in-Chief had prepared, the last meal they would eat in this farmhouse; they had heard the old man say the last grace.

He took down a tattered old cap from the wall, the battle-torn Kansas cap.

"Men. Get your arms. We will proceed to the Ferry."

At 7:05 in the morning of Monday, October 16, 1859, the Baltimore & Ohio train bound from the West to Baltimore arrived at the small village of Monocacy, Maryland. Before it came to a full stop, Phelps the conductor leaped from the caboose and went scrambling up the runway to the telegraph office. At 7:07 the operator was furiously tapping out a message to the master of transportation at Baltimore.

"Train held up five hours at Harper's Ferry by insurrectionists. One hundred and fifty strong. Baggage-master killed. Say they have come to free slaves. Leader says this is last train to pass bridge east or west. If attempted will be at peril of lives. Telegraph wires cut east and west of Ferry. Notify authorities at once."

By 10:27 the head of the Baltimore & Ohio, John W. Garret, had telegraphed to President Buchanan of the United States; John Floyd, Secretary of War; Governor Wise of Virginia; and Major-General George Stewart, commanding the First Light Division, Maryland Volunteers. By noon three companies of artillery from Fort Monroe, a detachment of Marines from the Washington navy-yard, and the Fredericksburg militia were speeding toward the scene of the reported disturbance; Colonel Robert E. Lee of the Second United States Cavalry in command, Lieutenant J. E. B. Stuart second in command.

Floyd, Secretary of War, pale, pacing back and forth in his Washington office, remembered a letter which some weeks ago had come to him. He had swept it into the basket as the work of a crank, a madman. ("Sir: . . . information of a movement of so great importance that I feel it my duty to impart it to you without delay . . . having for its general object the liberation of slaves by insurrection . . . he has been in Canada during the winter, drilling the Negroes there. . . .") Floyd had been too busy with certain furtive affairs of his own to pay attention to such a fantastic letter. For who could know, perhaps some day soon the South would have great need for guns and powder and cannon. Floyd, the United States War Secretary was in his heart more truly Floyd of Virginia. He was seeing to it well and secretly that huge supplies of military stores were being shifted from Northern arsenals to the South. Now, remembering the letter he cursed himself.

And in a thousand cities through the nation men were reading their newspapers with incredulous excitement:

" . . . The statements are fully confirmed. Two hundred Negroes and one hundred whites are in revolt, all armed with Minnie rifles, spears and pistols. They have all the arsenal buildings in their possession and access to thousands of weapons.

They expect, it is said, a reinforcement of twelve hundred slaves by morning. . . ."

" . . . Every light in the town had been previously extinguished by the lawless mob. All the streets, every road and lane leading to the Ferry has been barricaded and guarded. . . ."

" . . . He has refused to let anyone pass. All the east-bound trains are lying west of the Ferry. Your correspondent has just seen a letter from a merchant of the town, which was carried by two boys over the mountain, and who had to swim the river in order to escape. The letter states that almost all the leading citizens have been imprisoned and many have been killed. Beckham the Mayor was shot twice by the gang, and died. They are said to be disguised, the whites being painted as blacks. . . ."

" . . . The ringleader, who is said to be named Anderson, made his appearance at Harper's Ferry five or six days ago, and since that time has been driving around the place in an elegant barouche drawn by four horses. . . ."

" . . . The captain of the outlaw band was an old man with a white beard. He was heard to say in addressing the conductor 'If you knew me and understood my motives as well as I and others understand them you would not blame me so much.'"

" . . . The citizens were in a terrible state of consternation, most of them being shut up in their houses, and not a light to be seen in the streets or anywhere. It is difficult to describe the excitement throughout the entire section. Rumours of every sort are flying about. As yet it is impossible to divine the cause of this outbreak. Some are of the opinion it is a bold concerted scheme to rob the Government pay-house of funds deposited there on Saturday. We are informed by others that the leader of the rioters is a noted Abolitionist agent of the Underground Railroad. He is from Troy, New York and has made frequent visits to the Ferry. His conduct towards the black people had been noticed on other occasions and involved him in suspicion. He is represented as a most desperate and dangerous man, and one who is likely to cause a great deal of trouble before he will yield. The marauder chief was heard to exclaim, 'If you knew my heart and history you would not blame me.' The Negroes rely upon him, and will implicitly obey his directions. There are said to be more than six hundred armed slaves and whites. . . ."

They had buckled on their arms. They had thrown the long grey shawls over their shoulders and filed out to the cold wet darkness of the fall night, the Sabbath night. Owen had driven the horse and wagon to the door; it was filled with pikes, faggots, a sledge-hammer, and a crow-bar. The old man clambered up. "Come, boys," he said. The wagon began to creak down the lane, the men swinging behind, two and two, hiding their rifles under the shawls. Watson as he moved by found Owen's hand; they gave a quick deep squeeze. Edwin Coppoc, in the last of the line, halted for an instant, embraced his young brother, their lips meeting. Then, to the three remaining behind at the farmhouse, Owen, frail Merriam, and Barclay Coppoc, their comrades became shadows fading in the damp lonely night.

A bad wind was blowing up from the river-gloom. The little fat man walked slowly across the bridge, swinging the lantern, pressing his coat tighter about himself. He yawned, shivering a little, thinking vaguely: twelve noon to twelve the middle of the night is a rotten long dull time to mind a bridge, nothing ever happens, the sleepiest job in the sleepiest town. For seventeen years Will Williams had been watching the Potomac train-crossing and having the same drowsy glum feeling as the night closed on. Will Williams came to his tiny watch-coop at the Maryland entrance of the bridge. He settled inside on his bench with a sigh; he relaxed, nothing coming in till the 1:25 A.M. west-to-Baltimore. He carefully drew the stub of a cigar from his outer breast pocket. He put it into his mouth, rolled it luxuriously, bit on it. He lit a match, he——

"Come out of there!"

Will Williams' jaw hung. The match burned down to his fingers. A big man with a black beard and shining eyes stood in the coop door; Williams stared down the glistening barrel of a rifle.

"Come out, quick."

"Quit jokin'."

He came out, scared and incredulous. A lean young fellow was standing there too, with a rifle. "Quit jokin'," Williams kept saying. Then from the darkness a wagon came creaking on to the bridge and fat Williams saw a line of men. He saw their set hard faces, the shine of rifle-barrels; it was no joke. But it must be a joke. Why, there was Cook, John Cook the boy who tended the canal-lock. He knew the boy well, he'd married sweet Mary Turner, blessed luck. And there was that old gentleman sitting up on the seat, Mr. Smith, the new farmer at the Kennedy place, Isaac Smith who had

127

a quick straight way and you respected him. Why, they were up to some joke! But Will Williams felt the rifle murderous against his paunch.

"Oliver Brown. Will Thompson. Newby. Guard the bridge. Await orders. The rest, follow me."

Now they were moving along the bridge. Now they were over, they were in Harper's Ferry. They went along the narrow street; passed the railroad station with its green flaring lights; passed the saloon, seeing no one and not being seen. The wet night was with them; folks were close by hearth-fires, not dreaming danger. The Ferry had known its last belligerent men during the Revolution, beyond the remembrance of living citizens. This October of 1859 they would as soon expect lava to rage up from the gentle Virginia hills as bloodshed in their streets, as eighteen men moving desperate in the night with guns, like ghosts risen from a grave. Suddenly ahead the whole village darkened, lights dotting the obscurity clean up the Bolivar Heights suddenly snuffed out. Tidd was at work. In another instant the armoury loomed black by the Potomac bank. Old Dan Whelan would be drowsing in the arsenal yard. Thousands of arms would come into their possession. Hazlett and Jeremiah Anderson crept forward to the gate.

Five miles south of the Ferry, in an upstairs room of his plantation, Colonel Lewis Washington, great-grandnephew of the First President, slept fitfully. Downstairs, hanging above the fireplace, were an old pistol and a sword. The pistol had been presented to George Washington by Lafayette; the sword was the gift of Frederick the Great.

A little after midnight Lewis Washington stirred in his bed, vague sounds threading his sleep. Then two loud knocks came upon the heavy oak door. He sat up, startled. "Open up!" a voice boomed. He slipped from the bed, thrust his feet hastily into slippers, and went in his nightshirt to the door. He pulled it open. Four men stood there with levelled rifles. One, a Negro, held a burning flambeau.

"You're our prisoner," said the black-bearded man. "Get into your clothes."

Washington stared. "Will you have the courtesy to tell me what this means?"

"Yes. You're coming with us. And your slaves too. Get dressed, quick."

He prodded the thunderstruck Washington with his rifle. The colonel dressed, as in a fantastic dream. "Where are you taking me?" he asked, trying to speak with dignity as he slipped on a boot.

" Osawatomie Brown wants to see you."

" And who, pray, is Osawatomie Brown?"

" Have you never heard of Kansas?"

They went downstairs. The colonel's sister, grey-haired, wrapped in a dressing gown, sat proud in an arm-chair. Her look was eloquent: Lewis, cowhide these ruffians out of the house. Old Bettina, the Negress, was glaring defiantly at two armed men. One was a mulatto, the other a slim dark fellow.

" Good evening, Colonel Washington," the dark fellow said.

" Mr. Cook! What does this outrage mean?"

" I've been trying to calm Miss Washington. You will come to no harm."

" What does it mean, I say?"

" We're freeing the slaves of the South. We're prepared to do it."

The black-bearded man broke in roughly, " Enough talk. You, Mr. Washington, take down that sword, and that pistol too. Quick. . . . Now hand the sword over to Emperor Green. . . . Now the pistol, to Leary."

The Southerner was pale with the indignity.

" It's Captain Brown's orders," said Cook, half-proud, half-ashamed. " He said we'd start the work with a symbol."

Tidd came in growling through the front door: " The wagon's ready."

" Sir, your carriage awaits you." Stevens bowed low in mockery.

They went out, leaving the two women behind in the darkness. In the driveway was the colonel's small phaeton. Behind it was a large four-horse farm wagon. Six slaves stood startled and bewildered by the wagon. " Come on and fight to get free," Tidd had told them. Now they looked fearfully at their master, cringing. Colonel Washington stepped up into the carriage with hauteur. He felt more like himself now that he was out of his nightshirt. Stevens got beside him, taking the reins. The rest, whites and Negroes, climbed in to the wagon. The first hostage was taken. The first bondmen were freed.

A little past twelve, Pat Higgins, night-watchman, walked out on the Maryland bridge to relieve Will Williams. A shameful night, he growled in his thought, may it go quick. He puffed on his pipe as he trudged along the trestle and cursed himself for not bringing his ancient outer coat.

"Halt!"

Three forms rose dark before him. Instantly, intuitively, Higgins turned and began to run. A rifle sounded, a bullet snipped a furrow in the Irishman's scalp. His leathery old body dodged from side to side up the trestle. He made the town entrance and leaped behind the wing of the station. He stood listening; there was only silence again.

At 1:25 the Baltimore & Ohio train drew in at the Ferry. ". . . but I didn't know what 'halt' mint any more than a hog knows about a holiday!" said Patrick Higgins in great excitement to the conductor, Phelps. "There's no sign anywhere of Will, and sure there's somethin' evil about!"

Phelps and the engineer, half-incredulous, walked up the tracks to investigate. Rifle-fire came from the bridge. Hastily the train was backed away out of danger. Phelps ran to the telegraph office. The wires had been cut.

Shephard Hayward, a free Negro and baggage master at the Ferry, rolled his hand-truck down the platform as the train came in. It was a good job. He had held it for seven years now and they had been the happiest of his life. The little fund at the bank was growing; the whites all respected him, only yesterday old Mayor Beckham himself had inquired in a true friendly fashion about his family in the small new house at the foot of the Heights, was the boy better and how was the flower-bed coming along. It was a good deal for a "nigger" to have reached such a secure place in a Southern community, to have pulled himself up from the slime to a man's place. Shephard Hayward, not seeing the watchman about, not seeing the swing of Higgins' red lamp, walked around the corner of the hotel and on toward the bridge to look for him; Shephard Hayward walked crooning to himself. Dangerfield Newby, Negro with a wife and seven children enslaved, waiting with rifle poised over the railing, saw a man moving up in the dimness of the trestle. His finger trembled on the trigger. He called "Stop!" The man kept moving up, Newby's finger pulled in sharp. Shephard Hayward gave a little choked cry, he turned and staggered back along the bridge. Just over the end he dropped and lay moaning, with a bullet and agonised bewilderment in his heart. The first deathblow for the cause of blacks had been struck.

Back at the darkened farmhouse, Owen Brown, Merriam and

the Coppoc boy were waiting through the slow fearful hours. They could only wait. Their share would come later. The others would put the spark to the touchwood; these three would heap the fuel. When the first bullet cut to a soft living wall of flesh, making it dead; when the first oppressor sank lifeless before a black man's eyes, showing a way to freedom, the slaves would come in wild crowds to the Kennedy farm. These three would give them guns, old Brown had said; this was the point from which their strength would swell, would swirl. Now his son and the two boys waited throbbing, hoping.

And soon through the hills a boy of the South was streaking on a horse. By dawn he would be in Charlestown, eight miles away. By dawn the alarm bells would be ringing, tolling on —insurrection, civil war. The Jefferson Guards, men and boys with old muskets and squirrel-guns, would be falling into line before the court-house. In Martinsburg from bed or breakfast men would hurry armed to the town square. Bells ringing terror over the countryside, bells tolling, slaves rising bloody, the Shepherdstown troop forming, the Hamtramck Guards rushing, tighter, tighter the net drawing about an old man and some boys.

The first grey cold light came into the arsenal yard. The men were ranged about the gate with rifles, watching the still empty street. Across the town the bell of the Lutheran church had begun a steady ominous ringing. Close by the watch-house some of the prisoners paced, scared and hollow-eyed. Forty-two had been brought in during the night; now the rest were huddled inside. The handful of liberated slaves stood stupidly about, furtively training their pikes, ashamed to look full at the masters they were guarding. They were cold, they were hungry, the cabins on the plantations would be warm, food would be smelling good in the fires. But they were afraid of the old man with the fierce eyes. He kept moving about the yard, watching everything like a hawk. Now he strode over to Lewis Washington standing pale and outraged against the wall. The sword of Frederick was gripped in the old man's hand. He held it proudly, as if it were a true fit weapon for this leader. He began to speak to Washington, earnestly; his words were almost an appeal for justification:

" I am very attentive to you, sir. I may get the worst of it in my first encounter, and if so your life is worth as much as mine. I took you first for the moral effect it would give our cause having one of your name as prisoner." Or again turning to the prisoner of illustrious lineage: " You will find a fire in there, sir. It is quite cold this morning." But Washington would never answer, as if it were beneath him, and all the time his keen glance would take in the other—the gleaming bluish mettle of the eyes, the stiff whitening hair projecting close above on the low brow, the mouth like a sabre-thrust—and even as he hated the sight of the face he felt its awful unsmiling strength.

Just before daylight, in the flare of torches, the old man had addressed the prisoners, " I came here from Kansas, and this is a slave state. I want to free all the slaves, and I have possession now of the armoury. I hope that no harm will come to you. But if the citizens interfere I must only burn the town, and there will be blood. I am here in the name of the Great Jehovah."

As the first greyness was showing, the Baltimore & Ohio train began to pull up very slowly to the bridge entrance. At three o'clock old Brown had sent word to the conductor by a Negro that the train might proceed; but Phelps would not trust the word; surely the arches or timbers were cut. The old man left the armoury now and walked out on the trestle with Phelps to reassure him. The train drew across, took on speed, soon was lost wailing in the swell of the hills, in the direction of Monocacy. (Bend low over the keys, operator, tap tap frantic tap to Buchanan to Lee to Governor tapping drawing the net tighter, ever tighter!) Meanwhile Boerly the grocer stepped from his doorway a little beyond the arsenal to see what the unusual early noises were about, the church bells ringing so strangely, a train whistling through the town at such an hour. Boerly was broad and red-faced, he was the town's wit, the jolly-man. He could take two ends of a cider cask in his huge hands and hoist it up on the counter to be bunged, and he and his childless " old lady " would drink more of it than they sold. Now, in his blue cotton shirt, his face shining red with a fresh cold wash, he stepped out into the street, into the autumn air, the brisk living day. Three steps from the door a bullet ploughed his brain. He fell with his head twisted in the gutter, his bare white feet sticking up grotesquely above the walk, the blood oozing down the red shining cheek. Dauphin Thompson, white as the mists rising in the wooded heights, stared aghast; the smoking carbine quivered in his nerveless hands. His young vision had not

connected the vague beautiful idea of Liberty with men stiffening in the streets.

Kagi, holding the rifleworks with Copeland and Leary, saw
the train pull across the bridge, and smiled calm and bitter.
The old fool, he thought, why did he let it pass? The news
will spread hours before we want it to. We could have held
these farmers off indefinitely, but this will mean the troops.
Kagi felt the imploring harassed eyes of yellow Leary upon
him, the proud fine eyes of Copeland the Oberlin student, and
the same question was in each pair, what now, what now? Poor
devils, thought Kagi, this does mean everything for you, this
does mean your hope, your life. Instantly he took out a small
note-book and pencil from his pocket:

" Get back over Maryland bridge to hills. Why do you
linger? Your purpose accomplished, terror struck through
country and blacks roused. Trapped here if stay. Kagi."

In the armoury yard too the men were wondering, apprehensive. For a short time they had been stirred to vast hope,
flushed with the incredible success of the plan. Everything had
gone like clock-work, all the vital points were theirs: the
Potomac bridge was under guard, Kagi held the rifleworks,
Hazlett and Osborn Perry the arsenal, they themselves the
armoury. They had hostages. But now a fear began to grip
them. Where were the hordes of slaves, where was Owen
leading down thousands to their aid? From time to time they
turned their heads from the gate to look back at the old man.
They felt the golden minutes slipping; but he gave them no
sign, only stood there with that cold-frenzied face. He
seemed to be waiting, possessed of some deep invincible secret,
and somehow, seeing him thus, blindly they had faith—save
one. Look, thought Stewart Taylor, he is paralysed, he does
not know what to do now. He has thought nothing out further
than this. He has the town, but what he shall do with it he
does not know. Every minute of delay rouses the country
more, and still we stand here guarding a yard. Kill, burn,
escape, advance, die, only do something that will achieve
a positive end. But no, behold God and one man overturning
the universe!

Now old Brown was portioning out to the prisoners the
coffee and biscuits which he had ordered brought in from
the Wager House (he would himself take nothing nor would
he give his men any for fear the food had been poisoned).
Now he was opening the gate to allow young Reason Cross to
return home for a moment under guard. " My aunt will be

frantic with worry," pleaded the lame boy with the long patrician face. " I have been out all night. She will think I am killed. She is very ill. I'll come back." Or old Brown would be talking courteously to the huddled prisoners: " I think after a while, possibly, I shall be enabled to release you, but only on the condition of getting your friends to send in a stout Negro as a ransom, as a new member of the army of the Lord."

The sun rose up over the Bolivar Heights. The sun ran blazing cold golden down the stained autumn hills into the Ferry streets. The dawn swiftly sharply brightened blue, the Potomac caught rays, the Shenandoah, and there was a gleaming over the pure morning waters; but death in the town, panic in the town, and the Lutheran bell tolling, tolling. For years patrols had ridden and men had watched the night-roads; now the dreaded thing was upon them, slaves in revolt, slave-stealers murdering and pillaging. There must be thousands of the vengeful whites and blacks; only men with powerful numbers would dare to attack the slave border. And with the rise of the sun the whole populace was gathered upon the Bolivar hill, the women and young ones clustered in terror higher up, the townsmen running about, shouting, dazed. Some few had weapons, ancient flintlocks, axes, small rusty fowling-pieces. Starry, the young doctor, rode on his sorrel from group to stricken group, trying to calm them, to get them into some kind of organisation. But far down the central street they could see a heap in the gutter, Boerly dead; they were doomed. In their apprehension they seemed not to observe the very slaves they dreaded shrinking in their midst, terror-struck equally with the masters.

" Tell Kagi, stand firm," the old man said, crumpling the paper in his hand. Stevens stood there, hesitating. " We could make it," he said, not meeting his leader's eyes, looking off to the gates. " We have the bridge."

" No."

" You owe the men a chance. We'll be hemmed in. There's no sight of Owen and the slaves."

" The slaves will come."

" Kagi's in danger."

" Yes. I know."

" Kagi's exposed, he's isolated."

" Tell Kagi, stand firm."

Stevens' hand came up in a half-salute. (He had once been in the Army, a soldier in the Mexican war under Taylor; had been tried for " mutiny, engaging in a drunken riot and

134

assaulting Major Blake of First United States Dragoons"; he had escaped into Kansas.) Now his eyes gleamed with a proud fatal look as he strode quickly to the gates. Stand firm, throbbed in the old man's mind, the slaves will come, the slaves will come. Not back, we must not go back. It will mean the ruin of my plan, we will be at the beginning again. And I am old, it is the last of my strength. His eyes fastened hungrily upon the bridge entrance. They must come, the labour of his life hung on it. We will move into Africa, he thought fiercely, or we will die here. Let Kagi call, let Stevens plead, have we not sworn to a sacrifice? No, not back. Ahead, southward, down into the great Black Way, or let us die here.

Now among the townsmen the first paralysing consternation was over; they saw that they had vastly overrated the number of the raiders, that the little band in the yard was receiving no reinforcement, that the separated detachments could be harassed and cut off. A boy came running up excited: he had discovered that one of the end workshops beyond the confines of the yard was open; it was filled with guns that had been placed there for protection against possible freshets at high water. There was a rush for the shop. Soon men were sniping from the houses nearby, and the rocks and trees of the lower hill. By ten o'clock a steady point-blank fire was being directed upon the armoury and the yard. The bullets splintered and spattered about the prisoners shrinking in the flimsy watch house.

A handkerchief on a rifle showed in the yard, a flag of truce. Joseph Brua, one of the hostages, slipped through the gates. In a silence, he called up, pleading: " For God's sake, stop shooting! You endanger the lives of your friends! The captain offers you a truce! Leave the armoury in his possession and let the firing stop on both sides!" Brua ran back, the gates opened, he slipped in. Immediately the shooting began anew, heavier. Old Brown was fighting for time; but his parley had only succeeded in convincing the townsmen that the raiders were on the defensive. Soon the "miners" were being attacked at each point. A dozen men crossed the Potomac a short distance above the Ferry, sneaked down the tow-path of the canal and concealed themselves in the brush above the bridge entrance. Oliver Brown, Newby and Will Thompson were exposed on the trestle to a cunning, almost unanswerable fire. Another party crossed the Shenandoah and took a sheltered position opposite Kagi at the rifleworks. Hazlett and the consumptive Osborn Perry, across the street from the yard, alone had a fighting chance; they had the arsenal building at their backs, and then the Shenandoah.

It was a question of time. On one side the Jefferson Guards, speeding by train, the Shepherdstown troop, the Winchesters, the Hamtramck battalion, Lee, Stuart, the Marines; on the other an old man staring at the bridge entrance: they will come, they will come!

It was noon. The machinists, the workers of the arsenal would have been leaving the buildings; some to sit in the yard with their lunch boxes, out in the warming sun; others to walk home through the quiet streets for a hot meal. But now above the desultory cracking of rifles a sudden murderous fusillade blazed in the direction of the bridge, then a great mingled sound rose, the running tramp of many feet, voices shouting. Old Brown leaped for the gate, his eyes taking on a wild life. At last! At last! The slaves were coming, Owen was leading down the slaves! Then even as the thought formed exultant, a man came running from the trestle entrance, two followed hard behind—Will, Newby, Oliver. They were fleeing toward the armoury. The slaves had not come. The Jefferson Guards had come. A blackness crushed down upon the old man's heart. But swiftly he flung the gate open, calling with fierceness: "Cover them up!" and strode into the street. The raiders followed to a man, forming a desperate deadly line. The Jefferson Guards came in a ragged rush. The little band held. The old man cried "Let go on them!" There was a volley; the attackers halted, then scattered hastily, towards the Wager House. The guns behind had been silent, as if the townsmen were merely witness to the drama of the manœuvre. But now as the detachment of three came panting up to the gates a sniper hidden in a house at the foot of the heights took quick savage aim; fired. Halfway up the street Newby staggered, Dangerfield Newby dropped with a ball through the arteries of his throat, instantly dead. Slave woman, slave mother of seven slave children, do not write again of Newby's babe "just commenced to crawl"; do not beg: "buy us soon, for if you don't get me somebody else will." Bow your head in the fields, in the darkness by the cabin croon your darkened heart out: "Oh dear Dangerfield, come this fall without fail, money or no money I want to see you so much, that is one bright hope I have before me."

The other half of the Charlestown men had meanwhile come down from Bolivar Heights and occupied the saloon on the

Shenandoah side. A detachment had swarmed into the houses between the hill and the arsenal, from which they were sending a direct fire into the yard. Tighter, tighter the net. Now there was no way of retreat into Maryland, no means of communication with the Kennedy farm, they were cut off from Kagi at the rifleworks, from Hazlett and Osborn Perry in the arsenal.

" Oliver. Was there no sign of your brother?"

" There was no sign."

The men heard, and the last hope died on their faces. Leeman's eyes desperately sought the rear gate. He was the youngest, only eighteen. But the Potomac lay there, a full half-mile across; a man swimming could never make it, he would be riddled by a hundred guns. Leeman's eyes hungered upon the river. He was the youngest. They were all so young, they might have been boys in a college—Dauphin twenty-one, Edwin Coppoc twenty-four, Barclay twenty, Hazlett twenty-two, Tidd twenty-five, so young Watson, Merriam, Copeland, Cook, Stewart Taylor twenty-two, Will Thompson twenty-six, Oliver twenty, oh so young and doom in their hearts, there was no sign of Owen.

And the old man with the flowing white beard and the sunken terrible eyes stood there, shooting, ordering, brooding defiantly: it was not over, he was not beaten. Time, only time, and they would yet come through; flaming in his mind was the thought of Owen. Aye, no surrender, the protection of night would surely bring them in; even now they must be lying on Maryland Heights, waiting for the darkness. Hold on, stand firm, this is the labour of my life. And the hostages, he thought, he still had them as an overpowering threat. Long ago a concerted attack could have wiped out his band, but in such a charge the prisoners would also go down, and these Southerners would never sacrifice their kindred. He, John Brown, would not hesitate thus; let there be a true just reason and he would offer up every life. But these men would not; and now John Brown went into the watch-house. He surveyed the forty-odd prisoners. " I want you, sir," he said, pointing at Lewis Washington. " Come, Mr. Brua. And you, sir. . . . And you . . ." Eleven of them, the most prominent, were taken from the watch-room and crowded into the back part of the small engine-house. Then the old man ordered in the slaves he had armed, and posted the remnant of his men close about. The engine-house would be their last refuge. That, and the hostages.

" Gentlemen, you are the most influential." With stiff

dignity he addressed the chosen prisoners, with solemnity as in a speech. "I have only to say now that you will share the same fate that your friends extend to my men."

The Shepherdstown troop was in, the Hamtramck Guards, three companies from Martinsburg; a thousand surrounded the town. But the struggle was not alone against the desperate odds of men. Time. Time. "Will Thompson!" called the old man.

Agatha Thompson's boy came up.

"Take the lame fellow with you into the street. Keep him ahead of you. Treat with them for a stop to the firing."

A moment later Will Thompson was a prisoner in the Wager House. Time, time, night will bring them in, beat in the old man's head. "Stevens! Watson Brown!" The two came up, waited. "Put a handkerchief on your gun. Take Mr. Kitzmiller with you and negotiate so that we may leave the yard."

"Captain Brown," said Stevens. "You saw what happened to Thompson."

"You have my orders."

"Damn your——! Why don't you run things so we'll have a chance? . . . You have the prisoners! Put a bullet in one, throw him out of the gate! Send a nigger to say we'll kill 'em all if we can't get clear!"

"You have my orders. We will injure no unarmed man."

Stevens glared at Watson. The boy stood blanched, his eyes pleading: I have Bell, I want to live, the babe's just born. But no, there was the face like granite, unrelenting: let the grand reason that one course is right and another wrong be kept continually before your mind. The boy turned his face, hopeless, undone, toward the street, toward his fate. And into the blackbearded man's eyes again came the fiercely proud fatal look. His hand rose sharp in the habitual half-salute, and the man who once in the far West had been imprisoned for insubordination under a commuted sentence of death, now strode to the engine-house door.

"Kitzmiller!"

The two raiders and the prisoner walked slowly across the yard. Stevens was waving his rifle high; it was topped with a white handkerchief. The firing ceased, save at a distance where Kagi was trapped. Watson Brown opened the gate entrance. Kitzmiller went first, shrinking with fear. The three began to walk slowly up the street, toward the Wager House. Ten feet. Fifteen, the surrounding stillness deep. Twenty. Twenty-five, a rolling whining volley, rifles recoiling in the upper windows of the saloon. Stevens slumped, the white handkerchief dropping, slugs in his side and breast. Watson plunged to his knees, face agonised, his hand clutching his belly. Kitzmiller was clumping frantically toward the hotel. Watson Brown got to one knee. Again the intense silence, with a devil's tattoo faint down the rifleworks. Watson Brown began to drag himself back up the street, dropping, writhing, rising, moaning, a hundred shamed staring eyes riveted. Watson Brown reached the gate, suddenly there was another rattle of firing, poured in from the hillside. But not at Watson. Leeman the imp-eyed was taking his chance for life.

He had seen two comrades shot down. He went icy trembling cold, then like a madness the blood rushed in his head. Suddenly swift as a hound he whipped for the rear gate. He sprang clawing, slipping, then fell back. The volley rattled, he sprang again, held, pulled up, leaped the seven-foot gate. He darted along the river ledge. It ceased, it turned down sharp to the water. Leeman stood quivering still, his eyes moving like a cornered weasel's. The rifles were finding the range, bullets were crumbling the shale at his feet. Leeman slid down the bank to the water's edge. He pulled out his bowie, slashed at the accoutrements, the cartridge belt, the rifle-sling, flung his two revolvers away, tore off his boots; and ran into the river. He waded furiously a dozen steps, he cast himself upon the waters and began to swim. All about him the bullets were flicking up white jets. He made for the cover of a tiny green-rock islet fifty yards out. Now the militiamen were down to the water, now ten of them were wading out. Leeman draggled up on the islet, a bullet smashed his shoulder. He lay there, panting, at bay, watching the men wade closer, closer through the shallows with guns uplifted. Leeman threw up his arms, gasped, "Don't shoot! I surrender!" But they came up, one eagerly savagely in the lead, bearing his rifle high. An instant later Billy Leeman was dead, half his head blown away. All afternoon the boy's body lying on the edge of the rock, hands dangling in the water, blood staining the water, would be a target for hundreds of marksmen. Later it would slide down somehow and float in slow ghastly eddies toward the bridge.

Joseph Brua said, "I will go." He walked past the old man, crossed the yard. As he went without fear down the street toward Stevens sprawled in the gutter, a shot flicked the walk. But it was the only one; he was recognised. Brua lifted huge Stevens to his back. He sagged under the burden, moving in a zig-zag toward the Wager House. He went up the steps, went in. He came out alone and walked back toward the yard. He took his place again among the prisoners in the engine-house.

"A doctor is looking after him," he said.

"Thank you, sir," said old Brown.

But Brua's act was like a briefest gleam in a mad black chaos—snuffed out by the beating drowning lust. Gentle old Fontaine Beckham, Mayor of the Ferry and chief agent for the railroad, nervously ventured out on the trestlework, despite warnings. His heart was sickened, oh this violence in his streets, poor dead Shephard Hayward his helper. He must do something. Maybe he could reason with these outlaws, stop the bloodshed.

Edwin Coppoc, crouching in the doorway of the engine-house, saw a man sneak behind the water tank near the bridge. The young Quaker levelled his rifle; you murderers, you filthy murderers, he cried inside himself, thinking of Watson Brown all torn in the engine-house. The man showed his head. Coppoc fired, missed. Behind him, Alstadt the slave-owner cried, "It's Beckham, it's old Mayor Beckham! Don't fire!" Young Terence Burns laughed hysterically, "For God's sake, don't fire!" Coppoc fired, the dark wings again brushed the little town, and Fontaine Beckham crumpled upon the timbers. *Peace, Quaker, peace, thou shalt not kill.* And in Will Book No. 16 page 142 Jefferson Court Records, Charlestown, a recent entry showed that Fontaine Beckham (he was the greatest friend of the black man in all the country) had provided for the liberation upon his death of one Isaac Gilbert, Negro, his slave-wife and three children. The Quaker boy's shot had liberated them.

The two men ran toward the Wager House, Chambers the saloon-keeper, and young Harry Hunter. "The bitches, the god-damned bitches!" Hunter was crying. "They murdered my uncle!" The two men rushed up the steps of the Hotel, burst savagely into the room where Will Thompson was being guarded. In another moment they were dragging him out by the throat. They headed for the trestle where Beckham had fallen, and the crowd mad for revenge followed howling. "I don't care!" Will Thompson kept crying blindly as they dragged him, "Kill me, I don't care! Eighty million will rise up to free the slaves! I don't care!" Hunter and Chambers placed their revolvers against Thompson's head. "Die, you bastard!" They fired, he twisted crazily, before he fell a dozen balls had ploughed his young body. They threw him through the opening in the trestle, he dropped forty feet to the river rocks. All day Will Thompson's carcass would be riddled, his white face ghastly with agony of death staring up.

And you, Kagi, look out! They're creeping up, they're closing in on you! Oh Kagi, quick, breathe in the last sweet shining air, Oh drink the sun with your eyes; Bullets bullets close about thick as a tomb thick fatal shutting out light. Back, Kagi, back, Copeland and Leary, climb hard, desperate up on the Winchester tracks. Leap down, splash gasp swish into the ice of the waters Shenandoah. Storm of lead behind, Virginia guns opposite in a blazing wall of hate. Turn desperate, not back, not forward, turn with the downflow, east as the river flows to the sea, labour, wrench, the flat rock juts. Scream, Leary, flail screaming the stained waters, own no more the workin' place an' the honey-bab just born, cough gurgle blood, nevermore be back befo' the summer turns. Old Kagi, here it is, cease wondering, now you know the last darkness. Sink easily, move with the waters moving seaward, flow deep to the peace of the dark shining Sea the Father ancient before earth. Tremble, Copeland, alone alive. Be dragged back, a nigger living is sport. Knot the white handkerchiefs, townsmen tie them tight, lynch lynch nigger Copeland the student of Oberlin.

Now the rifleworks are empty. Now they are silent.

Night is down. They are hemmed in at the armoury. The men from Martinsburg, trainmen chiefly, charged into the yard at dusk, many falling, and the raiders are hemmed in the enginehouse. It will be their last stand. Night is down. There is no shooting. The militia are picketing the engine-house; their work is done, soon the Marines will be in, the majesty the power of Government. A thousand men surround the tiny stone-building. Inside are eleven prisoners, four trembling slaves, one dead boy, two dying boys, five living raiders— Edwin Coppoc, Jeremiah Anderson, Dauphin Thompson, Emperor Green, and the Commander-in-Chief of the "Provisional Army," John Brown. Loop-holes have been knocked in the stone wall. The five men stand there, waiting in the obscurity, their rifles to hand.

The moon besieged between Saturn and Mars . . . the Lord of the First in a streaming Sign or infested of the Malevolents,

141

and the depositor of the Light of Time being also in a violent Sign and afflicted. . . .

Stewart Taylor lies dead in the engine-house.

On the brick floor close by the Canadian, Oliver Brown is moaning, bleeding his life away.

Watson Brown lies breathing quietly, deeper deeper into the gathering Darkness.

A message comes in, under cover of truce: Surrender. The painful peasant hand writes:

"Captain John Brown answers—In consideration of all my men, whether living, or dead, or wounded, being soon safely in and delivered up to me at this point with all their arms and ammunition, we will then take our prisoners and cross the Potomac bridge, a little beyond which we will set them at liberty; after which we can negotiate about the Government property as may be best. Also we require the delivery of our horse and wagon at the hotel. John Brown." The torch flared in the yard, outlining a form. "Approach!" the old man called back. The man came close slowly. Old Brown opened the door a hand's breadth; he held the sword of Frederick. The other raiders with cocked carbines stared out into the darkness; they were ready for trickery.

"What do you want?"

"I want to speak to you under a truce. Let me in. It is for your own good."

The door opened a little wider. The man slipped through, bearing the torch. The doors shut.

"I am Sinn. Captain Sinn of the Fredericksburg Company."

"Well, sir?"

The militiamen looked about the engine-house, saw the exhausted prisoners, the slaves, the prostrate boys, the four raiders by the loop-holes. God, what madness, he thought.

"Surrender," he said. "You have no chance."

"You have my terms."

"There can be no terms."

"You shot my men down like dogs under a flag of truce. And I, I had full possession of the town, I could have massacred every soul, burned it to ashes. These prisoners, they are not scratched, I have given them every courtesy. And you say no terms."

"Men who take up arms as outlaws must expect to be shot down like dogs."

"Sir, we knew what we would have to go through before coming here. I have weighed the responsibility. I will not shrink from it now."

"Sinn!" It was Brua. "For mercy's sake, let them leave! They've been punished enough. His two sons are dying here."

The militiaman said, "It can't be, Mr. Brua." He turned to the old man again. "I wish to avoid danger to these citizens. I wish to save your men from further bloodshed. I beg you, surrender. I promise you protection from the crowds, a safe——"

"You have my terms. A free way to the mountains."

A groan came from Oliver Brown. Sinn looked down, watched the boy by the dim light of the torch; felt pity.

"You have no chance. For the last time, I beg you. Give in."

"We will die just here."

Sinn bowed, turned to the door. Old Brown opened it. Sinn looked back once again, his eyes lingered over the three forms lying on the brick floor. "I'll send in the company's doctor," he said; and went.

They stood there in the dark, in the silence, waiting, waiting.

"Father."

The old man went to the bearded boy.

"Father. I'm dying."

"The surgeon is coming. Have courage, Watson."

"Oh, I mustn't die. But I'm dying."

"I would help you, my son, if I could."

The old man walked back, took his place by the loop-hole again.

The surgeon came. "Good evening," he said. The old man held the torch as the Southerner kneeled by Oliver.

"He is my son," the old man said.

"Tell them to kill me," Mary Brown's youngest boy whispered. "I can't stand it."

The other's hands were swift and tender about his torn breast.

"Tell them to kill me. They won't kill me."

The doctor rose. His eyes met old Brown's. He moved to Watson's form; kneeled.

"He is my son too."

Quickly again the doctor rose, gathering his things together with finality. He went to the door.

"Will my sons live?" asked the old man.

"No," the lips formed. "They will not live." The old

man handed the torch back to the doctor who stood there an instant, thinking: I will always remember this. Strange, tragic. Men killing, conversing with one another, aiding the wounded, then killing again. "I will try to come again in the morning," he said; "good night," and went.

The old man stood once more in his place, holding the still watch. Now he trembled and his eyes were unseeing:

"O Lord God of truth, my rock and my fortress, have mercy upon me, for I am afflicted! Mine eye is consumed with grief, yea, my soul and my flesh! I trust in Thee, I say: Thou art my Lord. For this God is our God for ever and ever, He will be our guide even unto death."

In the engine-house the raiders kept the vigil. "I will come again in the morning," the doctor had said. But he would not come, they knew it; their fate would come, storming the hold at dawn. It was bitterly cold, a chill as of death lay about the stone floors and walls. The outside night, cloudy, moonless, crept through the loop-holes, deepening the blackness within. The drunken shouts of the militiamen ceased. They were resting from the heat of the day's valour; Dangerfield Newby's ears had been sliced from his head, the brutal indignities to his cold stiff body had been tired of; the poor white wretches from Loudon Heights had scavenged the dead; the riddled hulk of Will Thompson down in the trestle rocks was this hour being granted its first ghastly peace. A new sound was in the silence, the slow disciplined tread of the Marine guard cordon about the engine-house. "Rest," said the old man; "we have till morning"; and the prisoners and the Negroes and the raiders lay unsleeping side by side on the stone floor. He was still at his place by the door, now forty hours without food, without sleep; calling from time to time in the stillness of the night: "Men, are you awake?" And always there was the moaning of the dying boys.

"Father!"

"I am here, Oliver."

"I can't stand it! Shoot me!"

"No, Oliver. Have patience."

"Please! please! Oh, Martha would do it for me!"

"No, my son. I think you will get well."

Then later in the grievous black silence: "Father!"

"If you must die, die like a man does."

And golden Dolph Thompson, his hair matted with grime and blood, sat by the side of Watson; held the carbine in one hand, with the other stroked the head of his sister's young husband; rocked, heartbroken, Oh Wat, Wat, as the doomed boy sobbed with anguish; and the words which Brua had spoken earlier mingled with his present grief for a single throbbing horror.

"You are committing treason," Brua had said, "treason against your government."

Dolph Thompson had stared. "No, that isn't true! Captain Brown! Is it true that we are committing treason against our government?"

"Yes, I think it is, Dauphin. I think it is true."

"Then I won't fight more! I came to free slaves! I won't fight more, I won't commit treason!"

But the old man was at a distance, in this desperate lost moment he was far in the dream which his life had been. Yes, gentlemen, ran in his mind, ran so incalculably that he would never know whether it was speech or thought, if you realised my past history, if you knew my heart, you would not blame me for being here. I went to Kansas and the pro-slavery people from Kentucky and Virginia hunted me down like a wild animal. I lost one of my sons there. Yes, gentlemen, we are Abolitionists from the North, we've come to take and release your slaves. Our organisation is large, and must succeed. I suffered much in Kansas. I expect to suffer here, in the cause of human freedom. I have been well known as Old Brown of Kansas. I shed blood on Potawatomie. Slaveholders I regard as robbers and murderers, and I have sworn to abolish slavery and liberate my fellow men. And now I am here. . . . I have failed. . . . Two of my sons were killed here today.

"Oliver!" the old man called in the gloom.
No answer. Silence.
"I guess he's dead," old Brown said.

AN EGG FOR THE MAJOR

C. S. Forester

The major commanding the squadron of light tanks was just as uncomfortable as he had been for a number of days. For the officer commanding a light tank there is a seat provided, a sort of steel piano stool, but, in the opinion of the major, it had been designed for men of a physique that has no counterpart on earth. If one sat on it in the normal way, with the part of one which Nature provides for sitting on on the stool, one's knees bumped most uncomfortably on the steel wall in front. And contrariwise, if one hitched oneself back and sat on one's thighs, not only was the circulation interfered with to an extent which led to cramps but also the back of one's head was sore with being bumped against the wall of the turret behind. Especially when the tank was rolling over the desert, lurching and bumping from ridge to ridge; on a road one could look after oneself, but it was weeks and weeks since the major had set eyes on a road.

He left off thinking about the sort of shape a man should be who has to pass his days in a light tank, and gave the order for the tank to stop. He climbed out through the steel door with his compass to take a fresh bearing. Out in the desert here an army had to navigate like a ship at sea, with the additional difficulty that inside the steel walls, with the spark coils to complicate matters, a compass was no use at all. The only thing to do was to get out of the tank, carry one's compass well away from its influence, and look over the featureless landscape and mark some patch of scrub, some minor rise in the ground, on which one could direct one's course. He walked stiffly away from the tank, laid the compass level and stared forward. This was perhaps the five hundredth time he had done this, and he had learned by long experience the difficulties to be anticipated. There was never anything satisfactory directly ahead on which he could direct his course. There would be fine landmarks out to the right or left where they were no use to him, but nothing straight ahead. He would have to be content with some second best, the edge of that yellow patch on the brown, and he knew quite well that it would appear quite different when he got back into the tank again. Furthermore, it would appear

From: *The Saturday Evening Post*. By permission of the Author.

more different still when they had travelled a little way toward it—there had been times long ago, when the desert was new to him, when he had found at a halt that he was more than ninety degrees off his course. He was far more experienced now; five months of desultory warfare and now this last tremendous march across the desert had accustomed him to the difficulties.

Experience taught him to empty his mind of the hundreds of previous landscapes which he had memorised, to concentrate on this one, to note that yellow patch whose edge would be his guiding mark for the next ten miles, and to look back and absorb the appearance of the country in that direction as well. Then he went back to the tank, decided against the piano stool, slammed the door shut, and climbed up onto the roof before giving the word to start. On the roof he could lie on the unyielding steel to the detriment of hip and elbow, anchoring himself into position by locking his toe round the muzzle of the machine gun below him. After a time his leg would go to sleep at about the same time that his hip could bear it no longer; then he would have to change over; three changes—two turns with each foot and hip—would be as much as he could stand, and then it would be time to take a fresh bearing and go back to the piano stool and the other problem of which part to sit on.

He lounged on the steel roof while the tank pitched and rolled under him; it was as well to keep that foot firmly locked below the gun muzzle to save himself from being pitched off. It had happened to him sometimes; everything had happened to him at one time or another. The wind today was from ahead, which was a mercy; a gentle following wind meant that the dust of their progress kept pace with them and suffocated him. He looked away to the left and the right, and he could see a long line of great plumes of dust keeping pace with him as the other tanks of the squadron ploughed their way across the desert. The major was an unimaginative man, but that spectacle never failed to move him. That long line of dust plumes sweeping across the desert had menace and sinister beauty about it. There were the high yellow clouds, and at the base of each a little dot, a nucleus, as it were, sometimes concealed from view by the inequalities of the ground, and every cloud indicated the presence of one of the tanks of his squadron. There were other clouds behind, when the major turned his gaze that way; they showed where the stragglers were trying to regain their places in the line after some necessary halt. The ones farthest back were the ones who had had track trouble or engine trouble. There could be no waiting for them, not in the face of the orders which the wireless brought in, insisting on the utmost speed in this dash across the desert.

Already in the major's mind the total of days already consumed in the march was a little vague. If he set his mind to it, he could have worked it out, but he felt as if he had done nothing all his life except lead this squadron across the desert. Something enormous and of vital importance was happening to the north, he knew—Sidi Barrani and Tobruk had fallen, but his command had been plucked out of that attack and sent off on this wide flanking sweep, and were already a little in the dark about the situation. These Italian maps were of no use at all. They showed things which simply did not exist—he could swear to that from bitter experience —and, in consequence, the major did not know within twenty miles where he was. But somewhere ahead of him there was the sea, across the great hump of Northern Africa which he was traversing, and beside the sea ran the great road which Mussolini had built, and he knew he had only to arrive on that road to start making things unpleasant for the Italians. What the situation would be when he did arrive he could not imagine in the least, but the major had absorbed the philosophy of the desert, and left that problem to be solved when it arose, wasting no mental effort on hypothetical cases which probably would have no resemblance to the reality he would encounter sooner or later.

The squadron was moving on a wide front, impressive on account of the distant plumes of dust, but even so, the width of the front was nothing compared with the immensity of the desert. They had marched five hundred miles so far, and a thousand miles to the south of them the desert extended as far as the plains of the Sudan. Sometimes the major would allow his imagination to think about these distances, but more often he thought about eggs. Tinned beef and biscuits, day after day, for more days than he could count, had had their effect. Nearly every idle thought that passed through his mind was busy with food. Sometimes he thought about kippers and haddock, sometimes about the green vegetables he had refused to eat as a little boy, but mostly he thought about eggs—boiled eggs, fried eggs, scrambled eggs—mostly boiled eggs. The lucky devils who were doing the fighting in the north were in among the villages now which Mussolini had peopled with so much effort; they would have a hen or two for certain, and a hen meant an egg. A boiled egg.

For a day or two, eggs had formed a staple topic of conversation when he squatted at mealtimes with the gunner and the driver, until the major had detected a certain forbearing weariness mingled with the politeness with which his crew had received his remarks about eggs. Then he had left off talking about them; in this new kind of war, majors had to be careful not to become old bores in the eyes of the privates with whom they lived. But not being able to talk about them made him think about them all the more. The major swallowed hard in choking dust.

The sun was now right ahead of him, and low toward the horizon; the sky around it was already taking up the colours of the desert sunset, and the brassy blue overhead was miraculously blending into red and orange. To the major that only meant that the day's march was drawing to a close. Sunsets came every day, and eggs came only once a year, seemingly.

When darkness came, they halted; each tank where it happened to find itself, save for the outposts pushed forward in case the Italians should, incredibly, be somewhere near and should have the hardihood to attempt operations in the dark. The driver and the gunner came crawling out of the tank, dizzy with petrol fumes and stiff with fatigue, still a little deaf with the insensate din which had assailed their ears for the whole day. The most immediate duty was to service the tank and have it all ready for prolonged action again, but before they did that they washed their mouths round with a little of the precious water taken from the can which had ridden with them in the tank all day. It was at blood heat, and it tasted of the inside of a tank—indescribably, that is to say. But it was precious, all the same. There was always the possibility that their ration of water would not come up from the rear; and if it did, there was also the chance that there had been so much loss in the radiators during the day that no water could be spared for the men.

Once, long back, there had been a heavenly time when the day's ration had been a gallon a head a day. That had been marvellous, for a man could do simply anything with a gallon a day; he could shave, wash his face, sometimes even spare a little to wash off the irritating dust from his body. But the ration, now that they were so far from the base, was half a gallon, and a man, after a day in a tank, could drink half a gallon at a single draught if he were foolish enough to do so. Half a gallon meant only just enough water to keep thirst from coming to close quarters; only the most fussy among the men would spare a cupful for shaving, and the days when the radiators had been extra thirsty, so that the men's rations were cut in half, were days of torment.

The major and the gunner and the driver settled down in the desert for their supper. Long habit had blunted the surprise the major had once felt at finding himself, a field officer, squatting in the dust with a couple of privates, and, fortunately, long habit had done the same for the privates. Before this campaign opened they would have been tongue-tied and awkward at his presence. It had not been easy to reach adjustment, but they had succeeded—as witness the way in which, without saying a word, they had caused him to leave off talking about eggs. He was still "sir" to them, but almost the only other way in which his rank was notice-able in their personal relationships was that the two privates both suspected the major of being the guilty party in the matter of the loss of one of their three enamelled mugs. They had not ventured openly to accuse him, and he remained in ignor-ance of their suspicions, taking it for granted that the gunner —a scatterbrained fellow—had been at fault in the matter.

It was an infernal nuisance, being short of a mug; two mugs among three of them called for a whole lot of organisation, especially in the morning, when they had to clean their teeth, and sometimes to shave and sometimes to make tea—and the gunner liked his strong, and the driver liked his weak, and the major was the only one who did not want sugar in it. If ever the three of them were to quarrel, the major knew it would be over some difficulty arising out of the loss of the mug. Yet he did not see nowadays anything odd about a major worrying over the prospect of a disagreement with a couple of privates over an enamelled mug.

And tonight he was additionally unlucky, because the rations for the day were a tinned meat and vegetable con-coction that he particularly disliked. But the gunner and the driver were loud in their delight when they discovered what fate had brought them tonight. They ate noisily and apprecia-tively, while the major squatting beside them made only the merest pretence of eating and allowed his thoughts to stray back to memories of dinner at the Berkeley and the Gar-gantuan lunches at Simpson's in the Strand. And also of eggs.

It was dark now, and cold—before supper was over the major had to reach out for a blanket and wrap it round his shoulders as the treacherous desert wind blew chilly. The stars were out, but there was no moon yet and the darkness was impenetrable. There was nothing to do now except sleep. The major chose himself a spot where the scrub grew not too thickly, and where the rock did not jut entirely through the thin skin of earth which overlaid it. He spread his blankets over his fleabag and crawled in with the dexterity of long practice without disturbing the arrangement. The bit of tarpaulin stretched from the side of the tank to the earth kept off the dew, if there should be any, and the joints that had suffered on the steel piano stool and on the steel roof snuggled gratefully against the more kindly contact of the earth. And long habit was a help.

He awoke in the middle of the night with a shattering roar in his very ear. The driver had his own system of keeping his beloved motor warm enough to start. He slept only under two blankets, and when the cold awoke him he knew that it was necessary to warm up the motor. He would crawl out of bed, start it up, allow it to run for five minutes, and then switch it off. That meant that the light tank was always ready for instant action, but the major had never been able to acquire the habit of sleeping through the din of the motor. The only habit he had been able to form was that of cursing to himself at the driver, feebly, half awake, and then of turning over and completing his night's sleep. The gunner, on the other hand, slept stolidly through the whole racket, snoring away stubbornly—the major suspected him of dreaming about eggs.

Before dawn they were up and doing. Two inches of sand in the bottom of a petrol tin made an admirable wick; petrol soaked into it burned with an almost clear flame and heated the water for their tea in a flash. They had grown cunning lately and brushed their teeth after breakfast, using the remains of the tea for the purpose; that gave them an additional two swallows of water apiece to drink at the midmorning halt for filling up. The motor started, shatteringly noisy as usual. Then they were off, the long line of tanks heaving and rolling over the desert, the familiar plumes of dust trailing behind them, the familiar weary ache beginning to grow in the joints of the major as he settled himself on the piano stool.

The major's calculation of his position was a hazy one, and through no fault of his own. Erratic compasses, ridiculous Italian maps and strict wireless silence combined, after a march hundreds of miles long, to make it very doubtful where they were. But the major was philosophic about it. British light tanks were capable of fighting almost anything in Africa, and what they could not fight they could run away from; they had learned that lesson in innumerable untold skirmishes in the old days of the beginning of the war. The major felt ready for anything that might happen, as he stared out through the slit of the conning tower across the yellowish brown plain.

Yet all the same it is doubtful if he was really ready for the sight that met his eyes. The tank came lurching up a sharp slope. It heaved itself over the crest—the note of the motor changing ever so little as the gradient altered—and a new landscape was presented to the major's eyes.

First of all he saw the sea, the blue sea, the wonderful blue sea, flecked with white. The major wriggled on the piano stool and yelled involuntarily at the top of his voice when he saw it. That marvellous horizon, that beautiful colour, that new-found sense of achievement and freedom—they were simply intoxicating. The driver and the gunner were as intoxicated as he was screwing their necks round to grin at him, the fluffy immature beard of the gunner wagging on his chin.

And then they cleared the next curve of the crest, and the major saw the road, that long coastal road for the construction of which Mussolini had poured out so much treasure. The major had expected to see it from the moment when he had seen the sea—in fact, he was craning his neck for a sight of it. But he was not ready for the rest of what he saw. For twenty miles the road was black with the fleeing Italian army —an enormous column of men and vehicles, jamming the road from side to side, hastening westward—Bergenzoli's army escaping from Bengasi and from the wrath of the English behind them. From a point nearly ahead of them away off to the right stretched that hurrying column. From his point of vantage the major could see it looping like some monstrous water snake along the curves of the road. Now he knew why his squadron had been hurled across the desert at such a frantic speed. It had been planned to cut off Bergenzoli's retreat, and the object had been achieved, with no more than ten minutes to spare.

Those ten minutes were only to spare if the major did the right thing on the instant. But twenty years of training had prepared the major for that very purpose. He was still a hussar, even though his squadron's horses had long ago been replaced by light tanks. His mental reactions were instantaneous; there was no need to stop and ponder the situation. The trained tactical eye took in the lie of the land even while he was shouting into the wireless transmitter the vital information that he was ahead of the Italians. He saw the road and the ridge beside it, and the moment that the information had been acknowledged he was speaking again, quietly already, giving his orders to the squadron. The long line of tanks wheeled and swooped down upon the road.

So close was the race that they were barely in position before the head of the column was up to them. An hour later and the Italians would have been able to post a flank guard behind whose shelter most of them would have been able to slip away. As it was, the major just had time to give his orders to his two troops as the head of the Italian column came down upon them.

The tanks bucked themselves into position and the machine guns spoke out, pouring their fire into the trucks packed with infantry which were so recklessly coming down upon them. It was slaughter, the dire punishment of a harebrained attack. The major watched the trucks swerve off the road, saw the startled infantry come tumbling out while the machine-gun fire cut swaths through them. Truck piled upon truck. The poor devils in them were deserving of pity. At one moment they had thought themselves safe, rolling along a good road back to Tripoli, and then the next these grey monsters had come darting out of the desert across their path, spraying death.

With the checking of the head of the column, confusion spread up the road. The major could see movement dying away as each successive section bumped up against the one ahead; the sudden outburst of firing, taking everyone by surprise, was rousing panic among the weaker individuals. So much the better. From the major's point of view, there could not be too much panic. Somewhere up that column there were field guns and there were heavy tanks, and to neither of them could he offer any real resistance. The more confusion there was in the column, the longer would it take to extricate these, the only weapons that could clear its path. Time was of the utmost importance; he turned and looked back over his shoulder at where the sun was dipping toward the horizon and the blue sea. This time, by some curious chance, his mind was in a condition to take in the fact that the approaching sunset would be red and lurid. He was smiling grimly as he turned back to his work.

Someone over there was trying to urge the unarmoured infantry to the attack—to certain death, in other words, in the face of the two grim little groups of tanks that opposed them. Some of them came forward to the certain death too. And the sun was nearer the horizon.

Farther back down the column frantic officers were clearing a path for the artillery. There were eddies and swirls in the mass. Trucks were being heaved off the road as the guns came through. The major took his glasses from his eyes and gave another order. The tanks curvetted and wheeled, and next moment they had a ridge of solid earth between them and the guns. There was a dreary wait—the major had time for another glance at the sun sinking in a reddened sky—before the shells began to come over. Then the major could smile; they were shrieking over the crest and a good two yards above his head before they buried themselves in the ridge behind him. But there was infantry creeping forward again; there was still the chance that he might be forced sideways out of his position and have to leave a gap through which the mob might escape. He looked at the sun again, and then out to his right, the direction from which he had come, and he felt a glow of relief. The rest of the advance guard was coming—a battalion of motorised infantry with their battery of antitank guns. Now they had a chance. But where were the cruiser tanks, the only weapons in Africa that could stop the heavy tanks when they should be able to make their way out of the column?

It had been touch and go in the first place, when the light tanks had cut off the retreat of the column. It was touch and go now, when the light tanks and five hundred British soldiers were trying to stop the advance of fifty thousand Italians. But night was close at hand. Darkness blinded the Italian gunners and paralysed the efforts being made to clear the road for the heavy tanks. The major neatly withdrew his tanks over one more ridge, in case of a night attack—in all his extensive experience with the Italians they had never ventured a single operation in darkness—and went round his squadron to see that they were as well prepared as might be for a battle on the morrow.

The major always remembers that night as one when there was nothing he found it necessary to do. The British soldier was on the offensive. The veriest fool could see victory just ahead, victory of a crushing type, nothing less than annihilation of the enemy, if only the force of which the squadron formed a part could hold back Bergenzoli until pressure on his rear and the arrival of help to themselves should convince Bergenzoli of the hopelessness of his position. With victory depending on the proper lubrication of their tanks, on their precautions against surprise, they needed no telling, no inspection, to make them do their duty. The major was not an imaginative man, but something in his imagination was touched that night when he talked to his men. The final destruction of the Italians was what they had in mind; the fact that they would be opposed tomorrow by odds of a hundred to one, and that there was more chance of their being dead by evening than alive, did not alter their attitude in the least.

The major walked from one little group to another; the once khaki overalls worn by everyone, even himself, had been bleached almost white by exposure, and the oil stains somehow did not darken them in a bad light, so that the men he spoke to showed up as ghostly figures in the darkness. There was laughter in the voices of the ghosts he spoke to—laughter and delight in the imminent prospect of victory. And in the stillness of the desert night they could hear, across two valleys, the din of the heavy Italian tanks roaring up to take up positions for the charge that would try to clear the way for the Italians next day. That was the lullaby the major heard as he stretched out in the desert to try to snatch a couple of hours' sleep, side by side with the driver and the gunner. Only in the grave did officers and men sleep side by side until this war came.

Dawn—the first faint light that precedes dawn—showed, looming over the farther crest, the big Italian tanks which had been somehow forced forward during the night along the tangled column. They came forward ponderously, with fifty thousand men behind them, and in front of them there was only a thread of infantry, a single battery, a squadron of light tanks whose armour was only fit to keep out rifle bullets. It was as if the picadors and the matadors in the bull ring had to fight, not a single bull but a whole herd of bulls, all charging in the madness of desperation.

There is an art in the playing of a charging bull, even in the handling of a whole herd. Through a long and weary day, that was just what the major's squadron and the rest of the British force succeeded in doing. Since time immemorial —from Alexander to Hitler—it has been the fate of advance guards to be sacrificed to gain time for the manœuvre of the main body, to be used to pin the enemy to the ground, so that his flank can be safely assailed. Only troops of the highest discipline and training can be trusted to fulfil such a mission, however. The Italian tanks which were recklessly handled were lured into the fire of the battery; the timid ones were prevailed upon to procrastinate. The slow retreat of the British force was over ground marked with crippled tanks and littered with Italian dead; and there were British dead there, too, and knocked-out British guns, and burned-out British tanks.

It was an exhausted British force that still confronted the Italians. The line had shrunk, so that on its left flank, toward the sea, there was an open gap through which, among the sand dunes, some of the Italians were beginning to dribble on foot, creeping along the edge of the sea in the wild hope of escaping captivity. And then, at that last moment, came the decisive blow. At least to us here it seemed the last moment. That can only be a guess—no one can dare say that the British had reached the end of their resistance. But it was at that moment, when British riflemen were fighting hard to protect their headquarters, when two thirds of the British guns were out of action, when the major's squadron was reduced to three tanks, that help arrived. From out of the desert there came a sweeping line of huge British cruiser tanks. They came charging down on the Italian flank, enormous, invulnerable and terrifying. It is impossible to guess at the miracle of organisation, at the prodigy of hard work, which had brought these monstrous things across sands which had scarcely even been trodden by camels.

From out of the desert they came, wreathed in dust, spouting fire, charging down upon the tangled mass of the Italian army pent back behind the thin dam of the British line. The Italian tanks wheeled to meet them, and then and there the battle was fought out, tank to tank, under the brazen sky, over the sand where the dead already lay. The dust clouds wrapped them round, dimming the bright flames—visible even in the sunshine—which streamed from the wrecked tanks, the Viking pyres of their slain crews.

When it was over, the whole battle was finished. There was no fight left in the Italians. The desert had already vomited out three fierce attacks—first the major's light tanks, then the infantry, and last the cruiser tanks, and no one could guess what next would come forth. And from the rear came the news that the pursuing British were pressing on the rear guard; at any moment the sea might bring its quota of death, should the British ships find a channel through the sandbanks which would bring their guns within range of the huddled army. Front, rear and both flanks were open to attack, and overhead the air force was about to strike. Nor was that all. Thirst was assailing them, those unhappy fifty thousand men massed without a single well within reach. There was nothing for it but surrender.

The major watched the fifty thousand men yield up their arms; he knew that he was witness to one of the great victories of history, and he was pleased about it. Through the dreadful fatigue that was overwhelming him he also was aware that he had played a vital part in the gaining of that victory, and that somewhere in the future there would be mentions in dispatches and decorations. But his eyelids were heavy and his shoulders drooping.

Then came the gunner; his faded, oil-stained overalls made more shocking that ever by the stains of the blood of the wounded driver, and that horribly fluffy yellow beard of his, like the down on a baby chick, offending the sunlight. Now that they had reached the sea, the distillation plants would supply them with a sufficiency of water and that beard could be shaved off. But the gunner was grinning all over his face, his blue eyes nearly lost in the wrinkles round them, lines carved by the blinding light of the desert. The gunner had heard a cock crowing down beside the solitary white farmhouse toward the sea on the edge of the battlefield, and he had walked there and back on stiff legs. The gunner held out a big fist before the major, and opened the fingers like a man doing a conjuring trick. In his hand was an egg.

TANK FIGHTING IN LIBYA

Alan Moorehead

On the night of Nov. 17 a line of squat British Army trucks bounced over the camel's-thorn to the barbed-wire fence that divides Egypt from Libya. Engineers in greatcoats and battle-dress stepped down briskly in the darkness and began snipping some 20 holes in the 10-ft. thickness of the wire. There was no need for silence. A storm of extraordinary violence was sweeping across the desert and forked lightning played above the fence as the men sheared through the last strands dividing them from Libya.

Before the morning, while the same wild storm was rushing from the sea and the men read into it a portent of what was to come, the British Army passed through the broken fence into Libya. At the head rode the force of U.S.-built tanks that had never seen battle. Many of the crews were old in the desert—British youngsters of 20, maybe a little more, who had fought their way through to the coast beyond Bengasi last winter and held the southern desert flank ever since. But their vehicles were brand new—M3 light tanks with a brand new 37-mm. gun, new armour, new airplane motors that drove them forward over the rough gravel and salt-bush flats at an even noisy 10 m.p.h. Each tank commander sat up high in his open hatch holding his communication mouthpiece in his hand. The men's bedding and camping gear strapped on the open sides soaked steadily in the rain. Each vehicle bore its striped regimental colours with perhaps some painted name above liked " Gladys," " Phyllis," " Betty." Each flew its pennants from its wireless antennae that waved about like an ear of corn in the wind.

Riding close upon his leading squadrons and ahead of the scattered supply columns following behind went the brigadier in command—a huge man with a strong dark face, a hawk nose, a black tank corps beret on his head and a flash of red on the lapels of his tunic. Like most of the others he had wound a khaki woollen scarf round his neck, and he gave his orders over the radio quietly, quickly, incessantly. By midday, when the clouds were breaking, the little brigade was well into Libya. Enemy outposts that had watched the advance had disappeared over the horizon to break the news to General

From: *Life Magazine.* Copyright 1941 by the *Daily Express.*

Erwin Rommel at his headquarters near the coast. All the rest of that day U.S. tanks rode on into an empty enemy desert, meeting no opposition, sending scouts prying ahead but finding nothing.

The British plan was simple in structure but complex in detail. Four concentric rings were being laid round the enemy positions in the triangle of open desert between Tobruk, Fort Maddalena and Bardia. Wheeling northwest out of Egypt, two inner rings were closing upon Axis border pockets around Salûm, Bardia, Fort Capuzzo and Sidi Omár. The fourth and southernmost ring was describing a great arc from Maddalena northwest toward Tobruk. Stiffening and protecting these three layers like a band of metal through a slab of concrete went the British armoured forces. This mass of hundreds of tanks, 25-pounder guns, armoured fighting vehicles, armoured cars, anti-tank guns, machine gun and ack-ack units was pledged to one essential job—to seek out Rommel's two armoured divisions and destroy them. No one that first day knew where Rommel would strike or how. But lest he should choose not to strike at all and fall back westward, British tanks ran a cordon around him. It too reached from Tobruk to Maddalena. It was a host of thousands upon thousands of vehicles stretching across 100 miles of desert and with every hour expanding and changing as many thousands more came pouring through the gaps in the wire.

U.S.-built tanks took up position near Sidi Omár and in the evening, when the boys quietly boiled their tea and pried open their tins of bully, it was pretty certain that Rommel would be brought to battle on the morrow. Yet still, on the morning of the 19th, hardly a shot had been fired. I drove up to a tanks' supply column and was talking with Colonel Bonar Fellers, the American military attaché from Cairo. Then it came. For ten miles in the east between us and Egypt the horizon lit up with gun bursts. Some thought it was bombing and dispersed for shelter; the others thought it was artillery shooting on Sidi Omár. Most of them clambered into their vehicles and peered at the smoke that was gradually gathering itself into a continuous curtain on the horizon. Then clearly it sounded—that dry quick coughing that is a tank gun and nothing else. The war was starting. Rommel had come south with more than 100 medium tanks and the American "lights" had pitched into him.

Unless you are in a tank yourself, you don't see anything very clearly in a tank battle. The enemy appears as just a line of tiny silhouettes where the sky hits the desert, dark silhouettes

159

shaped exactly like distant battleships, each one spitting out a yellow flash from time to time. Your own tanks, weaving in to attack disappear behind the wake of their own dust. Within a few minutes it is just so much smoke, dust, flame and noise. That is what happened now and what I have seen half a dozen times since.

"There they come," yells someone on his radio blower. Listening on a headquarters communication vehicle you hear the tanks talking to one another right in the battle. You hear:

"Get to hell out of it Bill so that I can get at this ———. Easy boy, easy boy, now at him. . . . Bill, you ———, you're blocking my way again. . . . Look out, right behind you." And through it all you hear the bursting of shells, the tearing and screaming of the tank treads, the gears grunting into reverse and forward. No one, remember, who wasn't right in this first fight had any clear idea of what was going on. We had to wait and just watch that pall of battle smoke widen, darken and move westward into the sun.

Then a staff major came out of it and told us: "They came right at us off the rising ground with the sun behind their backs. Right smack at us. They opened up with their 50-mm. gun at 1,500 yd.—much too far for our 37s. So the boys just went into the barrage hull down at 40 m.p.h. to get into range. Then they mixed it. I tell you no one on God's earth can follow what's going on. The boys are just weaving in and between the Jerries, passing right through them, then turning and coming back into it again. They're passing 50 and 60 yd. apart and firing at point-blank range. As soon as you see a Swastika you just let fly. There's everything in the air—tracers, shells, bullets, ricochets, incendiaries and bits of red-hot metal whanging off the burning tanks. Some of the tanks are blowing right up into the air, their petrol exploding, their ammunition popping off in every direction."

R.A.F. bombers and fighters swept over but held their fire because they could not sort the battle out. Every few minutes a tank would stay out of the battle, rush to a supply vehicle, fling in petrol and shells, then zigzag into the arena again. The battle died down little by little as dusk fell, a blue-green dusk lightened in the east by the red glare of burning tanks. In the darkness tanks called to one another, found their friends, felt their way back to their own lines bringing what wounded they could. Other wounded walked back or crawled; or merely lay there in the dark with the acrid smell of cordite round them. And the piercing desert cold advanced degree by degree through the night.

The Nazis held the battlefield. Up from their lines flew star shells and Very lights in green, red, purple. Before midnight their breakdown wagons were there hooking on to partial wrecks, dragging guns and broken tracks away. The Germans were not unkind to our wounded. They took their rations but gave them hot tea, covered some with blankets, bandaged one or two sufficiently to give them a 50-50 chance of living till the next day. Many were left lying on the wet sand through the night. Marvellously, a British squadron leader, with both legs gone, survived till we picked him up in the morning. He described how the Nazis were round him all night salvaging their gear. Through the night we laboured, gathered our unarmoured vehicles into a close bunch, posted tanks in a ring outside.

Riding out at 5 o'clock in the morning, we watched the battle begin afresh when it was still only possible to see 100 yd. British and German tanks that had lain close to one another through the night simply aimed and blitzed off at one another again, though it was almost too cold to bear the touch of the metal. At 9 a.m. Rommel suddenly broke off and veered westward. He had lost some 30 tanks. We had learned too, at heavy cost, some of the great lessons that have governed this desert tank fighting ever since. Hear them out of the mouth of a young Scots sergeant, "We have got to get 50- and 75-mm. guns like the Germans. They start firing at 1,500 yd. and we have got to come right in to 800 yd. before our '37' can make any reply. But 'Honeys' (the group word for American tanks) are wonderful on speed and weaving about. It would go fine if we could just get our 25-pounder artillery right up forward to cover our first advance and the R.A.F. to bomb."

The armour plating on the Honeys can take it. One German shell landing on the turret knocked the gun mounting into the British gunner's head but it didn't pierce. However, there were neat six-pounder holes through some of the turrets, close-range stuff, and the Nazi incendiaries seemed to burn the very metal off the tanks. Swiftly then on this second morning of the battle, the tank officers checked up, refilled the tanks and before nightfall they were swept into action again.

Rommel, binding most of his two armoured divisions into one column, was moving westward across our line, feeling for a soft spot to burst through to the south. Finding none, he wheeled suddenly northwest and fell upon the extreme top of the British armoured wing holding the Sidi Rezegh airfield near Tobruk. A U.S. force was launched in pursuit.

They caught up with a Nazi supply column, demolished half of it and swept on again, fighting the German rearguard all the time.

Another night Honeys, expecting re-inforcement, sent out a staff officer to welcome a column of new tanks that hove up over the horizon. The newcomers were Germans. They charged straight through the brigade's headquarters, blowing up staff cars, petrol and food wagons while the British tanks scattered to new positions. There were moments of grim humour, too. A captured British officer tried to make a bolt for it when R.A.F. Blenheims came over bombing the German lines. A Nazi guard fired a burst from a tommy gun over his head. Out of a neighbouring ditch popped a platoon of Italians with their hands up, surrendering. The Briton eventually, like hundreds of others, was recaptured. I met another officer who, with bad wounds, crawled 1,000 yd. out of the fight. Others have walked 20 or 30 miles to freedom, lying doggo by day, bluffing past challenges at night.

I stopped by a British concentration camp, just a few strands of barbed wire in the open desert, where I found 50 prisoners. The Germans kept to one group, the Italians to another. The Germans had nothing with them, the Italians all had bulging suitcases which they swiftly packed as they surrendered. A German captain from Saxony was bitter. " I've had no hot food since I was captured twelve hours ago," he told me. The men in the Honeys had not had any for three days. From that first fight nearly a fortnight ago they had never ceased fighting for more than an hour or two. Consider them now on this twelfth day of battle. There is not much left. The brigadier has lost his kit and wears a blanket wrapped round his legs. He sits on a wooden chair on top of his tank in which he has entered every engagement to direct his squadrons over the radio. He has eaten perhaps once daily, slept a few hours each night, been cut off half a dozen times and never remained more than two hours each night on one spot. His tank is blackened with blast, chipped and holed with shell. He gives his men ten minutes to eat. At midday we attack again.

We cover the advance of infantry over last week's battlefield. It is a bare, utterly flat stretch of gravel now strewn with burnt-out tanks, a few crashed aircraft, and all the forlorn, pathetic wreckage of deadmen's clothing—bedding, mess tins, letters and papers. There is a litter of rifles which have been flung away, piles of British and German shell cases, tens of thousands of petrol tins, German water containers, broken tank tracks spilled along the sand like great lizards, up-ended trucks, biscuit and bully tins; and among all this the inter-mingled graveyards of British and German dead. These men were buried at the height of their battles beside their tanks. Most have a cross or some symbol like an empty cartridge belt placed by a comrade. As we pass, a half-demolished tank takes fire again. If fills the western sky with black smoke, its shells blowing off in mad, roaring volleys, its petrol sending up wave after wave of flame.

Two Messerschmitts come over machine-gunning briefly. British artillery starts up, sending its 25-pounders over our heads onto a formation of enemy tanks a mile or two ahead. R.A.F. bombers lay a 300 ft. curtain of dust and explosives across the battlefield. The Honeys deploy. The brigadier says quietly into his mouthpiece, " All right, go ahead." The British artillery covers the Honeys' first charge. It is working out the way the sergeant wanted it. The Nazis are coming on for a collision, dropping their shells among us already. One tank catches fire before it can get into action. Another hit below the turret lurches, stops, belches smoke. The wounded crew crawl out as a doctor in a little ambulance car races across. The Nazis are running right into our 25-pounder barrage and as far as the eye can see four more tanks, ours or theirs or both, are burning. In the last yellow light of the day the enemy seem to be veering east to open up a new attack. There is too much dust to see yet. I am told to go back for the night. The Honeys will stay there fighting in the dust as long as they can see.

BLOWING UP A TRAIN

T. E. Lawrence

Blowing up trains was an exact science when done deliberately, by a sufficient party, with machine-guns in position. If scrambled at it might become dangerous. The difficulty this time was that the available gunners were Indians; who, though good men fed, were only half-men in cold and hunger. I did not propose to drag them off without rations on an adventure which might take a week. There was no cruelty in starving Arabs; they would not die of a few days' fasting, and would fight as well as ever on empty stomachs; while, if things got too difficult, there were the riding camels to kill and eat; but the Indians, though Moslems, refused camel-flesh on principle.

I explained these delicacies of diet. Ali at once said that it would be enough for me to blow up the train, leaving him and the Arabs with him to do their best to carry its wreck without machine-gun support. As, in this unsuspecting district, we might well happen on a supply train, with civilians or only a small guard of reservists aboard, I agreed to risk it. The decision having been applauded, we sat down in a cloaked circle, to finish our remaining food in a very late and cold supper (the rain had sodden the fuel and made fire not possible) our hearts somewhat comforted by the chance of another effort.

At dawn, with the unfit of the Arabs, the Indians moved away for Azrak, miserably. They had started up country with me in hope of a really military enterprise, and first had seen the muddled bridge, and now were losing this prospective train. It was hard on them; and to soften the blow with honour I asked Wood to accompany them. He agreed, after argument, for their sakes; but it proved a wise move for himself, as a sickness which had been troubling him began to show the early signs of pneumonia.

The balance of us, some sixty men, turned back towards the railway. None of them knew the country, so I led them to Minifir, where, with Zaal, we had made havoc in the spring. The re-curved hill-top was an excellent observation-post, camp, grazing ground and way of retreat, and we sat

From: *Seven Pillars of Wisdom*: Copyright, 1926, 1935 by Doubleday, Doran & Co. Inc.

there in our old place till sunset, shivering and staring out over the immense plain which stretched map-like to the clouded peaks of Jebel Druse, with Um el Jemal and her sister-villages like ink-smudges on it through the rain.

In the first dusk we walked down to lay the mine. The rebuilt culvert of kilometre 172 seemed still the fittest place. While we stood by it there came a rumbling, and through the gathering darkness and mist a train suddenly appeared round the northern curve, only two hundred yards away. We scurried under the long arch and heard it roll overhead. This was annoying; but when the course was clear again, we fell to burying the charge. The evening was bitterly cold, with drifts of rain blowing down the valley.

The arch was solid masonry, of four metres span, and stood over a shingle water-bed which took its rise on our hill-top. The winter rains had cut this into a channel four feet deep, narrow and winding, which served us as an admirable approach till within three hundred yards of the line. There the gully widened out and ran straight towards the culvert, open to the sight of anyone upon the rails.

We hid the explosive carefully on the crown of the arch, deeper than usual, beneath a tie, so that the patrols could not feel its jelly softness under their feet. The wires were taken down the bank into the shingle bed of the watercourse, where concealment was quick; and up it as far as they could reach. Unfortunately, this was only sixty yards, for there had been difficulty in Egypt over insulated cable and no more had been available when our expedition started. Sixty yards was plenty for the bridge, but little for a train: however, the ends happened to coincide with a little bush about ten inches high, on the edge of the watercourse, and we buried them beside this very convenient mark. It was impossible to leave them joined up to the exploder in the proper way, since the spot was evident to the permanent way-patrols as they made their rounds.

Owing to the mud the job took longer than usual, and it was very nearly dawn before we finished. I waited under the draughty arch till day broke, wet and dismal, and then I went over the whole area of disturbance, spending another half-hour in effacing its every mark, scattering leaves and dead grass over it, and watering down the broken mud from a shallow rain-pool near. Then they waved to me that the first patrol was coming, and I went up to join the others.

Before I had reached them they came tearing down into their prearranged places, lining the watercourse and spurs each side.

A train was coming from the north. Hamud, Feisal's long slave, had the exploder; but before he reached me a short train of closed box-wagons rushed by at speed. The rainstorms on the plain and the thick morning had hidden it from the eyes of our watchman until too late. This second failure saddened us further and Ali began to say that nothing would come right this trip. Such a statement held risks as prelude of the discovery of an evil eye present; so, to divert attention, I suggested new watching posts be sent far out, one to the ruins on the north, one to the great cairn of the southern crest.

The rest, having no breakfast, were to pretend not to be hungry. They all enjoyed doing this, and for a while we sat cheerfully in the rain huddled against one another for warmth behind a breastwork of our streaming camels. The moisture made the animals' hair curl up like a fleece, so that they looked queerly dishevelled. When the rain paused, which it did frequently, a cold moaning wind searched out the unprotected parts of us very thoroughly. After a time we found our wetted shirts clammy and comfortless things. We had nothing to eat, nothing to do and nowhere to sit except on wet rock, wet grass or mud. However, this persistent weather kept reminding me that it would delay Allenby's advance on Jerusalem, and rob him of his great possibility. So large a misfortune to our lion was a half-encouragement for the mice. We would be partners into next year.

In the best circumstances, waiting for action was hard. Today it was beastly. Even enemy patrols stumbled along without care, perfunctorily, against the rain. At last near noon, in a snatch of fine weather, the watchmen on the south peak flagged their cloaks wildly in signal of a train. We reached our positions in an instant, for we had squatted the late hours on our heels in a streaming ditch near the line, so as not to miss another chance. The Arabs took cover properly. I looked back at their ambush from my firing point, and saw nothing but the grey hillsides.

I could not hear the train coming, but trusted, and knelt ready for perhaps half an hour, when the suspense became intolerable, and I signalled to know what was up. They sent down to say it was coming very slowly, and was an enormously long train. Our appetites stiffened. The longer it was the more would be the loot. Then came word that it had stopped. It moved again.

Finally, near one o'clock, I heard it panting. The locomotive was evidently defective (all these wood-fired trains were bad), and the heavy load on the up-gradient was proving too much for its capacity. I crouched behind my bush, while it crawled slowly into view past the south cutting, and along the bank above my head towards the culvert. The first ten trucks were open trucks, crowded with troops. However, once again it was too late to choose, so when the engine was squarely over the mine I pushed down the handle of the exploder. Nothing happened. I sawed it up and down four times.

Still nothing happened; and I realised that it had gone out of order, and that I was kneeling on a naked bank, with a Turkish troop train crawling past fifty yards away. The bush, which had seemed a foot high, shrank smaller than a fig-leaf; and I felt myself the most distinct object in the country-side. Behind me was an open valley for two hundred yards to the cover where my Arabs were waiting, and wondering what I was at. It was impossible to make a bolt for it, or the Turks would step off the train and finish us. If I sat still, there might be just a hope of my being ignored as a casual Bedouin.

So there I sat, counting for sheer life, while eighteen open trucks, three box-wagons, and three officers' coaches dragged by. The engine panted slower and slower, and I thought every moment that it would break down. The troops took no great notice of me, but the officers were interested, and came out to the little platforms at the ends of their carriages, point-ing and staring. I waved back at them, grinning nervously, and feeling an improbable shepherd in my Meccan dress, with its twisted golden circlet about my head. Perhaps the mud-stains, the wet and their ignorance made me accepted. The end of the brake van slowly disappeared into the cutting on the north.

As it went, I jumped up, buried my wires, snatched hold of the wretched exploder, and went like a rabbit uphill into safety. There I took breath and looked back to see that the train had finally stuck. It waited, about five hundred yards beyond the mine, for nearly an hour to get up a head of steam, while an officers' patrol came back and searched, very carefully, the ground where I had been seen sitting. However the wires were properly hidden: they found nothing: the engine plucked up heart again, and away they went.

Mifleh was past tears, thinking I had intentionally let the train through; and when the Serahin had been told the real cause they said " bad luck is with us." Historically they were right; but they meant it for a prophecy, so I made sarcastic reference to their courage at the bridge the week before, hinting that it might be a tribal preference to sit on camel-guard. At once there was uproar, the Serahin attacking me furiously, the Beni Sakhr defending. Ali heard the trouble, and came running.

When we had made it up the original despondency was half forgotten. Ali backed me nobly, though the wretched boy was blue with cold and shivering in an attack of fever. He gasped that their ancestor the Prophet had given to Sherifs the faculty of "sight," and by it he knew that our luck was turning. This was comfort for them: my first instalment of good fortune came when in the wet, without other tool than my dagger, I got the box of the exploder open and persuaded its electrical gear to work properly once more.

We returned to our vigil by the wires, but nothing happened, and evening drew down with more squalls and beastliness, everybody full of grumbles. There was no train; it was too wet to light a cooking fire; our only potential food was camel. Raw meat did not tempt anyone that night; and so our beasts survived to the morrow.

Ali lay down on his belly, which position lessened the hunger-ache, trying to sleep off his fever. Khazen, Ali's servant, lent him his cloak for extra covering. For a spell I took Khazen under mine, but soon found it becoming crowded. So I left it to him and went downhill to connect up the exploder. Afterwards I spent the night there alone by the singing telegraph wires, hardly wishing to sleep, so painful was the cold. Nothing came all the long hours, and dawn, which broke wet, looked even uglier than usual. We were sick to death of Minifir, of railways, of train watching and wrecking, by now. I climbed up to the main body while the early patrol searched the railway. Then the day cleared a little. Ali awoke, much refreshed, and his new spirit cheered up. Hamud, the slave, produced some sticks which he had kept under his clothes by his skin all night. They were nearly dry. We shaved down some blasting gelatine, and with its hot flame got a fire going, while the Sukhar hurriedly killed a mangy camel, the best spared of our riding-beasts, and began with entrenching tools to hack it into handy joints.

Just at that moment the watchman on the north cried a train. We left the fire and made a breathless race of the six hundred yards down-hill to our old position. Round the bend, whistling its loudest, came the train, a splendid two-engined thing of twelve passenger coaches, travelling at top speed on the favouring grade. I touched off under the first driving wheel of the first locomotive, and the explosion was terrific. The ground spouted blackly into my face, and I was sent spinning, to sit up with the shirt torn to my shoulder and the blood dripping from long, ragged scratches on my left arm. Between my knees lay the exploder, crushed under a twisted sheet of sooty iron. In front of me was the scalded and smoking upper half of a man. When I peered through the dust and steam of the explosion the whole boiler of the first engine seemed to be missing.

I dully felt that it was time to get away to support; but when I moved, I learnt that there was a great pain in my right foot, because of which I could only limp along, with my head swinging from the shock. Movement began to clear away this confusion, as I hobbled towards the upper valley, whence the Arabs were now shooting fast into the crowded coaches. Dizzily I cheered myself by repeating aloud in English, " Oh, I wish this hadn't happened."

When the enemy began to return our fire, I found myself much between the two. Ali saw me fall, and thinking that I was hard hit, ran out, with Turki and about twenty men of his servants and the Beni Sakhr, to help me. The Turks found their range and got seven of them in a few seconds. The others, in a rush, were about me—fit models, after their activity, for a sculptor. Their full white cotton drawers drawn in, bell-like, round their slender waists and ankles; their hairless brown bodies; and the love-locks plaited tightly over each temple in long horns, made them look like Russians dancers.

We scrambled back into cover together, and there, secretly, I felt myself over, to find I had not once been really hurt; though besides the bruises and cuts of the boiler-plate and a broken toe, I had five different bullet-grazes on me (some of them uncomfortably deep) and my clothes ripped to pieces.

From the watercourse we could look about. The explosion had destroyed the arched head of the culvert, and the frame of the first engine was lying beyond it, at the near foot of the embankment, down which it had rolled. The second locomotive had toppled into the gap, and was lying across the ruined tender of the first. Its bed was twisted. I judged them both beyond repair. The second tender had disappeared over the further side; and the first three wagons had telescoped and were smashed in pieces.

The rest of the train was badly derailed, with the listing coaches butted end to end at all angles, zigzagged along the track. One of them was a saloon, decorated with flags. In it had been Mehmed Jemal Pasha, commanding the Eighth Army Corps, hurrying down to defend Jerusalem against Allenby.

His chargers had been in the first wagon; his motor-car was on the end of the train, and we shot it up. Of his staff we noticed a fat ecclesiastic, whom we thought to be Assad Shukair, Imam to Ahmed Jemal Pasha, and a notorious pro-Turk pimp. So we blazed at him till he dropped.

It was all long bowls. We could see that our chance of carrying the wreck was slight. There had been some four hundred men on board, and the survivors, now recovered from the shock, were under shelter and shooting hard at us. At the first moment our party on the north spur had closed, and nearly won the game. Mifleh on his mare chased the officers from the saloon into the lower ditch. He was too excited to stop and shoot, and so they got away scathless. The Arabs following him had turned to pick up some of the rifles and medals littering the ground, and then to drag bags and boxes from the train. If we had had a machine-gun posted to cover the far side, according to my mining practice, not a Turk would have escaped.

Mifleh and Adhub rejoined us on the hill, and asked after Fahad. One of the Serahin told how he had led the first rush, while I lay knocked out beside the exploder, and had been killed near it. They showed his belt and rifle as proof that he was dead and that they had tried to save him. Adhub said not a word, but leaped out of the gully and raced downhill. We caught our breaths till our lungs hurt us, watching him; but the Turks seemed not to see. A minute later he was dragging a body behind the left-hand bank.

Mifleh went back to his mare, mounted, and took her down behind a spur. Together they lifted the inert figure on to the pommel, and returned. A bullet had passed through Fahad's face, knocking out four teeth, and gashing the tongue. He had fallen unconscious, but had revived just before Adhub reached him, and was trying on hands and knees, blinded with blood, to crawl away. He now recovered poise enough to cling to a saddle. So they changed him to the first camel they found, and led him off at once.

The Turks, seeing us so quiet, began to advance up the slope. We let them come half-way, and then poured in volleys which killed some twenty and drove the others back. The ground about the train was strewn with dead, and the broken coaches had been crowded: but they were fighting under the eye of their Corps Commander, and undaunted began to work round the spurs to outflank us.

We were now only about forty left, and obviously could do no good against them. So we ran in batches up the little stream-bed, turning at each sheltered angle to delay them by pot-shots. Little Turki much distinguished himself by quick coolness, though his straight-stocked Turkish cavalry carbine made him so expose his head that he got four bullets through his head-cloth. Ali was angry with me for retiring slowly. In reality my raw hurts crippled me, but to hide from him this real reason I pretended to be easy, interested in and studying the Turks. Such successive rests while I gained courage for a new run kept him and Turki far behind the rest.

At last we reached the hill-top. Each man there jumped on the nearest camel, and made away at full speed eastward into the desert, for an hour. Then in safety we sorted our animals. The excellent Rahail, despite the ruling excitement, had brought off with him, tied to his saddle-girth, a huge haunch of the camel slaughtered just as the train arrived. He gave us the motive for a proper halt, five miles farther on, as a little party of four camels appeared marching in the same direction. It was our companion, Matar, coming back from his home village to Azrak with loads of raisins and peasant delicacies.

So we stopped at once, under a large rock in Wadi Dhuleil, where was a barren fig-tree, and cooked our first meal for three days. There, also, we bandaged up Fahad, who was sleepy with the lassitude of his severe hurt. Adhub, seeing this, took one of Matar's new carpets, and, doubling it across the camel-saddle, stitched the ends into great pockets. In one they laid Fahad, while Adhub crawled into the other as make-weight: and the camel was led off southward towards their tribal tents.

The other wounded men were seen to at the same time. Mifleh brought up the youngest lads of the party, and had them spray the wounds with their piss, as a rude antiseptic. Meanwhile we whole ones refreshed ourselves. I bought another mangy camel for extra meat, paid rewards, compensated the relatives of the killed, and gave prize-money, for the sixty or seventy rifles we had taken. It was small booty, but not to be despised. Some Serahin, who had gone into the action without rifles, able only to throw unavailing stones, had now two guns apiece. Next day we moved into Azrak, having a great welcome, and boasting—God forgive us—that we were victors.

WAR IS THE PROVINCE OF CHANCE

In no sphere of human activity is such a margin to be left for this intruder because none is so much in constant contact with him on all sides. He increases the uncertainty of every circumstance, and deranges the course of events.

From this uncertainty of all intelligence and suppositions, this continual interposition of chance, the actor in War constantly finds things different from his expectation; and this can not fail to have an influence on his plans, or at least on the presumptions connected with these plans. If this influence is so great as to render the pre-determined plan completely null, then, as a rule, a new one must be substituted in its place; but at the moment the necessary data are often wanting for this, because in the course of action circumstances press for immediate decision, and allow no time to look about for fresh data, often not enough for mature consideration.

TURN ABOUT

William Faulkner

The American—the older one—wore no pink Bedfords. His breeches were of plain whipcord, like the tunic. And the tunic had no long London-cut skirts, so that below the Sam Browne the tail of it stuck straight out like the tunic of a military policeman beneath his holster belt. And he wore simple puttees and the easy shoes of a man of middle age, instead of Savile Row boots, and the shoes and the puttees did not match in shade, and the ordnance belt did not match either of them, and the pilot's wings on his breast were just wings. But the ribbon beneath them was a good ribbon, and the insigne on his shoulders were the twin bars of a captain. He was not tall. His face was thin, a little aquiline; the eyes intelligent and a little tired. He was past twenty-five; looking at him, one thought, not Phi Beta Kappa exactly, but Skull and Bones perhaps, or possibly a Rhodes scholarship.

One of the men who faced him probably could not see him

at all. He was being held on his feet by an American military policeman. He was quite drunk, and in contrast with the heavy-jawed policeman who held him erect on his long, slim, boneless legs, he looked like a masquerading girl. He was possibly eighteen, tall, with a pink-and-white face and blue eyes, and a mouth like a girl's mouth. He wore a pea-coat, buttoned awry and stained with recent mud, and upon his blond head, at that unmistakable and rakish swagger which no other people can ever approach or imitate, the cap of a Royal Naval Officer.

"What's this, corporal?" the American captain said. "What's the trouble? He's an Englishman. You'd better let their M.P.s take care of him."

"I know he is," the policeman said. He spoke heavily, breathing heavily, in the voice of a man under physical strain; for all his girlish delicacy of limb, the English boy was heavier —or more helpless—than he looked. "Stand up!" the policeman said. "They're officers!"

The English boy made an effort then. He pulled himself together, focusing his eyes. He swayed, throwing his arms about the policeman's neck, and with the other hand he saluted, his hand flicking, fingers curled a little, to his right ear, already swaying again and catching himself again. "Cheer-o, sir," he said. "Name's not Beatty, I hope."

"No," the captain said.

"Ah," the English boy said. "Hoped not. My mistake. No offence, what?"

"No offence," the captain said quietly. But he was looking at the policeman. The second American spoke. He was a lieutenant, also a pilot. But he was not twenty-five and he wore the pink breeches, the London boots, and his tunic might have been a British tunic save for the collar.

"It's one of those navy eggs," he said. "They pick them out of the gutters here all night long. You don't come to town often enough."

"Oh," the captain said. "I've heard about them. I remember now." He also remarked now that, though the street was a busy one—it was just outside a popular café—and there were many passers, soldiers, civillian, women, yet none of them so much as paused, as though it were a familiar sight. He was looking at the policeman. "Can't you take him to his ship?"

"I thought of that before the captain did," the policeman said. "He says he can't go aboard his ship after dark because he puts the ship away at sundown."

"Puts it away?"

"Stand up, sailor!" the policeman said savagely, jerking at his lax burden. "Maybe the captain can make sense out of it. Damned if I can. He says they keep the boat under the wharf. Run it under the wharf at night, and that they can't get it out again until the tide goes out tomorrow."

"Under the wharf? A boat? What is this?" He was now speaking to the lieutenant. "Do they operate some kind of aquatic motorcycles?"

"Something like that," the lieutenant said. "You've seen them—the boats. Launches, camouflaged and all. Dashing up and down the harbour. You've seen them. They do that all day and sleep in the gutters here all night."

"Oh," the captain said. "I thought those boats were ship commanders' launches. You mean to tell me they use officers just to—"

"I don't know," the lieutenant said. "Maybe they use them to fetch hot water from one ship to another. Or buns. Or maybe to go back and forth fast when they forget napkins or something."

"Nonsense," the captain said. He looked at the English boy again.

"That's what they do," the lieutenant said. "Town's lousy with them all night long. Gutters full, and their M.P.s carting them away in batches, like nursemaids in a park. Maybe the French give them the launches to get them out of the gutters during the day."

"Oh," the captain said, "I see." But it was clear that he didn't see, wasn't listening, didn't believe what he did hear. He looked at the English boy. "Well, you can't leave him here in that shape," he said.

Again the English boy tried to pull himself together. "Quite all right, 'sure you," he said glassily, his voice pleasant, cheerful almost, quite courteous. "Used to it. Confounded rough *pavé*, though. Should force French do something about it. Visiting lads jolly well deserve decent field to play on, what?"

"And he was jolly well using all of it too," the policeman said savagely. "He must think he's a one-man team, maybe."

At that moment a fifth man came up. He was a British military policeman. "Nah then," he said. "What's this? What's this?" Then he saw the Americans' shoulder bars. He saluted. At the sound of his voice the English boy turned, swaying, peering.

"Oh, hullo, Albert," he said.

"Nah then, Mr. Hope," the British policeman said. He said to the American policeman, over his shoulder: "What is it this time?"

"Likely nothing," the Americans said. "The way you guys run a war. But I'm a stranger here. Here. Take him."

"What is this, corporal?" the captain said. "What was he doing?"

"He won't call it nothing," the American policeman said, jerking his head at the British policeman. "He'll just call it a thrush or a robin or something. I turn into this street about three blocks back a while ago, and I find it blocked with a line of trucks going up from the docks, and the drivers all hollering ahead what the hell the trouble is. So I come on, and I find it is about three blocks of them, blocking the cross streets too; and I come on to the head of it where the trouble is, and I find about a dozen of the drivers out in front, holding a caucus or something in the middle of the street, and I come up and I say, 'What's going on here?' and they leave me through and I find this egg here laying—"

"Yer talking about one of His Majesty's officers, my man," the British policeman said.

"Watch yourself, corporal," the captain said. "And you found this officer—"

"He had done gone to bed in the middle of the street, with an empty basket for a pillow. Laying there with his hands under his head and his knees crossed, arguing with them about whether he ought to get up and move or not. He said that the trucks could turn back and go around by another street, but that he couldn't use any other street, because this street was his."

"His street?"

The English boy had listened, interested, pleasant. "Billet, you see," he said. "Must have order, even in war emergency. Billet by lot. This street mine; no poaching, eh? Next street Jamie Wutherspoon's. But trucks can go by that street because Jamie not using it yet. Not in bed yet. Insomnia. Knew so. Told them. Trucks go that way. See now?"

"Was that it, corporal?" the captain said.

"He told you. He wouldn't get up. He just laid there, arguing with them. He was telling one of them to go somewhere and bring back a copy of their articles of war—"

"King's Regulation; yes," the captain said.

"—and see if the book said whether he had the right of way, or the trucks. And then I got him up, and then the captain come along. And that's all. And with the captain's permission I'll now hand him over to His Majesty's wet nur—"

"That'll do, corporal," the captain said. "You can go. I'll see to this." The policeman saluted and went on. The British policeman was now supporting the English boy. "Can't you take him home?" the captain said. "Where are their quarters?"

"I don't rightly know, sir, if they have quarters or not. We —I usually see them about the pubs until daylight. They don't seem to use quarters."

"You mean, they really aren't off ships?"

"Well, sir, they might be ships, in a manner if speaking. But a man would have to be a bit sleepier than him to sleep in one of them."

"I see," the captain said. He looked at the policeman. "What kind of boats are they?"

This time the policeman's voice was immediate, final and completely inflectionless. It was like a closed door. "I don't rightly know, sir."

"Oh," the captain said. "Quite. Well, he's in no shape to stay about pubs until daylight this time."

"Perhaps I can find him a bit of a pub with a back table, where he can sleep," the policeman said. But the captain was not listening. He was looking across the street, where the lights of another café fell across the pavement. The English boy yawned terrifically, like a child does, his mouth pink and frankly gaped as a child's.

The captain turned to the policeman:

"Would you mind stepping across there and asking for Captain Bogard's driver? I'll take care of Mr. Hope."

The policeman departed. The captain now supported the English boy, his hand beneath the other's arm. Again the boy yawned like a weary child. "Steady," the captain said. "The car will be here in a minute."

"Right," the English boy said through the yawn.

11

Once in the car he went to sleep immediately with the peaceful suddenness of babies, sitting between the two Americans. But though the aerodrome was only thirty minutes away, he was awake when they arrived, apparently quite fresh, and asking for whisky. When they entered the mess he appeared quite sober, only blinking a little in the lighted room, in his raked

176

cap and his awry-buttoned pea-jacket and a soiled silk muffler, embroidered with a club insignia which Bogard recognised to have come from a famous preparatory school, twisted about his throat.

"Ah," he said, his voice fresh, clear now, not blurred, quite cheerful, quite loud, so that the others in the room turned and looked at him. "Jolly. Whisky, what?" He went straight as a bird dog to the bar in the corner, the lieutenant following. Bogard had turned and gone on to the other end of the room, where five men sat about a card table.

"What's he admiral of?" one said.

"Of the whole Scotch navy, when I found him," Bogard said.

Another looked up. "Oh, I thought I'd seen him in town." He looked at the guest. "Maybe it's because he was on his feet that I didn't recognise him when he came in. You usually see them lying in the gutter."

"Oh," the first said. He, too, looked around. "Is he one of those guys?"

"Sure. You've seen them. Sitting on the curb, you know, with a couple of limey M.P.s hauling at their arms."

"Yes, I've seen them," the other said. They all looked at the English boy. He stood at the bar, talking, his voice loud, cheerful. "They all look like him too," the speaker said. "About seventeen or eighteen. They run those little boats that are always dashing in and out."

"Is that what they do?" a third said. "You mean, there's a male marine auxilliary in the Waacs? Good Lord, I sure made a mistake when I enlisted. But this war never was advertised right."

"I don't know," Bogard said. "I guess they do more than just ride around."

But they were not listening to him. They were looking at the guest. "They run by clock," the first said. "You can see the condition of one of them after sunset and almost tell what time it is. But what I don't see is, how a man that's in that shape at one o'clock every morning can even see a battleship the next day."

"Maybe when they have a message to send out to a ship," another said, "they just make duplicates and line the launches up and point them towards the ship and give each one a duplicate of the message and let them go. And the ones that miss the ship just cruise the harbour until they hit a dock somewhere."

"It must be more than that," Bogard said.

He was about to say something else, but at that moment the guest turned from the bar and approached, carrying a glass. He walked steadily enough but his colour was high and his eyes were bright, and he was talking, loud, cheerful, as he came up.

"I say. Won't you chaps join—" He ceased. He seemed to remark something; he was looking at their breasts. "Oh, I say. You fly. All of you. Oh, good gad! Find it jolly, eh?"

"Yes," somebody said. "Jolly."

"But dangerous, what?"

"A little faster than tennis," another said. The guest looked at him, bright, affable, intent.

Another said quickly, "Bogard says you command a vessel."

"Hardly a vessel. Thanks, though. And not command. Ronnie does that. Ranks me a bit. Age."

"Ronnie?"

"Yes. Nice. Good egg. Old, though. Stickler."

"Stickler?"

"Frightful. You'd not believe it. Whenever we sight smoke and I have the glass, he sheers away. Keeps the ship hull down all the while. No beaver then. Had me two down a fortnight yesterday."

The Americans glanced at one another. "No beaver?"

"We play it. With basket masts, you see. See a basket mast. Beaver! One up. The Ergenstrasse doesn't count any more, though."

The men about the table looked at one another. Bogard spoke. "I see. When you or Ronnie see a ship with basket masts, you get a beaver on the other. I see. What is the Ergenstrasse?"

"She's German. Interned. Tramp steamer. Foremast rigged so it looks something like a basket mast. Booms, cables, I dare say. I didn't think it looked very much like a basket mast, myself. But Ronnie said yes. Called it one day. Then one day they shifted her across the basin and I called her on Ronnie. So we decided to not count her any more. See now, eh?"

"Oh," the one who had made the tennis remark said, "I see. You and Ronnie run about in the launch, playing beaver. H'm'm. That's nice. Did you ever pl—"

"Jerry," Bogard said. The guest had not moved. He looked down at the speaker, still smiling, his eyes quite wide.

The speaker still looked at the guest. "Has yours and Ronnie's boat got a yellow stern?"

178

"A yellow stern?" the English boy said. He had quit smiling, but his face was still pleasant.

"I thought that maybe when the boats had two captains, they might paint the stern yellow or something."

"Oh," the guest said. "Burt and Reeves aren't officers."

"Burt and Reeves," the other said, in a musing tone. "So they go, too. Do they play beaver too?"

"Jerry," Bogard said. The other looked at him. Bogard jerked his head a little. "Come over here." The other rose. They went aside. "Lay off of him," Bogard said. "I mean it, now. He's just a kid. When you were that age, how much sense did you have? Just about enough to get to chapel on time."

"My country hadn't been at war going on four years, though," Jerry said. "Here we are, spending our money and getting shot at by the clock, and it's not even our fight, and these limeys that would have been goose-stepping twelve months now if it hadn't been——"

"Shut it," Bogard said. "You sound like a Liberty Loan."

"——taking it like it was a fair or something. 'Jolly.'" His voice was now falsetto, lilting. "'But dangerous, what?'"

"Sh-h-h-h," Bogard said.

"I'd like to catch him and his Ronnie out in the harbour, just once. Any harbour. London's. I wouldn't want anything but a Jenny, either. Jenny? Hell, I'd take a bicycle and a pair of water wings! I'll show him some war."

"Well, you lay off him now. He'll be gone soon."

"What are you going to do with him?"

"I'm going to take him along this morning. Let him have Harper's place out front. He says he can handle a Lewis. Says they have one on the boat. Something he was telling me—about how he once shot out a channel-marker light at seven hundred yards."

"Well, that's your business. Maybe he can beat you."

"Beat me?"

"Playing beaver. And then you can take on Ronnie."

"I'll show him some war, anyway," Bogard said. He looked at the guest. "His people have been in it three years now, and he seems to take it like a sophomore in town for the big game." He looked at Jerry again. "But you lay off him now."

As they approached the table, the guest's voice was loud and cheerful: ". . . if he got the glasses first, he would go in close and look, but, when I got them first, he'd sheer off where I couldn't see anything but the smoke. Frightful

179

stickler. Frightful. But Ergenstrasse not counting any more. And if you make a mistake and call her, you lose two beaver from your score. If Ronnie were only to forget and call her we'd be even."

III

At two o'clock the English boy was still talking, his voice bright, innocent and cheerful. He was telling them how Switzerland had been spoiled by 1914, and instead of the vacation which his father had promised him for his sixteenth birthday, when that birthday came he and his tutor had had to do with Wales. But that he and the tutor had got pretty high and that he dared to say—with all due respect to any present who might have had the advantage of Switzerland, of course—that one could see probably as far from Wales as from Switzerland. "Perspire as much and breathe as hard, anyway," he added. And about him the Americans sat, a little hard-bitten, a little sober, somewhat older, listening to him with a kind of cold astonishment. They had been getting up for some time now and going out and returning in flying clothes, carrying helmets and goggles. An orderly entered with a tray of coffee cups, and the guest realised that for some time now he had been hearing engines in the darkness outside.

At last Bogard rose. "Come along," he said. "We'll get your togs." When they emerged from the mess, the sound of the engines was quite loud—an idling thunder. In alignment along the invisible tarmac was a vague rank of short banks of flickering blue-green fire suspended apparently in midair. They crossed the aerodrome to Bogard's quarters, where the lieutenant, McGinnis, sat on a cot fastening his flying boots. Bogard reached down a Sidcott suit and threw it across the cot. "Put this on," he said.

"Will I need all this?" the guest said. "Shall we be gone that long?"

"Probably," Bogard said. "Better use it. Cold upstairs."

The guest picked up the suit. "I say," he said. "I say. Ronnie and I have a do ourselves, tomor—today. Do you think Ronnie won't mind if I am a bit late? Might not wait for me."

"We'll be back before teatime," McGinnis said. He seemed quite busy with his boot. "Promise you." The English boy looked at him.

180

" What time should you be back?" Bogard said.

" Oh, well," the English boy said, " I dare say it will be all right. They let Ronnie say when to go, anyway. He'll wait for me if I should be a bit late."

" He'll wait," Bogard said. " Get your suit on."

" Right," the other said. They helped him into the suit. " Never been up before," he said, chattily, pleasantly. " Dare say you can see farther than from mountains, eh?"

" See more, anyway," McGinnis said. " You'll like it."

" Oh, rather. If Ronnie only waits for me. Lark. But dangerous, isn't it?"

" Go on," McGinnis said. " You're kidding me."

" Shut your trap, Mac," Bogard said. " Come along. Want some more coffee?" He looked at the guest, but McGinnis answered:

" No. Got something better than coffee. Coffee makes such a confounded stain on the wings."

" On the wings?" the English boy said. " Why coffee on the wings?"

" Stow it, I said, Mac," Bogard said. " Come along."

They recrossed the aerodrome, approaching the muttering banks of flame. When they drew near, the guest began to discern the shape, the outlines, of the Handley-Page. It looked like a Pullman coach run upslanted aground into the skeleton of the first floor of an incomplete skyscraper. The guest looked at it quietly.

" It's larger than a cruiser," he said in his bright, interested voice. " I say, you know. This doesn't fly in one lump. You can't pull my leg. Seen them before. It comes in two parts: Captain Bogard and me in one; Mac and 'nother chap in other. What?"

" No," McGinnis said. Bogard had vanished. " It all goes up in one lump. Big lark, eh? Buzzard, what?"

" Buzzard?" the guest murmured. " Oh, I say. A cruiser. Flying. I say, now."

" And listen," McGinnis said. His hand came forth; something cold fumbled against the hand of the English boy— a bottle. " When you feel yourself getting sick, see? Take a pull at it."

" Oh, shall I get sick?"

" Sure. We all do. Part of flying. This will stop it. But if it doesn't. See?"

" What? Quite. What?"

" Not overside. Don't spew it overside."

" Not overside?"

"It'll blow back in Bogy's and my face. Can't see. Bingo. Finished. See?"

"Oh, quite. What shall I do with it?" Their voices were quiet, brief, grave as conspirators.

"Just duck your head and let her go."

"Oh, quite."

Bogard returned. "Show him how to get into the front pit, will you?" he said. McGinnis led the way through the trap. Forward, rising to the slant of the fuselage, the passage narrowed; a man would need to crawl.

"Crawl in there and keep going," McGinnis said.

"It looks like a dog kennel," the guest said.

"Doesn't it, though?" McGinnis agreed cheerfully. "Cut along with you." Stooping, he could hear the other scuttling forward. "You'll find a Lewis gun up there, like as not," he said into the tunnel.

The voice of the guest came back: "Found it."

"The gunnery sergeant will be along in a minute and show you if it is loaded."

"It's loaded," the guest said; almost on the heels of his words the gun fired, a brief staccato burst. There were shouts, the loudest from the ground beneath the nose of the aeroplane. "It's quite all right," the English boy's voice said. "I pointed it west before I let it off. Nothing back there but Marine office and your brigade headquarters. Ronnie and I always do this before we go anywhere. Sorry if I was too soon. Oh, by the way," he added, "my name's Claude. Don't think I mentioned it."

On the ground, Bogard and two other officers stood. They had come up running. "Fired it west," one said. "How in hell does he know which way is west?"

"He's a sailor," the other said. "You forgot that."

"He seems to be a machine gunner too," Bogard said.

"Let's hope he doesn't forget that," the first said.

IV

Nevertheless, Bogard kept an eye on the silhouetted head rising from the round gunpit in the nose ten feet ahead of him. "He did work that gun, though," he said to McGinnis beside him. "He even put the drum on himself, didn't he?"

"Yes," McGinnis said. "If he just doesn't forget and think

that that gun is him and his tutor looking around from a Welsh alp."

"Maybe I should not have brought him," Bogard said. McGinnis didn't answer. Bogard jockeyed the wheel a little. Ahead, in the gunner's pit, the guest's head moved this way and that continuously, looking. "We'll get there and unload and haul air for home," Bogard said. "Maybe in the dark —Confound it, it would be a shame for his country to be in this mess for four years and him not even to see a gun pointed in his direction."

"He'll see one to-night if he don't keep his head in," McGinnis said.

But the boy did not do that. Not even when they had reached the objective and McGinnis had crawled down to the bomb toggles. And even when the searchlights found them and Bogard signalled to the other machines and dived, the two engines snarling full speed into and through the bursting shells, he could see the boy's face in the searchlight's glare, leaned far overside, coming sharply out as a spotlighted face on a stage, with an expression upon it of childlike interest and delight. "But he's firing that Lewis," Bogard thought. "Straight too"; nosing the machine farther down, watching the pinpoints swing into the sights, his right hand lifted, waiting to drop into McGinnis' sight. He dropped his hand; above the noise of the engines he seemed to hear the click and whistle of the released bombs as the machine, freed of the weight, shot zooming in a long upward bounce that carried it for an instant out of the light. Then he was pretty busy for a time, coming into and through the shells again, shooting athwart another beam that caught and held long enough for him to see the English boy leaning far over the side, looking back and down past the right wing, the undercarriage. "Maybe he's read about it somewhere," Bogard thought, turning, looking back to pick up the rest of the flight.

Then it was all over, the darkness cool and empty and peaceful and almost quiet, with only the steady sound of the engines. McGinnis climbed back into the office, and standing up in his seat, he fired the coloured pistol this time and stood for a moment longer, looking backward toward where the searchlights still probed and sabered. He sat down again.

"O.K.," he said. "I counted all four of them. Let's haul air." Then he looked forward. "What's become of the King's Own? You didn't hang him onto a bomb release, did you?" Bogard looked. The forward pit was empty. It was in dim silhouette again now, against the stars, but there was nothing there now save the gun. "No," McGinnis said; "there he is. See? Leaning overside. Dammit, I told him not to spew it! There he comes back!" The guest's head came into view again. But again it sank out of sight.

"He's coming back," Bogard said. "Stop him. Tell him we're going to have every squadron in the Hun Channel group on top of us in thirty minutes."

McGinnis swung himself down and stooped at the entrance to the passage. "Get back!" he shouted. The other was almost out; they squatted so, face to face like two dogs, shouting at another above the noise of the still-unthrottled engines on either side of the fabric walls. The English boy's voice was thin and high.

"Bomb!" he shrieked.

"Yes," McGinnis shouted. "They were bombs! We gave them hell! Get back I tell you! Have every Hun in France on us in ten minutes! Get back to your gun!"

Again the boy's voice came, high, faint above the noise: "Bomb! All right?"

"Yes! Yes! All right. Back to your gun, damn you!"

McGinnis climbed back into the office. "He went back. Want me to take her awhile?"

"All right," Bogard said. He passed McGinnis the wheel. "Ease her back some. I'd just as soon it was daylight when they come down on us."

"Right," McGinnis said. He moved the wheel suddenly. "What's the matter with that right wing?" he said. "Watch it. . . . See? I'm flying on the right aileron and a little rudder. Feel it."

Bogard took the wheel a moment. "I didn't notice that. Wire somewhere, I guess. I didn't think any of those shells were that close. Watch her, though."

"Right," McGinnis said. "And so you are going with him on his boat tomorrow—today."

"Yes, I promised him. Confound it, you can't hurt a kid, you know."

"Why don't you take Collier along, with his mandolin? Then you could sail and sing."

"I promised him," Bogard said. "Get that wing up a little."

"Right," McGinnis said.

Thirty minutes later it was beginning to be dawn; the sky was grey. Presently McGinnis said: "Well, here they come. Look at them! They look like mosquitoes in September. I hope he don't get worked up now and think he's playing beaver. If he does he'll just be one down to Ronnie, provided the devil has a beard. . . . Want the wheel?"

v

At eight o'clock the beach, the Channel, was beneath them. Throttled back, the machine drifted down as Bogard ruddered it gently into the Channel wind. His face was strained, a little tired.

McGinnis looked tired, too, and he needed a shave.

"What do you guess he is looking at now?" he said. For again the English boy was leaning over the right side of the cockpit, looking backward and downward past the right wing.

"I don't know," Bogard said. "Maybe bullet holes." He blasted the port engine. "Must have the riggers——"

"He could see some closer than that," McGinnis said. "I'll swear I saw tracer going into his back at one time. Or maybe it's the ocean he's looking at. But he must have seen that when he came over from England." Then Bogard levelled off; the nose rose sharply, the sand, the curling tide edge fled along-side. Yet still the English boy hung far overside, looking backward and downward at something beneath the right wing, his face rapt, with utter and childlike interest. Until the machine was completely stopped he continued to do so. Then he ducked down, and in the abrupt silence of the engines they could hear him crawling in the passage. He emerged just as the two pilots climbed stiffly down from the office, his face bright, eager; his voice high, excited.

"Oh, I say! Oh, good gad! What a chap! What a judge of distance! If Ronnie could only have seen! Oh, good gad! Or maybe they aren't like ours—don't load themselves as soon as the air strikes them."

The Americans looked at him. "What don't what?" McGinnis said.

"The bomb. It was magnificent; I say, I shan't forget it. Oh, I say, you know! It was splendid!"

After a while McGinnis said, "The bomb?" in a fainting voice. Then the two pilots glared at each other; they said in unison: "That right wing!" Then as one they clawed down through the trap and, with the guest at their heels, they ran around the machine and looked beneath the right wing. The bomb, suspended by its tail, hung straight down like a plumb bob beside the right wheel, its tip just touching the sand. And parallel with the wheel track was the long delicate line in the sand where its ultimate tip had dragged. Behind the English boy's voice was high, clear, childlike:

"Frightened, myself. Tried to tell you. But realised you knew your business better than I. Skill. Marvellous. Oh, I say, I shan't forget it."

VI

A marine with a bayoneted rifle passed Bogard onto the wharf and directed him to the boat. The wharf was empty, and he didn't even see the boat until he approached the edge of the wharf and looked directly down into it and upon the backs of two stooping men in greasy dungarees, who rose and glanced briefly at him and stooped again.

It was about thirty feet long and about three feet wide. It was painted with grey-green camouflage. It was quarter-decked forward, with two blunt, raked exhaust stacks. "Good Lord," Bogard thought, "if all that deck is engine—" Just after the deck was the control seat; he saw a big wheel, an instrument panel. Rising to a height of about a foot above the freeboard, and running from the stern forward to where the deck began, and continuing on across the after edge of the deck and thence back down the other gunwale to the stern, was a solid screen, also camouflaged, which enclosed the boat save for the width of the stern, which was open. Facing the steerman's seat like an eye was a hole in the screen about eight inches in diameter. And looking down into the long, narrow, still, vicious shape, he saw a machine gun swivelled at the stern, and he looked at the low screen—including which the whole vessel did not sit much more than a yard above water level—with its single empty forward-staring eye, and he thought quietly: "It's steel. It's made of steel." And his face was quite sober, quite thoughtful, and he drew his trench coat about him and buttoned it, as though he were getting cold.

He heard steps behind him and turned. But it was only an orderly from the aerodrome, accompanied by the marine with the rifle. The orderly was carrying a largish bundle wrapped in paper.

"From Lieutenant McGinnis to the captain," the orderly said.

Bogard took the bundle. The orderly and the marine retreated. He opened the bundle. It contained some objects and a scrawled note. The objects were a new yellow silk sofa cushion and a Japanese parasol, obviously borrowed, and a comb and a roll of toilet paper. The note said:

Couldn't find a camera anywhere and Collier wouldn't let me have his mandolin. But maybe Ronnie can play on the comb.

Mac

Bogard looked at the objects. But his face was still quite thoughtful, quite grave. He rewrapped the things and carried the bundle on up the wharf a way and dropped it quietly into the water.

As he returned toward the invisible boat he saw two men approaching. He recognised the boy at once—tall, slender, already talking, voluble, his head bent a little toward his shorter companion, who plodded along beside him, hands in pockets, smoking a pipe. The boy still wore the pea-coat beneath a flapping oilskin, but in place of the rakish and casual cap he now wore an infantryman's soiled Balaclava helmet, with, floating behind him as though upon the sound of his voice, a curtainlike piece of cloth almost as long as a burnous.

"Hullo, there!" he cried, still a hundred yards away.

But it was the second man that Bogard was watching, thinking to himself that he had never in his life seen a more curious figure. There was something stolid about the very shape of his hunched shoulders, his slightly down-looking face. He was a head shorter than the other. His face was ruddy, too, but its mould was a profound gravity that was almost dour. It was the face of a man of twenty who has been for a year trying, even while asleep, to look twenty-one. He wore a high-necked sweater and dungaree slacks; above this a leather jacket; and above this a soiled naval officer's warmer that reached almost to his heels and which had one shoulder strap missing and not one remaining button at all. On his head was a plaid fore-and-aft deer stalker's cap, tied on by a narrow scarf brought across and down, hiding his ears, and then wrapped once about his throat and knotted with a hangman's noose beneath his left ear. It was unbelievably soiled, and with his hands elbow-deep in his pockets and his hunched shoulders and his bent head, he looked like someone's grandmother hung, say, for a witch. Clamped upside down between his teeth was a short brier pipe.

"Here he is!" the boy cried. "This is Ronnie. Captain Bogard."

"How are you?" Bogard said. He extended his hand. The other said no word, but his hand came forth, limp. It was quite cold, but it was hard, calloused. But he said no word; he just glanced briefly at Bogard and then away. But in that instant Bogard caught something in the look, something strange—a flicker; a kind of covert and curious respect, something like a boy of fifteen looking at a circus trapezist.

But he said no word. He ducked on; Bogard watched him drop from sight over the wharf edge as though he had jumped feet first into the sea. He remarked now that the engines in the invisible boat were running.

"We might get aboard too," the boy said. He started toward the boat, then he stopped. He touched Bogard's arm. "Yonder!" he hissed. "See?" His voice was thin with excitement.

"What?" Bogard also whispered; automatically he looked backward and upward, after old habit. The other was gripping his arm and pointing across the harbour.

"There! Over there. The Ergenstrasse. They have shifted her again." Across the harbour lay an ancient, rusting, sway-backed hulk. It was small and nondescript, and, remembering, Bogard saw that the foremast was a strange mess of cables and booms, resembling—allowing for a great deal of license or looseness of imagery—a basket mast. Beside him the boy was almost chortling. "Do you think that Ronnie noticed?" he hissed. "Do you?"

"I don't know," Bogard said.

"Oh, good gad! If he should glance up and call her before he notices, we'll be even. Oh, good gad! But come along." He went on; he was still chortling. "Careful," he said. "Frightful ladder."

He descended first, the two men in the boat rising and saluting. Ronnie had disappeared, save for his backside, which now filled a small hatch leading forward beneath the deck. Bogard descended gingerly.

"Good Lord," he said. "Do you have to climb up and down this every day?"

"Frightful, isn't it?" the other said, in his happy voice. "But you know yourself. Try to run a war with makeshifts, then wonder why it takes so long." The narrow hull slid and surged, even with Bogard's added weight. "Sits right on top, you see," the boy said. "Would float on a lawn, in a heavy dew. Goes right over them like a bit of paper."

"It does?" Bogard said.

"Oh, absolutely. That's why, you see." Bogard didn't see, but he was too busy letting himself gingerly down to a sitting posture. There were no thwarts; no seats save a long, thick, cylindrical ridge which ran along the bottom of the boat from the driver's seat to the stern. Ronnie had backed into sight. He now sat behind the wheel, bent over the instrument panel. But when he glanced back over his shoulder he did not speak. His face was merely interrogatory. Across his face there was now a long smudge of grease. The boy's face was empty, too, now.

"Right," he said. He looked forward, where one of the seamen had gone. "Ready forward?" he said.

"Aye, sir," the seaman said.

The other seaman was at the stern line. "Ready aft?"

"Aye, sir."

"Cast off." The boat sheered away, purring, a boiling of water under the stern. The boy looked down at Bogard. "Silly business. Do it shipshape, though. Can't tell when silly fourstriper—" His face changed again, immediate, solicitous. "I say. Will you be warm? I never thought to fetch—"

"I'll be all right," Bogard said. But the other was already taking off his oilskin. "No, no," Bogard said. "I won't take it."

"You'll tell me if you get cold?"

"Yes. Sure." He was looking down at the cylinder on which he sat. It was a half cylinder—that is, like the hot-water tank to some Gargantuan stove, sliced down the middle and bolted, open side down, to the floor plates. It was twenty feet long and more than two feet thick. Its top rose as high as the gunwales and between it and the hull on either side was just room enough for a man to place his feet to walk.

"That's Muriel," the boy said.

"Muriel?"

"Yes. The one before that was Agatha. After my aunt. The first one Ronnie and I had was Alice in Wonderland. Ronnie and I were the White Rabbit. Jolly, eh?"

"Oh, you and Ronnie have had three, have you?"

"Oh, yes," the boy said. He leaned down. "He didn't notice," he whispered. His face was again bright, gleeful. "When we come back," he said. "You watch."

"Oh," Bogard said. "The Ergenstrasse." He looked astern, and then he thought: "Good Lord! We must be going—travelling." He looked out now, broadside, and saw the harbour line fleeing past, and he thought to himself that the boat was well-nigh moving at the speed at which the

Handley-Page flew, left the ground. They were beginning to bound now, even in the sheltered water, from one wave crest to the next with a distinct shock. His hand still rested on the cylinder on which he sat. He looked down at it again, following it from where it seemed to emerge beneath Ronnie's seat, to where it bevelled into the stern. " It's the air in here, I suppose," he said.

" The what?" the boy said.

" The air. Stored up in here. That makes the boat ride high."

" Oh, yes. I dare say. Very likely. I hadn't thought about it." He came forward, his burnous whipping in the wind, and sat down beside Bogard. Their heads were below the top of the screen.

Astern the harbour fled, diminishing, sinking into the sea. The boat had begun to lift now, swooping forward and down, shocking almost stationary for a moment, then lifting and swooping again; a gout of spray came aboard over the bows like a flung shovelful of shot. " I wish you'd take this coat," the boy said.

Bogard didn't answer. He looked around at the bright face. " We're outside, aren't we?" he said quietly.

" Yes. . . . Do take it, won't you?"

" Thanks, no. I'll be all right. We won't be long, anyway, I guess."

" No. We'll turn soon. It won't be so bad then."

" Yes. I'll be all right when we turn." Then they did turn. The motion became easier. That is, the boat didn't bang head-on, shuddering, into the swells. They came up beneath now, and the boat fled with increased speed, with a long, sickening, yawning motion, first to one side and then the other. But it fled on, and Bogard looked astern with the same soberness with which he had first looked down into the boat. " We're going east now," he said.

" With just a spot of north," the boy said. " Makes her ride a bit better, what?"

" Yes," Bogard said. Astern there was nothing now save empty sea and the delicate needlelike cant of the machine gun against the boiling and slewing wake, and the two seamen crouching quietly in the stern. " Yes. It's easier." Then he said: " How far do we go?"

The boy leaned closer. He moved closer. His voice was happy, confidential, proud, though lowered a little: " It's Ronnie's show. He thought of it. Not that I wouldn't have, in time. Gratitude and all that. But he's the older, you see.

Thinks fast. Courtesy, *noblesse oblige*—all that. Thought of it soon as I told him this morning. I said, 'Oh, I say. I've been there. I've seen it'; and he said, 'Not flying?'; and I said, 'Strewth'; and he said 'How far? No lying now'; and I said, 'Oh, far. Tremendous. Gone all night'; and he said, 'Flying all night. That must have been to Berlin'; and I said, 'I don't know. I dare say'; and he thought. I could see him thinking. Because he is the older, you see. More experience in courtesy, right thing. And he said, 'Berlin. No fun to that chap, dashing out and back with us.' And he thought and I waited, and I said, 'But we can't take him to Berlin. Too far. Don't know the way, either'; and he said—fast, like a shot—said, 'But there's Kiel'; and I knew—"

"What?" Bogard said. Without moving, his whole body sprang. "Kiel? In this?"

"Absolutely. Ronnie thought of it. Smart, even if he is a stickler. Said at once 'Zeebrugge no show at all for that chap. Must do best we can for him. Berlin,' Ronnie said. 'My Gad! Berlin.'"

"Listen," Bogard said. He had turned now, facing the other, his face quite grave. "What is this boat for?"

"For?"

"What does it do?" Then, knowing beforehand the answer to his own question, he said, putting his hand on the cylinder: "What is this in here? A torpedo, isn't it?"

"I thought you knew," the boy said.

"No," Bogard said. "I didn't know." His voice seemed to reach him from a distance, dry, cricketlike: "How do you fire it?"

"Fire it?"

"How do you get it out of the boat? When that hatch was open a while ago I could see the engines. They were right in front of the end of this tube."

"Oh," the boy said. "You pull a gadget there and the torpedo drops out astern. As soon as the screw touches the water it begins to turn, and then the torpedo is ready, loaded. Then all you have to do is turn the boat quickly and the torpedo goes on."

"You mean—" Bogard said. After a moment his voice obeyed him again. "You mean you aim the torpedo with the boat and release it and it starts moving, and you turn the boat out of the way and the torpedo passes through the same water that the boat just vacated?"

"Knew you'd catch on," the boy said. "Told Ronnie so. Airman. Tamer than yours, though. But can't be helped.

Best we can do, just on water. But knew you'd catch on."

"Listen," Bogard said. His voice sounded to him quite calm. The boat fled on, yawing over the swells. He sat quite motionless. It seemed to him that he could hear himself talking to himself: "Go on. Ask him. Ask him what? Ask him how close to the ship do you have to be before you fire. . . . Listen," he said in that calm voice. "Now, you tell Ronnie, you see. You just tell him—just say—" He could feel his voice ratting off on him again, so he stopped it. He sat quite motionless, waiting for it to come back; the boy leaning now, looking at him face. Again the boy's voice was solicitous:

"I say. You're not feeling well. These confounded shallow boats."

"It's not that," Bogard said. "I just—Do your orders say Kiel?"

"Oh, no. They let Ronnie say. Just so we bring the boat back. This is for you. Gratitude. Ronnie's idea. Tame, after flying. But if you'd rather, eh?"

"Yes, some place closer. You see, I—"

"Quite. I see. No vacations in wartime. I'll tell Ronnie." He went forward. Bogard did not move. The boat fled in long, slewing swoops. Bogard looked quietly astern, at the scudding sea, the sky.

"My God!" he thought. "Can you beat it? Can you beat it?"

The boy came back; Bogard turned to him a face the colour of dirty paper. "All right now," the boy said. "Not Kiel. Nearer place, hunting probably just as good. Ronnie says he knows you will understand." He was tugging at his pocket. He brought out a bottle. "Here. Haven't forgot last night. Do the same for you. Good for the stomach, eh?"

Bogard drank, gulping—a big one. He extended the bottle, but the boy refused. "Never touch it on duty," he said. "Not like you chaps. Tame here."

The boat fled on. The sun was already down the west. But Bogard had lost all count of time, of distance. Ahead he could see white seas through the round eye opposite Ronnie's face, and Ronnie's hand on the wheel and the granite-like jut of his profiled jaw and the dead upside-down pipe. The boat fled on.

Then the boy leaned and touched his shoulder. He half rose. The boy was pointing. The sun was reddish; against it, outside them and about two miles away, a vessel—a trawler, it looked like—at anchor swung a tall mast.

"Lightship!" the boy shouted. "Theirs." Ahead Bogard could see a low, flat mole—the entrance to a harbour. "Channel!" the boy shouted. He swept his arm in both directions. "Mines!" His voice swept back on the wind. "Place filthy with them. All sides. Beneath us too. Lark, eh?"

VII

Against the mole a fair surf was beating. Running before the seas now, the boat seemed to leap from one roller to the next; in the intervals while the screw was in the air the engine seemed to be trying to tear itself out by the roots. But it did not slow; when it passed the end of the mole the boat seemed to be standing almost erect on its rudder, like a sail-fish. The mole was a mile away. From the end of it little faint lights began to flicker like fireflies. The boy leaned. "Down," he said. "Machine guns. Might stop a stray."

"What do I do?" Bogard shouted. "What can I do?"

"Stout fellow! Give them hell, what? Knew you'd like it!"

Crouching, Bogard looked up at the boy, his face wild. "I can handle the machine gun!"

"No need," the boy shouted back. "Give them first innings. Sporting. Visitors, eh?" He was looking forward. "There she is. See?" They were in the harbour now, the basin opening before them. Anchored in the channel was a big freighter. Painted midships of the hull was a huge Argentine flag. "Must get back to stations!" the boy shouted down to him. Then at that moment Ronnie spoke for the first time. The boat was hurtling along now in smoother water. Its speed did not slacken and Ronnie did not turn his head when he spoke. He just swung his jutting jaw and the clamped cold pipe a little, and said from the side of his mouth a single word:

"Beaver."

The boy, stooped over what he had called his gadget, jerked up, his expression astonished and outraged. Bogard also looked forward and saw Ronnie's arm pointing to starboard. It was a light cruiser at anchor a mile away. She had basket masts, and as he looked a gun flashed from her after turret. "Oh, damn!" the boy cried. "Oh, you putt! Oh, confound you, Ronnie! Now I'm three down!" But he had already stooped again over his gadget, his face bright and empty and alert again; not sober; just calm, waiting. Again Bogard looked forward and felt the boat pivot on its rudder and head directly for the freighter at terrific speed. Ronnie now with one hand on the wheel and the other lifted and extended at the height of his head.

But it seemed to Bogard that the hand would never drop. He crouched, not sitting, watching with a kind of quiet horror the painted flag increase like a moving picture of a locomotive taken from between the rails. Again the gun crashed from the cruiser behind them, and the freighter fired point-blank at them from its poop. Bogard heard neither shot.

"Man, man!" he shouted. "For God's sake!"

Ronnie's hand dropped. Again the boat spun on its rudder. Bogard saw the bow rise, pivoting; he expected the hull to slam broadside on into the ship. But it didn't. It shot off on a long tangent. He was waiting for it to make a wide sweep, heading seaward, putting the freighter astern, and he thought of the cruiser again. "Get a broadside, this time, once we clear the freighter," he thought. Then he remembered the freighter, the torpedo, and looked back towards the freighter to watch the torpedo strike, and saw to his horror that the boat was now bearing down on the freighter again, in a skidding turn. Like a man in a dream, he watched himself rush down upon the ship and shoot past under her counter, still skidding, close enough to see the faces on her decks. "They missed and they are going to run down the torpedo and catch it and shoot it again," he thought idiotically.

So the boy had to touch his shoulder before he knew he was behind him. The boy's voice was quite calm: "Under Ronnie's seat there. A bit of a crank handle. If you'll just hand it to me—"

He found the crank. He passed it back; he was thinking dreamily: "Mac would say they had a telephone on board." But he didn't look at once to see what the boy was doing with it, for in that still and peaceful horror he was watching Ronnie, the cold pipe rigid in his jaw, hurling the boat at top speed round and round the freighter, so near that he could see the rivets in the plates. Then he looked aft, his face wild, importunate, and he saw what the boy was doing with the crank. He had fitted it into what was obviously a small windlass low on one flank of the tube near the head. He glanced up and saw Bogard's face. "Didn't go that time!" he shouted cheerfully.

"Go?" Bogard shouted. "It didn't—The torpedo—"

The boy and one of the seamen were quite busy, stooping over the windlass and the tube. "No. Clumsy. Always happening. Should think clever chaps like engineers—Happens, though. Draw her in and try her again."

"But the nose, the cap!" Bogard shouted. "It's still in the tube, isn't it? It's all right, isn't it?"

"Absolutely. But it's working now. Loaded. Screw's started turning. Get it back and drop it clear. If we should stop or slow up it would overtake us. Drive back into the tube. Bingo! What?"

Bogard was on his feet now, turned, braced to the terrific merry-go-round of the boat. High above them the freighter seemed to be spinning on her heel like a trick picture in the movies. "Let me have that winch!" he cried.

"Steady!" the boy said. "Mustn't draw her back too fast. Jam her into the head of the tube ourselves. Same bingo! Best let us. Every cobbler to his last, what?"

"Oh, quite," Bogard said. "Oh, absolutely." It was like someone else using his mouth. He leaned, braced, his hands on the cold tube, beside the others. He was hot inside, but his outside was cold. He could feel all his flesh jerking with cold as he watched the blunt, grained hand of the seaman turning the windlass in short, easy, inch-long arcs, while at the head of the tube the boy bent, tapping the cylinder with a spanner, lightly, his head turned with listening delicate and deliberate as a watchmaker. The boat rushed on in those furious, slewing turns. Bogard saw a long, dropping thread loop down from somebody's mouth, between his hands, and he found that the thread came from his own mouth.

He didn't hear the boy speak, nor notice when he stood up. He just felt the boat straighten out, flinging him to his knees beside the tube. The seaman had gone back to the stern and the boy stooped again over his gadget. Bogard knelt now, quite sick. He did not feel the boat when it swung again, nor hear the gun from the cruiser which had not dared to fire and the freighter which had not been able to fire, firing again. He did not feel anything at all when he saw the huge painted flag directly ahead, and increasing with locomotive speed, and Ronnie's lifted hand drop. But this time he knew that the torpedo was gone; in pivoting and spinning this time the whole boat seemed to leave the water; he saw the bow of the boat shoot skyward like the nose of a pursuit ship going into a wingover. Then his outraged stomach denied him. He saw neither the geyser nor heard the detonation as he sprawled over the tube. He felt only a hand grasp him by the slack of his coat, and the voice of one of the seamen: "Steady all, sir. I've got you."

VIII

A voice roused him, a hand. He was half sitting in the narrow starboard runway, half lying across the tube. He had been there for quite a while; quite a while ago he had felt someone spread a garment over him. But he had not raised his head. "I'm all right," he said, "You keep it."

"Don't need it," the boy said. "Going home now."

"I'm sorry I—" Bogard said.

"Quite. Confound shallow boats. Turn any stomach until you get used to them. Ronnie and I both, at first. Each time. You wouldn't believe it. Believe human stomach hold so much here." It was the bottle. "Good drink. Take enormous one. Good for stomach."

Bogard drank. Soon he did feel better, warmer. When the hand touched him later, he found that he had been asleep.

It was the boy again. The pea-coat was too small for him; shrunken, perhaps. Below the cuffs his long, slender, girl's wrists were blue with cold. Then Bogard realised what the garment was that had been laid over him. But before Bogard could speak, the boy leaned down, whispering; his face was gleeful: "He didn't notice!"

"What?"

"Ergenstrasse! He didn't notice that they had shifted her. Gad, I'd be just one down, then." He watched Bogard's face with bright, eager eyes. "Beaver, you know. I say. Feeling better, eh?"

"Yes," Bogard said. "I am."

"He didn't notice at all. Oh, gad! Oh, Jove!"

Bogard rose and sat on the tube. The entrance to the harbour was just ahead; the boat had slowed a little. It was just dusk. He said quietly: "Does this often happen?" The boy looked at him. Bogard touched the tube. "This. Failing to go out."

"Oh, yes. Why they put the windlass on them. That was later. Made first boat; whole thing blew up one day. So put on windlass."

"But it happens sometimes, even now? I mean, sometimes they blow up, even with the windlass?"

"Well, can't say, of course. Boats go out. Not come back.

Possible. Not ever know, of course. Not heard of one captured yet, though. Possible. Not to us, though. Not yet."

"Yes," Bogard said. "Yes." They entered the harbour, the boat moving still fast, but throttled now and smooth, across the dusk-filled basin. Again the boy leaned down, his voice gleeful.

"Not a word, now!" he hissed. "Steady all!" He stood up; he raised his voice: "I say, Ronnie." Ronnie did not turn his head, but Bogard could tell that he was listening. "That Argentine ship was amusing, eh? In there. How do you suppose it got past us here? Might have stopped here as well. French would buy the wheat." He paused, diabolical—Machiavelli with the face of a strayed angel. "I say. How long has it been since we had a strange ship in here? Been months, eh?" Again he leaned, hissing. "Watch, now!" But Bogard could not see Ronnie's head move at all. "He's looking, though!" the boy whispered, breathed. And Ronnie was looking, though his head had not moved at all. Then there came into view, in silhouette against the dusk-filled sky, the vague, basket-like shape of the interned vessel's foremast. At once Ronnie's arm rose, pointing; again he spoke without turning his head, out of the side of his mouth, past the cold, clamped pipe, a single word:

"Beaver."

The boy moved like a released spring, like a heeled dog freed. "Oh, damn you!" he cried. "Oh, you putt! It's the Ergenstrasse! Oh, confound you! I'm just one down now!" He had stepped one stride completely over Bogard, and he now leaned down over Ronnie. "What?" The boat was slowing in toward the wharf, the engine idle. "Aren't I, Ronnie? Just one down now?"

The boat drifted in; the seamen had again crawled forward onto the deck. Ronnie spoke for the third and last time. "Right," he said.

IX

"I want," Bogard said, "a case of Scotch. The best we've got. And fix it up good. It's to go to town. And I want a responsible man to deliver it." The responsible man came. "This is for a child," Bogard said, indicating the package. "You'll find him in the Street of the Twelve Hours, somewhere near the Café Twelve Hours. He'll be in the gutter. You'll know him. A child about six feet long. Any English

M.P. will show him to you. If he is asleep, don't wake him. Just sit there and wait until he wakes up. Then give him this. Tell him it is from Captain Bogard."

X

About a month later a copy of the English Gazette which had strayed onto an American aerodrome carried the following item in the casualty lists:

MISSING; *Torpedo Boat* XOOI. Midshipmen R. Boyce Smith and L. C. W. Hope, R.N.R., Boatswain's Mate Burt and Able Seaman Reeves, Channel Fleet, Light Torpedo Division. Failed to return from coast patrol duty.

Shortly after that the American Air Service headquarters also issued a bulletin:

For extraordinary valour over and beyond the routine of duty, Captain H. S. Bogard, with his crew, composed of Second Lieutenant Darrel McGinnis and Aviation Gunners Watts and Harper, on a daylight raid and without scout protection, destroyed with bombs an ammunition depot several miles behind the enemy's lines. From here, beset by enemy aircraft in superior numbers, these men proceeded with what bombs remained to the enemy's corps headquarters at Blank and partially demolished this château, and then returned safely without loss of a man.

And regarding which exploit, it might have been added, had it failed and had Captain Bogard come out of it alive, he would have been immediately and thoroughly court-martialled.

Carrying his remaining two bombs, he had dived the Handley-Page at the château where the generals sat at lunch, until McGinnis, at the toggles below him, began to shout at him, before he ever signalled. He didn't signal until he could discern separately the slate tiles of the roof. Then his hand dropped and he zoomed, and he held the aeroplane so, in its wild snarl, his lips parted, his breath hissing, thinking: "God! God! If they were all there—all the generals, the admirals, the presidents and the kings—theirs, ours—all of them."

198

AIR BATTLE

Charles Nordhoff
and
James Norman Hall

One early morning in November, Harvey McKail, Golasse, and I were loafing around the messroom stove. The other members of Spad 597, with the exception of Captain Clermont, were out on an eight to ten o'clock patrol. A new motor was being installed in the captain's Spad, so he was doubtless having as luxurious a morning in his own barrack as we were in ours. The other three squadrons of Group 31 had gone off at eight-thirty to furnish protection to a lot of Brequet bombing planes sent out to drop huge bombs on ammunition dumps near Metz. McKail, Golasse and I were to go up at ten-fifteen for a high patrol so we had slept till nine, and now, a quarter of an hour later, still dressed in pyjamas, we were crunching buttered toast and drinking chocolate. McKail was reading Henry James' *Gabrielle de Bergerac*, and Golasse and I were exchanging boyhood reminiscences. Our lives up to the war had been as different as possible. His had been spent wholly in Paris; he had never been farther from the boulevards than to St. Cloud, and it was hard for him to understand what ranch life in California could be like. Still less could he picture the South Seas.

"Do you mean to say you really enjoyed being there?" he asked incredulously.

"Enjoyed it! That's a mild way of stating it," I replied. "I'm going back after the war; Forbes and I are going together if we get through."

Golasse shook his head. "You Americans are a queer lot. Well, you can have your South Sea island. Give me Paris. Give me the *Café Maxeville* on a fine summer evening, with a glass of *porto* on the table beside me, plenty of money to buy more when it's gone, and nothing to do till to-morrow. Give me——"

He didn't finish the sentence. Just then Old Felix came in, and his beard fairly bristled with excitement. "Gentlemen! I don't like to disturb you, but there's a Boche coming this way! I thought you might like to see him."

From: *Falcons of France*, by permission of Little, Brown & Co. and the Atlantic Monthly Press.

We rushed outside, and heard at once the far-off brisk detonations of anti-aircraft fire. It was a windless, cloudless morning; eight or ten miles away to the southeast the sky was dotted with the tiny white smoke blossoms of French seventy-fives. The smoke from the French anti-aircraft shells was always white and that of the Germans black, so we knew at once that the plane was a Boche. He was still too far away to be seen, but we could follow his course by the shell bursts, and he was evidently coming our way.

"Another of those photographic buses," said Golasse. "Selden, there's some cold meat for us. Let's go after it. What do you say, McKail?"

I looked at my watch—a quarter to ten. "Haven't time," I said. "We're due for high patrol in half an hour."

Just then an orderly from Group headquarters scorched across the field on a motor-cycle. It was Flingot, the chauffeur who had met me at Chalons the night I joined the squadron.

"Now then! Now then!" he said. "Don't stand there looking at him. That won't win the war. Hop along, you two! Captain's orders."

He handed Golasse a pencilled note which read:

Golasse. You and Selden take off at once after that two-seater. Never mind the ten-fifteen patrol. McKail will wait for the scheduled information. Good luck!

There was no time to dress, of course. We sprinted down the field, bearskin coats over our pyjamas. Orders had already been sent to hangars; the mechanics had trundled out our Spads and were warming up the motors by the time we had arrived. We jumped into our flying suits and were ready for the take-off within three minutes. At least I was, but Golasse's mechanics were having trouble with his motor. It spluttered and back-fired, and refused to turn up more than a thousand revolutions. Golasse was cursing and waving his arms. "Go on!" he yelled. "I'll be along in a minute." So I waved and started off alone.

My little ship had never climbed more beautifully. I took height over the aerodrome, watching it shrink and shrink until the great field with its rows of barracks and hangars looked no larger than a playing card. The horizons rolled back; soon I could see for miles in every direction, and above me, but still off to the right, the sky sparkled every little while with points of intense light where the French anti-aircraft shells were bursting. The minute puffs of smoke were climbing the sky in my direction. It looked as though the German meant to make a long sweep across the Salient and reënter his own territory somewhere to the northwest.

I turned northeast and climbed in a wide circle so that I could have the sun at my back when high enough to attack, at the same time keeping a sharp lookout for other Germans. There were none to be seen, however, but far to the eastward the sky, at about three thousand metres, was plentifully sprinkled with shell bursts, both black and white. There was no lack of aerial activity over the lines. Apparently the two-seater, taking altitude over his own territory, had sailed serenely across the front at a great height.

Presently I could make him out, a minute speck moving jauntily among the smoke blossoms. Every anti-aircraft battery along the sector seemed to be blazing away at him, and some of them were making good practice. They were putting them very close, in groups of three and four, but he moved in a leisurely fashion, flying in wide detours and circles. As I watched him I was convinced that Golasse was right in thinking it a photographic plane, sent out to take long range pictures with one of those marvellous high-altitude cameras the Germans had. The two men went about their business as calmly and methodically as though anti-aircraft fire was nothing to them and the possibility of pursuit by hostile planes had not crossed their minds.

I wondered whether they saw my Spad on their trail, climbing steadily up the sky. I could see them plainly enough now, not more than two miles away and about a thousand metres over me. "They must see me," I thought, "but it doesn't appear to worry them." Now and then they would make a wide turn, very slowly, as though they had throttled down for picture-taking, and then move leisurely on. I felt a little uneasy at their apparent disregard for me, and scrutinised the air below me, hoping to see Golasse. The sight of his Spad would have been a welcome one, but I was not to be granted it. No Golasse—no anybody save myself and the two Germans, who looked bigger and more sinister every moment.

While making a turn I was astonished to find that we were almost over the Senard aerodrome, which now appeared to be about the size of a postage stamp. I had been looking overhead constantly and had paid little attention to direction except to follow the Germans. We had turned west without knowing it, and were flying parallel to the front and about ten miles inside our lines. "Lord!" I thought. "Now's my time!

What luck if I could bring down a German right over my field!" He was almost directly above me now, but still a good five hundred metres higher. Useless to pull up and fire a burst at that distance, but I was rather surprised that the observer didn't spray a few bullets in my direction. He didn't, however, at least I saw no pencilled lines of smoke from tracers. They still flew in the most leisurely manner, as though they thought me not worth bothering about; and somehow their manner of flying told me that they were old pilots who knew their business thoroughly. Their ship, with its silvered undersurface and the huge black crosses on the wings, looked like a veteran too, long accustomed to making flights deep into enemy territory. By that time I had made it out to be a Rumpler.

I didn't like the way they ignored my little Spud, and felt a welcome flush of anger surging through me. "Just wait a minute, you two!" I thought. "You may be old hands at this game, and you maybe know that I'm a young one. Just the same you'll have to notice me."

I crept up, crept up, turning off from their course as I gained my last three hundred metres of altitude, and taking care to keep the sun at my back. "Now, my boy," I said, "Go to it!"

I made a half turn to the left, at the same time crooking my forefinger around the machine-gun trigger on the joy-stick, and started toward what I considered my prey. I had made my calculations with the utmost care, so that I could attack directly from behind and a little below the two-seater, approaching him under cover of his blind spot. The only mistake I made was in forgetting, momentarily, that the two Germans might do some calculating as well. As I have said, I started toward my prey, and to my great astonishment he wasn't there.

Then I heard a sound as peculiar as it was uncomfortable —flac! flac-flac! flac! I knew what that meant: bullets were going through the fabric of my bus. I made a steep turn and found that the German pilot had dived suddenly about fifty metres and levelled off again so that his observer could have me in full view. And so he did have me, and was giving me a full dose with both guns. I thought certainly I was lost; the muzzles of his two guns were pointing straight at me and my Spad seemed to be hanging motionless. But he didn't have me in his sights for long. I made a diving turn and had him broadside on a little above me again. I pulled the trigger. My gun popped once and jammed.

Of all the exasperating things that could happen in the air, a jammed gun was assuredly the worst, and it seemed always to occur at the most critical moment possible. It was by no means easy to clear a stoppage; and in order to do so it was necessary to withdraw from a fight for several moments, and a pilot was lucky if his opponent permitted him to withdraw. I was grateful to those Germans for allowing me to do so in this case. They flew steadily on, I was following at a safe distance, all the while hammering on my crank handle with the little wooden mallet we carried for such emergencies. I knew from the position of my crank handle that I had a bulged cartridge to deal with, but I got rid of it at last and went on again, full motor.

The two-seater was about half a mile in front of me now, flying at the same altitude. I gained on him rapidly, and in my excitement opened fire when still one hundred and fifty metres distant. My tracers appeared to be going directly into the plane, and yet, to my astonishment, and disgust, it showed no signs of being damaged. I must have fired between fifty and seventy-five rounds when of a sudden the Rumpler loomed up directly in front of me. I had not realised how much faster I was going, and as a result I nearly got him by running into him. He turned just as I zoomed over him, and I had a vivid glimpse of my opponents. The observer was sighting down through his camera, but looked up just as I passed and seized the handle of his guns with an air of annoyance and surprise as much as to say, "Oh——!! Here's that pest back again!" The pilot turned his head over his shoulder, and I had a fleeting view of the vacant stare of his goggles and a flowing blond moustache. I did an Immelmann turn to come back at them, and unfortunately, in making it, passed directly above them, whereupon the observer gave me another burst. I heard a loud *whang-g-g*, and knew that something had been hit, but it was not till several minutes later that I saw that one of my bracing wires had been cut through.

One of the most surprising things to me, in an air battle, was the rapidity with which two planes could separate. At one second you were close enough to see the colour of your opponent's moustache and the kind of flying clothes he wore; a few seconds later, as you turned to come back, you found that he was a half a mile or even three-quarters of a mile away. Two planes flying at a combined speed of perhaps two hundred and fifty miles per hour are soon separated when going in opposite directions.

My Rumpler was still not mine. He was a long way off, and I had to do my creeping all over again. This time I determined to keep cool and reserve my fire until within fifty yards of him. He let me approach as before, and I knew that the observer was busy with his long-range camera, for I could see the muzzles of his guns pointing idly in the air. The pilot flew straight on as though so thoroughly convinced of my poor marksmanship that he meant to let me blaze away to my heart's content; but he was not quite so indifferent as that. I was still about three hundred yards distant, and had my head steadily braced against my head-rest and my sights in beautiful alignment, when the Rumpler began to rise as though being drawn up by invisible wires. Despite my resolution to keep cool, I pulled up steeply and fired a burst of fifteen or twenty rounds which doubtless missed him by twice as many yards, slipped off on a wing, and had to dive into it to regain flying speed. In doing so I lost a good fifty metres of altitude, and when I turned once more in pursuit the Rumpler was a long way ahead and climbing as though there was no limit to his ceiling. There was nothing to do but climb after him.

All this while we had not, of course, been circling over the same area. Our general direction had been east and a little north, but I had been so busy that I failed to notice how far we had gone. Now, with nothing to do but climb for a while, I took notice of landmarks. Far below to the left I saw a great stretch of wooded country, another to the right and north of that one a city. "Now, what in the world can that town be?" I thought. Chalons was the first name that occurred to me, but I knew there were no forests near Chalons. I made a more careful scrutiny and presently recognised the Cathedral of Rheims. There was no doubt of it. I had never seen Rheims from the air,—or from the ground, for that matter,—but for more than three months I had been studying aeroplane maps and photographs of the western front from the channel coast to Switzerland, and knew it better than my native California. I easily identified the Marne-Vesle canal which makes a great loop from Epernay to Rheims. We were a good thirty-five miles from Senard, and evidently the Germans meant to go still farther. The Rumpler was headed for Rheims, and within a few moments we were directly over the city at a height of fifty-five hundred metres.

At least that was my own altitude; the Rumpler was at six thousand or more, and my Spad was doing its best to lessen the advantage. The motor sounded tacky; not the full-blooded roar to which I was accustomed. Something was wrong, but I didn't know what. By the time we had left Rheims behind I had climbed another fifty metres, but that was the best I could do. And there were my Germans, not five hundred metres higher, paying no further attention to me, knowing, apparently, that the only harm I could do now would be to get into the line of vision of their camera. Then it occurred to me that they might even want me there, provided that my Spad was far enough away and cut off the view of nothing essential on the ground. It would add a bit of local colour to their photographs to have a tiny French *chasse* plane clearly outlined over the towns, railroad junctions, aerodromes, ammunition dumps, and so forth, they were snapping. I could imagine them, a day or two later, bringing their developed films to their squadron or group commander, who would glance through them with interest.

" Splendid photographs, *Oberleutnant*. Just what we want."

" *Danke schön, Hauptmann*. We had excellent weather— a perfectly clear sky all the way from St. Mihiel to Rhiems. It would have been impossible not to have taken good pictures."

" And you weren't molested, all that way?"

" *Nein, Hauptmann*. We had very good luck. We were heavily shelled, of course, as usual."

" Hello! Here's a Spad showing—in the photograph taken over that aerodrome near St. Hilare."

" *Bitte schön?*"

" A Spad—a French Spad. He must have been about five hundred metres under you at the time. Yes, here it is again in the picture taken over the Montagne de Rheims. He must have been following you. Didn't you know he was there?"

" Oh, *ja*! . . . *Ja, ja*, I remember now. There was a Spad that trailed us all the way from the foot of the Argonne Forest. The pilot was quite harmless. We could have bagged him easily if we'd had time."

I could all but hear this conversation taking place, and it made me so angry to think that in all probability it *would* take place that I pulled up and fired another burst at the Rumpler, although he was a quarter of a mile in front of me and as much above. And I believe that I may have been lucky enough to hit him with a stray bullet, for the pilot made a leisurely turn, banking to look at me, then levelled out on his course again. The manœuvre said, as plainly as though he had spoken, " What! *You* still there?" It was as though he had waved his hand at a fly—troublesome, perhaps, but not troublesome enough to waste time over.

So it went for another ten or fifteen minutes. After leaving Rheims the Rumpler made another wide sweep into French territory, all the way from five to eight or nine miles behind the trenches. I had a map from the Verdun Sector in my map case, but we had long since flown out of that, over country I had never before seen from the air. The German pilot showed me everything worth seeing, from the military standpoint, behind our lines: aerodromes, hospitals, ammunition and supply dumps, and the like, all quite unknown to me. I wondered why I was not joined by some other friendly plane until it occurred to me that other Spads below, seeing me, would refrain from joining up. Pilots would think: " That Rumpler is his victim. I'll not horn in on his victory. Hope he gets the blighter. Awful crust he's got, that Boche, coming all this way back." The anti-aircraft batteries, too, had ceased firing, doubtless from the fear of hitting the wrong ship; for all this while I was trailing along very close behind, vainly trying to coax my Spad up the last short slope of sky that would give me another chance to attack. It was damnable to think that A-A battery commanders were perhaps watching me through binoculars, counting on me to do something and wondering why I didn't.

" I will!" I said. " I will! Don't worry. If he gives me half a chance." I had forgotten to be afraid, or even in the least uneasy about my own skin. I had forgotten my severed bracing wire and my coughing motor. I had forgotten what time it was, how long I had been flying, how much gas I had left—everything but my intense longing to knock down the cheeky Rumpler that had already flown with impunity across seventy-five miles of French territory.

And then my chance came, more quickly than I had bargained for. The Germans had just made a circle over a flying field I was later to know very well, deep in our territory, at the village of Fareen-Tardenois. It was not an aerodrome, but a small aviation-supply depot furnished only with two hangars. The Rumpler circled over it, so I circled too, as I had already done a score of times while they took their photographs. Then, their mission over apparently, they headed due north to cross their own lines. But they held that course for no longer than a minute. Suddenly the pilot went down in a steep turn and I saw the observer seize his guns and swing them around to fire at me.

This time I was not caught napping, and I wasted no precious seconds trying to get under his tail. I turned left as the Rumpler did, and got in a beautiful burst of about thirty rounds, again broadside on, and from a distance of not more than fifty yards. The observer repaid me with a shorter burst, but a murderously accurate one. Again I heard the ominous *flac! flac-flac-flac! flac-flac!* but it was only for a second. My Spad flopped over in a half turn and came back in the opposite direction so prettily that the thought, " Did I do that?" flashed through my mind. So it was always in the air: the manœuvres one made instinctively were always better than those made with deliberation. It was from that moment that I began to learn how to take care of myself in the air. Every old war-time pilot must have had some such illuminating experience which taught him more in three seconds than his flying instructions could do in five months. Thereafter, when I met a German ship, I kept my eye on that and let my Spad do its own manœuvring.

Turning, I found the Rumpler coming for me from a distance of two hundred yards—straight for me this time, the pilot firing the guns mounted on his motor hood. So I made for him, my guns crackling steadily. Our motors seemed to be eating each other's bullets; in fact they were, as I discovered later, but we flashed past each other, both seemingly intact. I made a vertical turn to the right and then saw something that made me shout for joy. The Rumpler was going off, and his propeller was standing stock-still. He had a " dead-stick," as we used to say. I thought for a second or two I had imagined this, for not infrequently pilots thought they saw what they hoped to see. It was true, however. The propeller was standing vertically, motionless. What a thrill it gave me to see it! " Now I've got them!" I thought. " I'll force them down in our lines!"

But the Germans had other plans about where they meant to land. They were planing very flatly, making a straight course for their own territory. I glanced at my altimeter. Forty-eight hundred metres. They had sufficient altitude to enable them to land behind their own lines if they were careful not to lose height unnecessarily. My motor was coughing and spitting as though at its last gasp, but I quickly overtook them. The rear gunner was waiting for me; I could see him turning his guns this way and that, trying to get a line on me; but his pilot was afraid of losing altitude which he could not regain, so I had little difficulty in keeping the observer guessing. He fired two or three bursts, but they went wide of the mark. " I'll have to shoot them," I thought. " These men are old hands. They can't be frightened into landing." So I went after them again, hoping that my marksmanship would be good enough to wing them both but not good enough to kill either. I had a wonderful chance now. They were planing all the while, of course, tail up at such an angle that I could see the surface of the underbody. I pressed the triggered. My gun fired twice and stopped. This time it wasn't a misfire or a bulged shell casing. I had run out through my entire belt of cartridges.

I didn't know what to do then. I had never thought of such an emergency as this. I confess that what I felt like doing was crying with vexation and disappointment. I had tried hard for that Rumpler, and to have him escape me at the last moment, when victory was all but in my hand—it was too much for me. And all the while the wide belt of desolate country that marked the trench lines was drawing nearer. Soon they would be sailing over it safely. I made a feint at an attack from the side so that both pilot and observer could see me, but that didn't frighten them in the least. The observer swung his guns round and gave me a dose of lead in the tail just as I passed under him. Had he been half a second quicker the chances are that I shouldn't be telling this story.

Help came in histrionic eleventh-hour fashion. Greased lightning decorated with tricolour *cocardes* streaked down the sky, turned left and fired, turned right and fired, flipped upside down, fired again, and vanished. I saw the German observer drop his guns and collapse in his seat as though he had been pushed down by strong, invisible hands. The little friendly plane flashed into view again; it was precisely as though it had the power of being everywhere at once, and visible or invisible as it chose. This time it came down from the side in plain view of the German pilot, but keeping well above him. The Frenchman, or whoever it was, did a barrel turn, at the same time cutting his motor down to come down on the Rumpler, but the German didn't wait for him to fire again. He turned away from his lines—slowly, and I could feel as well as see with what reluctance—and planed down into France.

We were right at his tail, the Frenchman on one side, I on the other. He was flying a Nieuport, type 27, and on the side of his fuselage was painted a black dragon, and another insignia which I made out to be a skull-and-crossbones design against a black background. I waved and he waved back, then reached out and went through the motions of shaking hands. He pulled up till he was opposite the German pilot's cockpit and I followed to the same position on the other side.

The Frenchman yelled something at the Boche and pointed down. The German looked over the side and waved his hand as much as to say, "All right." I looked, too, and saw the hangars of an aerodrome off to our left front. We were all three so close together that we could see each other's faces. It gave me a curious feeling to be flying wing to wing with a Rumpler. The pilot's yellow moustache was even longer than it had seemed when I had my first fleeting view of it. The ends fluttered back in the wind around the sides of his flying helmet. The observer was crumpled down in his cockpit, his head hanging to one side. We weren't long in coming down. Two or three minutes later the German landed with his "dead-stick." The Rumpler rolled a little way and stopped, and I saw a crowd of mechanics rushing out to it. The Frenchman and I followed him down.

MIRACLE AT DUNKIRK

Arthur D. Divine

I am still amazed about the whole Dunkirk affair. There was from first to last a queer, medieval sense of miracle about it. You remember the old quotation about the miracle that crushed the Spanish Armada, "God sent a wind." This time "God withheld the wind." Had we had one onshore breeze of any strength at all, in the first days, we would have lost a hundred thousand men.

The pier at Dunkirk was the unceasing target of bombs and shell-fire throughout, yet it never was hit. Two hundred and fifty thousand men embarked from that pier. Had it been blasted . . .

The whole thing from first to last was covered with that same strange feeling of something supernatural. We muddled, we quarrelled, everybody swore and was bad-tempered and made the wildest accusations of inefficiency and worse in high places. Boats were badly handled and broke down, arrangements went wrong.

And yet out of all that mess we beat the experts, we defied the law and the prophets, and where the Government and the Board of Admiralty had hoped to bring away 30,000 men, we brought away 335,000. If that was not a miracle, there are no miracles left.

When I heard that small boats of all sorts were to be used at Dunkirk, I volunteered at once, having no vast opinion of the navy as small-boat handlers. I had been playing with the navy off and on since the beginning of the year, mine sweeping and submarine hunting, convoying, and so on. So friends of mine at the Admiralty passed me through without formalities, and within two hours of my first telephone call I was on my way to Sheerness. From Sheerness I acted as navigator for a party of small boats round to Ramsgate, and at Ramsgate we started work. The evacuation went on for something over a week, but to me the most exciting time was the night before the last.

I was given a motorboat about as long as my drawing room at home, 30 feet. She had one cabin forward and the rest was open, but she had twin engines and was fairly fast.

From: *The Reader's Digest.* By permission of the Author.

For crew we had one sub-lieutenant, one stoker and one gunner. For armament we had two Bren guns—one my own particular pet which I had stolen—and rifles. In command of our boat we had a real live Admiral—Taylor, Admiral in charge of small boats.

We first went out to French fishing boats gathered off Ramsgate, boats from Caen and Le Havre, bright little vessels with lovely names—*Ciel de France, Ave Maria, Gratia Plena, Jeanne Antoine*. They had helped at Calais and Boulogne and in the preceding days at Dunkirk, and the men were very tired, but when we passed them new orders they set out again for Dunkirk.

They went as the leaders of the procession, for they were slow. With them went a handful of Dutch *schouts*, stumpy little coasting vessels commandeered at the collapse of Holland, each flying the white ensign of the Royal Navy, sparkling new, and each fitted out with a Lewis gun. Next went coasters, colliers, paddle steamers that in time of peace had taken trippers around the harbour for a shilling, tugs towing mud scows with brave names like *Galleon's Reach* and *Queen's Channel*.

There was a car ferry, surely on its first trip in the open sea. There were yachts; one the *Skylark*—what a name for such a mission! There were dockyard tugs, towing barges. There were sloops, mine sweepers, trawlers, destroyers. There were Thames fire floats, Belgian drifters, lifeboats from all around the coast, lifeboats from sunken ships. I saw the boats of the old *Dunbar Castle*, sunk eight months before. Rolling and pitching in a cloud of spray were open speedboats, wholly unsuited for the Channel chop.

There was the old *Brighton Belle* that carried holiday crowds in the days before the Boer War. She swept mines in the Great War, and she swept mines in this war through all the fury of last winter. I know; I sailed with her then. Coming back from her second trip to Dunkirk, she struck the wreck of a ship sunk by a magnetic mine and slowly sank. Her captain, a Conservative party agent in civil life, got 400 men safely off and at the last even saved his dog.

There was never such a fleet went to war before, I think. As I went round the western arm of the harbour near sunset, passing out orders, it brought my heart into my throat to watch them leave. They were so small! Little boats like those you see in the bight of Sandy Hook fishing on a fine afternoon. Some were frowsy, with old motorcar tyres for fenders, and some of them were bright with paint and chromium—little white boats that were soon lost to view across the ruffled water. And as they went there came round from the foreland a line of fishing boats—shrimp catchers and what not, from the east coast—to join the parade.

When this armada of oddments was under way, we followed with the faster boats—Royal Air Force rescue launches, picket boats and the like—and with us went an X-lighter, a flatboat, kerosene-powered built for landing troops at Gallipoli and a veteran of *that* evacuation more than 20 years ago.

It was the queerest, most nondescript flotilla that ever was, and it was manned by every kind of Englishman, never more than two men, often only one, to each small boat. There were bankers and dentists, taxi drivers and yachtsmen, longshoremen, boys, engineers, fishermen and civil servants. There were bright-faced Sea Scouts and old men whose skins looked fiery red against their white hair. Many were poor; they had no coats, but made out with old jerseys and sweaters. They wore cracked rubber boots. They were wet, chilled to the bone, hungry; they were unarmed and unprotected, and they sailed toward the pillars of smoke and fire and the thunder of the guns, into waters already slick with the oil of sunken boats, knowing perfectly well the special kind of hell ahead. Still, they went, plugging gamely along.

I had a feeling, then and after, that this was something bigger than organisation, something bigger than the mere requisitioning of boats. In a sense it was the naval spirit that has always been the foundation of England's greatness, flowering again and flowering superbly. I believe 887 was the official figure for the total of boats that took part over the ten days of the evacuation. But I think there were more than a thousand craft in all. I myself know of fishermen who never registered, waited for no orders, but, all unofficial, went and brought back soldiers. Quietly, like that.

It was dark before we were well clear of the English coast. It wasn't rough, but there was a little chop on, sufficient to make it very wet, and we soaked the Admiral to the skin. Soon, in the dark, the big boats began to overtake us. We were in a sort of dark traffic lane, full of strange ghosts and weird, unaccountable waves from the wash of the larger vessels. When destroyers went by, full tilt, the wash was a serious matter to us little fellows. We could only spin the wheel to try to head into the waves, hang on, and hope for the best.

Mere navigation was dangerous in the dark. Clouds hung low and blotted out the stars. We carried no lights, we had no signals, no means of recognition of friend or foe. Before we were halfway across we began to meet the first of the returning stream. We dodged white, glimmering bow waves of vessels that had passed astern, only to fall into the way of half-seen shapes ahead. There were shouts in the darkness, but only occasionally the indignant stutter of a horn. We went " by guess and by God."

From the halfway mark, too, there were destroyers on patrol crossing our line of passage, weaving a fantastic warp of foam through the web of our progress. There were collisions, of course. Dover for days was full of destroyers with bows stove in, coasting vessels with great gashes amidships, ships battered, scraped and scarred. The miracle is that there were not ten for every one that happened.

Even before it was fully dark we had picked up the glow of the Dunkirk flames, and now as we drew nearer the sailing got better, for we could steer by them and see silhouetted the shapes of other ships, of boats coming home already loaded, and of low dark shadows that might be the enemy motor torpedo boats.

Then aircraft started dropping parachute flares. We saw them hanging all about us in the night, like young moons. The sound of the firing and the bombing was with us always, growing steadily louder as we got nearer and nearer. The flames grew, too. From a glow they rose up to enormous plumes of fire that roared high into the everlasting pall of smoke. As we approached Dunkirk there was an air attack on the destroyers and for a little the night was brilliant with bursting bombs and the fountain sprays of tracer bullets.

The beach, black with men, illumined by the fires, seemed a perfect target, but no doubt the thick clouds of smoke were a useful screen.

When we got to the neighbourhood of the mole there was a lull. The aircraft had dispersed and apparently had done no damage, for there was nothing sinking. They had been there before, however, and the place was a shambles of old wrecks, British and French, and all kinds of odds and ends. The breakwaters and lighthouse were magnificently silhouetted against the flames of burning oil tanks—enormous flames that licked high above the town. Further inshore and to the east of the docks the town itself was burning furiously, but down near the beach where we were going there was no fire and we could see rows of houses standing silent and apparently empty.

We had just got to the eastward of the pier when shelling started up. There was one battery of 5.9s down between La

Panne and Nieuport that our people simply could not find and its shooting was uncannily accurate. Our place was in the corner of the beach at the mole and as they were shelling the mole, the firing was right over our heads. Nothing, however, came near us in the first spell.

The picture will always remain sharp-etched in my memory—the lines of men wearily and sleepily staggering across the beach from the dunes to the shallows, falling into little boats, great columns of men thrust out into the water among bomb and shell splashes. The foremost ranks were shoulder deep, moving forward under the command of young subalterns, themselves with their heads just above the little waves that rode in to the sand. As the front ranks were dragged aboard the boats, the rear ranks moved up, from ankle deep to knee deep, from knee deep to waist deep, until they, too, came to shoulder depth and their turn.

Some of the big boats pushed in until they were almost aground, taking appalling risks with the falling tide. The men scrambled up the sides on rope nets, or climbed hundreds of ladders, made God knows where out of new, raw wood and hurried aboard the ships in England.

The little boats that ferried from the beach to the big ships in deep water listed drunkenly with the weight of men. The big ships slowly took on lists of their own with the enormous numbers crowded aboard. And always down the dunes and across the beach came new hordes of men, new columns, new lines.

On the beach was a destroyer, bombed and burned. At the water's edge were ambulances, abandoned when their last load had been discharged.

There was always the red background, the red of Dunkirk burning. There was no water to check the fires and there were no men to be spared to fight them. Red, too, were the shell bursts, the flash of guns, the fountains of tracer bullets.

The din was infernal. The 5.9 batteries shelled ceaselessly and brilliantly. To the whistle of shells overhead was added the scream of falling bombs. Even the sky was full of noise —anti-aircraft shells, machine-gun fire, the snarl of falling planes, the angry hornet noise of dive bombers. One could not speak normally at any time against the roar of it and the noise of our own engines. We all developed "Dunkirk throat," a sore hoarseness that was the hallmark of those who had been there.

Yet through all the noise I will always remember the voices of the young subalterns as they sent their men aboard, and I will remember, too, the astonishing discipline of the men. They had fought through three weeks of retreat, always falling back, often without orders, often without support. Transports had failed. They had gone sleepless. They had been without food and water. Yet they kept ranks as they came down the beaches, and they obeyed commands.

Veterans of Gallipoli and of Mons agreed this was the hottest spot they had ever been in, yet morale held. I was told stories of French troops that rushed the boats at first so that stern measures had to be taken, but I saw nothing like that. The Frenchmen I brought off were of the rear guard, fine soldiers, still fighting fit.

Having the Admiral on board, we were not actually working the beaches but were in control of operations. We moved about as necessary, and after we had spent some time putting small boats in touch with their towing boats, the 5.9 battery off Nieuport way began to drop shells on us. It seemed pure spite. The nearest salvo was about 20 yards astern, which was close enough.

We stayed there until everybody else had been sent back, and then went pottering about looking for stragglers. While we were doing that, a salvo of shells got one of our troopships alongside the mole. She was hit clean in the boilers and exploded in one terrific crash. There were then, I suppose, about 1000 Frenchmen on the mole. We had seen them crowding along its narrow crest, outlined against the flames. They had gone out under shellfire to board the boat, and now they had to go back again, still being shelled. It was quite the most tragic thing I ever have seen in my life. We could do nothing with our little park dinghy.

While they were still filing back to the beach and the dawn was breaking with uncomfortable brilliance, we found one of our stragglers—a navy whaler. We told her people to come aboard, but they said that there was a motorboat aground and they would have to fetch off her crew. They went in, and we waited. It was my longest wait, ever. For various reasons they were terribly slow. When they found the captain of the motorboat, they stood and argued with him and he wouldn't come off anyway. Damned plucky chap. He and his men lay quiet until the tide floated them later in the day. Then they made a dash for it, and got away.

We waited for them until the sun was up before we got clear of the mole. By then, the fighting was heavy inshore, on the outskirts of the town, and actually in some of the streets.

Going home, the Jerry dive bombers came over us five

times, but somehow left us alone though three times they took up an attacking position. A little down the coast, towards Gravelines, we picked up a boatload of Frenchmen rowing off. We took them aboard. They were very much bothered as to where our "ship" was, said quite flatly that it was impossible to go to England in a thing like ours. Too, too horribly dangerous!

One of the rare touches of comedy at Dunkirk was the fear of the sea among French poilus from inland towns. They were desperately afraid to forfeit solid land for the unknown perils of a little boat. When, on the last nights of the evacuation, the little boats got to the mole many refused to jump in, despite the hell of shells and bombs behind them. I saw young sub-lieutenants grab poilus by the collar and the seat of the pants and rush them overside into waiting launches.

There was comedy of a sort, too, in the misadventures of the boats. The yachting season hadn't begun and most of the pleasure boats had been at their winter moorings when the call came; their engines had not been serviced and they broke down in the awkwardest places. The water supply at Dunkirk had been bombed out of use in the first days, and the navy ferried water across to keep the troops alive. Some of the water went in proper water cans, but most of it was put into two-gallon gasoline tins. *Of course* some of these tins got into the gasoline dumps, with lamentable results. I ran out of gasoline myself in the angle between Dunkirk mole and the beach, with heavy shelling going on and an Admiral on board. He never even said "damn." But we were lucky. A *schout* with spare fuel was lying a mile or so from the beach, near a buoy. I got to her with my last drop of reserve.

Then, for grim humour, there is the tale of the young sub-lieutenant, no more than a boy, whom I saw from time to time on one side of the Channel or the other. He was sent in the early days of the show to the beach east of Gravelines, where he was told there was a pocket of English troops cut off. He landed at the beach with only a revolver and walked off into the sand dunes to hunt for them. In the darkness he suddenly saw two faint shapes moving, and called out, " Here we are, boys, come to take you off."

There was silence, and then a guttural, " *Lieber Gott!*"

" So," the boy told me, " I shot them and came away."

He had walked right into the German army.

One of the greatest surprises of the whole operation was the failure of the German E-boats—motor torpedo boats. We crossed by a path that was well lit by light buoys, spread clean across from Godwins to Dunkirk Roads. Well-handled E-boats could have got among us in the dark and played havoc—either in the Channel or in Dunkirk Roads.

I had stopped once off one of the light buoys when a division of destroyers passed me. They could see me only as a small dark shape on the water, if at all, and had I had torpedoes I could have picked off the leaders. I might have been a German motorboat, and if the German navy had any real fighting spirit I ought to have been a German motorboat. They did send a few boats in, and I believe they claimed one of our destroyers somewhere off La Panne, but they never pressed the attack home, never came in force against our motley armada off the beaches. The German navy lost a great chance.

Germany, in fact, failed in three ways at Dunkirk. Against a routed army she failed on land to drive home her advantage, though she had strategic and numerical superiority. She failed in the air, though with half a million men narrowed into one small semi-circle, she should have been able—if air power ever could be decisive—to secure decisive victory. And at sea, her motorboats were so lamentably handled that we almost disregarded them. For long hours on end we were sheep for the slaughtering, but we got back to Ramsgate safely each time. There we watched the debarkations, two and three hundred men from each of the larger boats marching in an endless brown stream down the narrow curve of the east harbour wall. Among each load would be five or six wounded. The hospital ships went in to Dover; at Ramsgate we saw mainly the pitiful survivors of ships bombed on the way over—men with their skin flayed by oil burns, torn by bomb splinters, or wounded by machine-gun fire from the air. Most of them were unbandaged and almost untended. They were put ashore just as they were pulled from the water, the most pitiful wrecks of men. Yet they were surprisingly few.

Well, that's the story of Dunkirk, as I saw the show. Just afterwards, I volunteered for a new picnic farther down the coast. Our 51st Division had got cut off with a portion of the French army in the new battle which had developed from the Somme downward, and our job was to try to get it away.

I was given a Brighton Beach boat as warship this time, one of those things that takes trippers for a cruise around the bay. We left before dawn on a Wednesday morning and made the first half of the crossing in fog. We headed for Dieppe at first, but Dieppe had already fallen, and we veered toward

St. Valery-en-Caux, a little down the coast. I knew the place well, having been there two or three days before war broke out. We sighted the French coast in the early afternoon and closed to within about five miles of it. Our destroyer escort never turned up, though we heard it having a bright little scrap on its own just below the horizon to the southwest.

About the middle of the afternoon, we sighted two boats rowing toward us and picked them up. They were full of French seamen who said that they were the last survivors of St. Valery. They had fought the Germans from their ship with machine guns until she sank under them, and then had rowed out of the harbour. They were very badly shot about, many of them dead and a large number wounded. I was called onto the tug to give first aid. We stowed them on two of our faster boats and sent the wounded off.

The German planes were buzzing around most of the time, but high up. Just as I got back to my own boat we got the signal to scatter. Three Heinkels had come over to deal with us.

My engine wouldn't start, as I had not been on board to see that it was warmed up, and the boat ahead of me was out of action with a fouled propeller. Neither of us could move, so we had to sit and watch the attack. The bombing was pretty good, but not good enough. For a long time it looked as if bombs from the first Heinkel were falling absolutely straight at us, tiny black specks that grew most horribly. They fell about 15 or 20 yards clear, and though they blew us sideways over the water they did us no harm.

Then the second bomber dived and dropped eight bombs, and again they fell just clear. While the third was manœuvering, my engineer got the engine going. I threw a towline to the other fellow, and we got under way. I had the flight of the bombs pretty well judged by then, and we worked clear of the third attack.

We started out for England. The bombers, having used up all their bombs, left us and we had a spell of quiet. However, big fighters came out to have another smack. We were far from the rest of the fleet and going along lamely. They attacked the others from a height, but when they came to us—thinking we were helpless, I suppose—they dived low and machine-gunned us heavily.

I was standing at the tiller, steering, and there was no sort of cover. One of the bullets got me through the middle. It felt like the kick of a mule, and knocked me away from the tiller to the bottom boards. However, there was not much real pain then, and I got up and examined myself. From the looks of the hole, I didn't think I had much of a chance. I told them to put me on the bottom boards, forward, and gave my gunner the course for the English coast. The tug picked us up after a time, and we were towed to New Haven, arriving about six next morning.

I was weak from loss of blood and wasn't betting too heavily on my chances of survival. However, I was operated on within an hour of landing, and it was found that I had been amazingly lucky. The bullet had done no serious damage.

I went to a hospital at Brighton. After three weeks the Admiralty moved me to a country hospital so that I could have a quiet rest. I didn't. We had 28 siren warnings in 20 days, and were bombed one night.

I am now back in town. The Admiralty offers me a commission, as a reward of virtue, I suppose, but the medical examiners say that I cannot go to sea. I don't want a shore job, so I have turned down the offer. I shall be a good boy and sit in an office awhile until the wound is better. Then I shall wangle my way to sea. I think I know how.

Meanwhile we are all right here. Germany is not starving us out; she is not going to invade us out; and she isn't going to air-raid us out. If I can't quite see yet how we are going to win—the method and so on—I certainly can't see how we are going to be defeated.

Twenty miles of sea is still twenty miles of sea, and the Straits of Dover are the best tank trap the world has ever devised.

THE STOLEN RAILROAD TRAIN

Marquis James

On Sunday evening, the sixth of April, 1862, a tall, carefully dressed civilian with a heavy black beard and the inflection of the South in his speech, presented himself to the pickets of Mitchel's Division, encamped near Shelbyville, Tennessee. His papers were in order and he was admitted.

Major General O. M. Mitchel and the spy sat down over a map and it was daylight before they reached an agreement. The scheme offered by the secret agent was such that even a soldier as bold as Mitchel drew back. But step by step the civilian justified the proposal. Audacity would promote its success, he said, and success would be worth any risk. General Mitchel's caller asked for thirty picked men from whom to made his personal selections, and at length Mitchel agreed he should have them.

That forenoon thirty volunteers were culled from the veteran Second, Twenty-First and Thirty-Third Ohio Infantry Regiments, the colonels passing upon the qualifications of each man who was told that a detail was being made up for duty involving great personal peril. Though occupied with plans for a military advance, General Mitchel himself took the time to look over a few of the applicants. In the afternoon the chosen thirty were sent to Shelbyville to purchase civilian clothing and to report to J. J. Andrews, a tall civilian with a heavy beard who would be found on the streets of the town.

Shelbyville was full of soldiers, and, as soldiers often laid off their uniforms when going home on furlough, the thirty made their purchases without exciting comment. J. J. Andrews was easily identified. He sauntered about the streets, frequently entering a store to take an apparently idle interest in a soldier who was buying clothing. In the course of the afternoon all thirty approached him, singly or in small groups, for they were generally unknown to one another. He would ask what they were to report to him for. The soldiers would say that they did not know, or something of the sort. Andrews would ask them a few questions. Then in a casual tone he would say, "You may meet me to-night shortly after dark on

From: *They Had Their Hour*: Copyright 1934. Used by special permission of The Bobbs-Merrill Co.

the Wartrace Road a mile or so from town." To five or six he said, "There must be some mistake. I am not the man you are looking for." Their demeanour had not satisfied the Union spy.

Nor was Sergeant Major Marion Ross altogether satisfied with his interview. "A mile or so from town." "Shortly after dark." The instructions were so vague that he asked his friend Corporal William Pittenger what he thought of this Andrews. "I answered with enthusiasm," the Corporal related in after years. "The strong-influence this singular man never failed to exert over those who were brought in contact with him was already at work. His pensive manner, his soft voice, not louder than a woman's, his grace and dignity made me at once declare him above the ordinary type of manhood. He was more like a poet than an adventurer, but I would have trusted him to the end of the earth."

II

Such whole-hearted endorsement put Ross in entire agreement with his friend's estimate. In fact, his curiosity was now aroused and he wished that he knew more about their new leader. And General Mitchel himself would have liked to know more about James J. Andrews, but all he knew or ever learned was that he was a good spy and described himself as a resident of Flemingsburg, Kentucky.

This town was equally unsatisfied with the scope of its knowledge. Andrews had come there two years before the war—from Virginia, as he said, but he gave no particulars. Something about the man suggested an interesting past. Flemingsburg believed he " had a story."

Perhaps one person in Flemingsburg really knew. She was Elizabeth Layton to whom Mr. Andrews after a long court-ship, had just become engaged. They were to be married in two months, and a part of the bargain was that Andrews should abandon his perilous profession as a Union secret agent. The service he had proposed to Mitchel was intended to be his last. It was calculated to reveal to the world where his true loyalties lay, for in the South Andrews was known as a con-fidential agent of the Confederate armies.

The night following the interviews at Shelbyville was pitch dark and the rain fell in sheets. Twenty-four men, singly or in small parties, trudged through the mud of the Wartrace Road. Several of them were hopeless of meeting Andrews or anyone on such a night. Yet twenty-three of the twenty-four found him as readily as if they had had daylight and explicit directions to guide them. Andrews led them into a patch of woods near the road and began to speak in a quiet voice, stopping when the thunder was too loud for him to be heard distinctly.

He said that the expedition for which they had volunteered would take them into the enemy's country in disguise, which meant that any one captured and detected would probably be hanged as a spy. Therefore, any one unwilling to take the risk might now withdraw. Mr. Andrews paused. No one stirred and in a few sentences the speaker outlined the undertaking. In bands of two to four, the party would proceed to Marietta, Georgia, in the heart of the Confederacy, arriving on Thursday, four days hence. The following morning they would capture the north-bound mail train from Atlanta to Chattanooga, and run it to Bridgeport, Alabama, burning bridges behind them and rendering useless a hundred and thirty miles of railroad and telegraph. At Bridgeport, the party would meet Mitchel in the course of his southward advance. The destruction of these communications would paralyse the movement of southern armies in the Central West and embarrass Lee's operations in Virginia.

" I shall be in Marietta with you or before you," said Mr. Andrews, " and there will tell each man what to do."

The route from Shelbyville to Marietta was long and difficult, and Andrews gave his men a few pointers on travel. If questioned, the best thing to say was that they were Kentuckians on their way to join the southern armies. But the men were to use their heads. They had been selected because they were thought capable of independent action.

" But what if they take us at our word and insist that we enlist?" asked one.

" Oh, be looking for a special regiment that is some place else. But if diplomacy fails do not hesitate to enlist any place."

" What if they won't take us?"

" No danger about that," replied Andrews. " The difficulty is not to get in but to stay out of the rebel army."

Andrews distributed seven hundred dollars of Confederate money and shook hands with each man. " Good-bye. Good-bye, Sergeant. Marietta not later than five, Thursday afternoon. Now, move out, men. Not more than four together."

On the appointed Thursday—April 10, 1862—two of the twenty-three reached Marietta. They strolled about town until late and went to bed uneasy. All day Friday they waited without a sign of one of their comrades, so far as they were able to recognise, the party having been together but once and then in the dark. The evening train from Chattanooga, however, brought Andrews and the remainder of his men, except two who were never heard from.

Incessant rain had made travelling difficult. When the party converged at Chattanooga to take the train for Marietta, Mr. Andrews had passed the word that the raid should be postponed one day. Thus all but the two men who had outstripped their schedule by a few hours had lain over at Chattanooga. Andrews's reason for the delay was that he felt it better to run the captured train into Bridgeport a day late rather than risk getting there ahead of Mitchel whose advance, he figured, would be retarded by the weather.

At Marietta the men slept in different hotels and at dawn met Andrews in his room for final instructions. As usual the leader did not waste a word. "Buy tickets to different points up the line. Take seats in the same car. When the train stops at Big Shanty remain seated until I tell you to go. When the signal is given, if anybody interferes, shoot him."

The ranking soldier present was Sergeant Major Ross, whose courage was well known. Respectfully asking permission to speak, he suggested that the whole project be dropped or delayed for a reconsideration of all the factors involved. The delay of one day had altered everything, said Ross. Big Shanty was surrounded by troops; the line was congested by rolling stock being hurried out of Mitchel's reach; should Mitchel get to Bridgeport on time, the raiders, a day late, might miss him. Very courteously Mr. Andrews took up Ross's objections. He said the excitement and confusion caused by Mitchel's drive into Alabama would facilitate, not hinder, the flight of the fugitive train. "Boys," he concluded after dismissing the last of the sergeant major's arguments, "I will succeed in this or leave my bones in Dixie."

That was the nearest to an heroic speech that J. J. Andrews ever made. He closed his watch and picked up his tall silk hat. The depot was just across the street and there was barely time before the train came in to buy tickets.

An hour later Conductor William A. Fuller walked through the coaches. Fuller was a wiry young fellow, with a blond goatee and steady grey eyes.

"Big Shanty!" he called. "Twenty minutes for breakfast."

The sleepy passengers began to scramble toward the door, Andrews rose and beckoned to William Knight, who had been designated as engineer. The station was on the right side of the track. Four Georgia regiments were encamped on the left side and a bored sentry walked his post within a few feet of the cars. Andrews and Knight got off on the side next to the camp. They strolled forward and took a look at the engine. The cab was empty. Behind the tender were three empty freight cars. Andrews stopped beside the last one.

"Uncouple here," he told Knight.

He walked to the coach where the other men were waiting. Strolling part of the way down the aisle, Andrews paused and said in an ordinary tone, "Come on, boys, it's time to go."

IV

Wilson W. Brown, the relief engineer, and George D. Wilson, the fireman, swung off and darted toward the locomotive. Knight was in the cab with his hand on the throttle. Andrews signalled the others to tumble into the box-cars—all the work of probably twelve seconds. Knight pulled the throttle half-way open. The wheels spun on the track but the train did not move. Then the wheels "bit" and the engine, the three box-cars attached, shot forward with a bound that piled the box-car passengers in a heap.

They scurried to their feet to look from the doors and cheer. The start had been propitious beyond expectation. The picket, near enough to have used his bayonet, was staring in open-mouthed amazement—which, after all, was a fortunate negligence on the part of this green recruit as each of Andrews's men carried a cocked pistol in his coat.

The feeling of triumph was short-lived, however. Less than a mile from the Confederate camp the engine began to falter, which was strange, for this locomotive, the General, was rated one of the best on the Western & Atlantic road. Shortly this excellent engine stopped dead and Andrews, who was in the cab, called to the men in the cars to cut the telegraph wires. While John Scott, the smallest man in the party, was shinning up the telegraph pole, the trouble with the engine was located. The draft was shut off and the fire nearly out. Wood doused with oil soon had the firebox roaring and they were on their way again.

Nothing now, said Andrews who was not given to strong statements, could defeat them. Cutting the wires at this point was an excess precaution. There was no need for it so soon as Big Shanty lacked a telegraph office. Pursuit would be a matter of hours, the nearest engines available for this purpose being at Atlanta on the south and Kingston on the north, each about thirty miles from Big Shanty. Three south-bound trains from Chattanooga must be dealt with, but Andrews had arranged for that. He would adhere to the regular time on the mail train until Kingston was reached, and pass there a local freight, the first of these trains. After burning some eleven bridges beyond Kingston and keeping the wires cut to prevent word from getting ahead of them, the raiders could skirt Chattanooga by means of the " Y " below the town, and dash westward into Alabama where Mitchel would be waiting.

The schedule of the fast mail from Atlanta was sixteen miles an hour and Andrews had difficulty in holding his engineers down to that speed, even though the track was crooked and soft from the rains, and the rails light and worn by the constant travel of military trains. The local freight must be passed at Kingston and it would be better to take it easy en route than to get to Kingston early and have to wait. So they jogged along, stopping once to relieve a track repair gang of its tools, and again to cut wires and lift a rail. The rail-lifting was slow work as the tools they had taken were not the proper ones.

Half-way to Kingston Andrews received a surprise. Slowing up for a private switch that led to the Etowah Iron Works, five miles off the main line, he saw a locomotive fired up not forty feet from the main track. It was the veteran Yonah, owned by the iron works, and, carefully as he had explored the road, Andrews had not learned of its existence until now. Knight put on the brakes.

"We had better get rid of that," he suggested.

Andrews hesitated. "No," he said, " go ahead. It won't make any difference."

Andrews did not wish to risk a delay in meeting the freight at Kingston. Beyond Kingston he could destroy track and thwart pursuit by the Yonah as effectively as by attacking its crew and the iron works gang at the switch. The decision reveals an important difference in temperament between

Andrews and his men. The men would have preferred to disable the Yonah on the spot. They were soldiers, the pick of a first-class division, and accustomed to direct methods. Andrews's way was otherwise—to avoid clashes and to *finesse* his way through tight places where the flick of an eyelash might mean death.

V

Seven miles from Kingston was Cassville, a wood and water stop. The box-car doors were closed while the engine crew replenished the tender. The wood-yard foreman strolled up, curious to know about the small train running on the schedule of the morning mail, with the mail's locomotive but none of the regular hands. Mr. Andrews had put on his silk hat in place of the cap he wore while the train was under way. This was a powder train, he said, being taken through to General Beauregard, who was in a bad way for ammunition. The wood-yard foreman wished the powder-bearers luck.

Kingston was a good-sized town. The station platform was filled with people. The branch train for Rome was there, waiting for the Atlanta mail. Knight stopped alongside it and the Rome engineer called out:

"What's up? Fuller's engine and none of his men on board."

"I have taken this train by Government authority," said Andrews, "to run powder through to Beauregard." He waved his hand toward the box-cars in which his men were shut up.

The local freight was late. Andrews could get no information beyond that. Five minutes passed. Ten, fifteen minutes. To the men in the dark box-cars they seemed like hours.

Mr. Andrews walked up and down the station platform. One or two persons recognised him and saluted respectfully. He would stop and chat for a moment, belittling the alarming stories of Mitchel's advance into Alabama. People spoke of his poise in the face of the vexatious delay of the powder train.

Finally the freight came in. Andrews hastened to ask the conductor to pull up so that the powder train could move. The conductor was willing to oblige, but indicated a red flag on the end of his train. Another train was behind, made up, the freight conductor said, of everything on wheels that could be gleaned out of Mitchel's path. "And where," asked the conductor, "did you say you were to deliver this powder to Beauoregard?" "At Corinth, Mississippi," repeated Andrews. "Why, you can't get through," explained the conductor. "Mitchel is on the line at Huntsville." Andrews said he did not believe it, but the trainman said he knew, having just come from there.

Twenty minutes, thirty minutes dragged by. Andrews patrolled the station platform within ear-shot of the telegraph key. With one hand he raised his tall hat in polite greeting. The other hand enclosed the butt of a pistol in the pocket of his long black coat. Any attempt to send a suspicious message and the telegraph operator would have been a dead man. Andrews told Knight to get word to the men in the cars as to how the land lay and have them ready to fight.

Knight and his crew oiled their engine. An old switch tender who had spent a lifetime on southern railroads, hung around asking questions. The powder-train story did not concern him. The strange crew in the General's cab interested the veteran whose mind was an encyclopaedia of southern railway personnel. Where had they worked? Road? Division? Knight and his helpers answered in monosyllables. Fortunately Brown had once run a locomotive on the Mobile & Ohio, but there was no evading a certain discomfort in the old-timer's boring cross-examination.

Forty minutes is a long time to wait for a train under any circumstances. There was a whistle around the curve and Andrews met the refugee train as it pulled in, shouting directions for it to take its place on the already crowded sidings. The conductor also pointed to a red flag on his last car. The refugee train was running in two sections.

Fifty minutes. One hour—and a whistle that was music to the ears of twenty-two men. Section two rumbled in. Two regular trains from the north were now overdue. A prudent conductor would not have entertained a notion of leaving Kingston then. But Andrews said he would have to take the chance of passing the trains at Adairsville, ten miles farther on.

He waved for the switch admitting his train to the main line to be opened. But the old switch tender refused to budge. He had hung up his keys in the station and said that Andrews would have to show his authority to get them. The men inside the box-cars heard the old man's defiance and got their pistols ready. Not so the mannerly Mr. Andrews whose life was filled with escapes from apprehensive moments. He laughed at the veteran's distemper and said he would get the keys. He did so, and the General was off after a delay of one hour and five minutes at Kingston, making in all an elapse of three hours and thirteen minutes from Big Shanty, thirty-two miles away.

"Push her, boys, push her," Andrews urged, and the General simply flew.

VI

Well for Mr. Andrews that he had taken a chance and left for Adairsville. Four minutes after the General cleared the Kingston yards, a screaming whistle was heard from the south. The impatient passengers thought Fuller's train was coming and picked up their valises. It was Fuller—but he had not brought his train. The old Yonah rolled in, wheezing and blowing. Fuller swung off with the stunning story of the capture of the General at Big Shanty, and while the tracks were being cleared of the four trains congesting them, he managed to give a few of the details of his almost incredible pursuit.

At Big Shanty—now the town of Kenesaw—Fuller had just sat down at breakfast when a shout went up that his train had been stolen. He was on the platform in time to see the General and three box-cars glide around a curve. The station and camp were in an uproar. The dumbfounded sentry stammered his story. It flashed on Fuller that the engine had been seized by deserters who would run it up the track for a few miles and take to the woods.

"Let's get her back before we are badly out of time," he shouted and, with Engineer Cain and Superintendent Murphy of the machine shops, started up the track at a dead run. Two miles out the three were winded and about to give up when they met the track gang whose tools Andrews had appropriated.

"If we can find the old Yonah at our end of the branch, we will get the scoundrels at Kingston where those extras will hold them up," said Fuller.

Before any one could reply to this observation push-car and riders, sailing down a grade, were pitched into a ditch, having struck a lifted rail.

The Yonah was overtaken just as she started to leave the main line. This old engine was full of complaints, but she had had her day, and on this day she turned back the calendar. The sixteen miles to Kingston were covered in thirteen minutes.

The crowd at the station told Fuller that his quarry had eluded him by four minutes. The conductor dashed into the telegraph office and sent a message north. He came back to the platform to hear the powder story, but, of course, did not learn that the "powder" cars were filled with armed men. Otherwise, he and his few helpers would have proceeded much more cautiously. The trains still were in a snarl on the tracks and, rather than lose any more time in switching, Fuller decided to abandon the Yonah. He uncoupled the engine of the Rome train and was off in a little better than six minutes, or about eleven minutes behind the Yankees.

The message telegraphed from Kingston did not get through because Andrews had stopped above the town in a blinding rain and cut the wires. Here the men also started to lift a rail, but their ineffective tools made clumsy work of it. Two-thirds of the rail was loose from the ties and the fugitives were about to give it up as a bad job, when the unmistakable whistle of a locomotive was heard from the south. Pursuit! It could be nothing else. The lifting of the rail became a matter of life or death. Most of the members of the party were large muscular men. They grasped the loose end of the rail, and with the strength born of peril heaved and pulled and heaved and pulled again. The iron rail snapped and the men tumbled in a heap. In an instant they were on their feet, in the cars and away.

At Adairsville the raiders were cheered by the sight of the south-bound freight waiting on the siding. At the depot Andrews received positive information that Mitchel held several miles of the railroad in Alabama. To Andrews, the Yankee raider, this was welcome news. To Andrews, the Confederate powder-train official, it presented complications. The story of the powder train was rendered absurd on its face, but the marvellous address of the spy covered up the inconsistency long enough for him to get away. This took a little time, too. He tarried to reassure the freight crew and send them south with their train. With the pursuers coming north, the freight going south, and a broken rail between them, Andrews expected his adversaries to be delayed long enough to give him the lead he needed.

To accomplish this he took further risks. The south-bound passenger train, following the freight, was overdue. The station officials advised Andrews to wait for it. Quite truthfully Andrews said he could not afford to wait, but he promised to run slowly, sending a flagman ahead on curves. Thus Andrews hoped to reach Calhoun, nine miles farther on, and deal with the passenger train there.

So as not to arouse suspicion, the General rolled cautiously away from the Adairsville depot. A quarter of a mile of this and Andrews told Knight to let her go.

VII

The Yonah, ancient as she was, had been a faster locomotive than the engine Fuller took from the Rome train, but it was this fact—and an element of luck, as the conductor himself admitted—that averted disaster to the pursuit. Having struck one broken rail he was on the lookout for others, although the rain made it almost impossible to see anything. Nevertheless Fuller did see, or thought he saw, where the track had been tampered with in time to have his engineer throw the engine into reverse and stop it on the brink of the gap.

The conductor leaped from the useless locomotive and, motioning to his men to follow again, started another footrace up the track, sliding and slipping in the mud. He had not gone far when he saw the through freight headed toward him. He flagged it down and backed it into Adairsville. The freight engine was the Texas and there was no better locomotive on the line. It was detached and with a small party of armed men started, tender forward, toward Calhoun.

Fuller believed he had the Yankees now. Andrews was thought to be running slowly for fear of colliding with the south-bound passenger train. If so, Fuller's quarry was boxed between two trains. But if Andrews had succeeded in reaching Calhoun before the passenger left, Fuller himself would risk a collision—unless he took care. Fuller did not take care. The scent was hot and he sent the Texas racing ahead.

VIII

To this day Knight probably holds the speed record between Adairsville and Calhoun, Georgia. The nine miles were behind the stolen engine in seven and one-half minutes—over a track on which safe running was reckoned to be sixteen miles an hour. At that the Andrews party escaped destruction by thirty seconds. The passenger train had just pulled out from the station when the wild General was seen roaring toward it. The two locomotives, screaming under the pressure of their brakes, were stopped within a few yards of each other. The passenger engineer was trembling with fright—and he was angry. He refused to back up and let Andrews pass. A crisis seemed at hand, for Andrews literally did not have a moment to lose, as he had not yet cut the wires beyond Adairsville.

The rain still fell. The passenger conductor came up to see what was the trouble. Andrews addressed him in a tone of authority. He said he had requested the removal of his passenger train in order that powder for the front might not be delayed. Now he had no alternative but to issue orders. Without a word the conductor obeyed.

The spraddling hamlet of Calhoun diminished in the distance and the Yankees breathed more easily. Sergeant Major Ross had been right about a day's delay altering things. Yesterday it would have been smooth sailing—no extra trains, no excitement on the line, the powder-train story perfection itself. By now the raiders should have been near their triumphant journey's end. But to-day difficulties had been encountered only to be overcome. Five trains passed, a pursuit shaken off by a matter of minutes, and now they were on the main line once more with an open road ahead and a broken track behind.

IX

Fuller covered the nine miles to Calhoun in ten minutes—which still leaves the Yankee Knight in possession of the record, however. The passenger train was still waiting. One scare in a day had been enough for the engineer. Andrews had tried vainly to send him on his way, which would certainly have been the end of Conductor Fuller. Instead, the raider's Nemesis, saved by another stroke of luck, rushed the Texas, running backward, out of Calhoun. Fuller himself perched on the tender where he could get a better view of the track.

The General and crew were within a few minutes of the first bridge to be burned—a covered wooden structure over the Oostanaula River. Here Andrews planned to render his success secure. He stopped a couple of miles in front of the bridge to cut wires and take up track. While some of the men tugged at a rail, others collected wood to fire the bridge. This would not be easy as the downpour continued and everything was soaking wet. The toiling rail crew was having its usual difficulties when they saw a sight that would not have startled them more had it been a ghost. A locomotive whistled and hove in view, burning up the track from the south. For the first time during the chase, Fuller sighted his quarry. Those at the rail yanked like men possessed. They could not break the rail, but they bent a yard of it some inches out of line. That seemed sufficient to wreck any train and the men jumped into the box-cars and the General started off.

It did not, however, wreck the mysterious pursuer. As far as the fugitives could see the oncoming engine shot over the bent rail as if nothing was wrong. On the tender Fuller had been so engrossed in observing the men in possession of the General, that he overlooked the rail until it was too late to stop. Actually the rail had nearly thrown the pursuing crew from the cab and they thought they were lost. The bent rail was on the inside of a curve and the weight of the swiftly moving engine was on the outside rail. The bent rail simply straightened and the train kept on the track.

As for the Yankees, all their chances of getting away now depended on firing the bridge, and Andrews attempted a dramatic expedient to gain time for that. He reversed the General and charged his pursuers. When going full tilt the rear box-car was uncoupled, and the General was started forward leaving the box-car to continue the assault.

The bridge was reached. On a fair day a little oil and a faggot or two would have finished it, but it was raining harder than ever. Every stick of wood was soaked and the men kept their pistol ammunition dry with difficulty. Nevertheless a fire was kindled and coaxed to burn in one of the remaining cars. The plan was to leave the car in flames on the covered wooden bridge, but before the fire seemed the least encouraging here came the pursuers—pushing the raider's box-car in front of them. The southerners had had some more luck. On a down-grade the flying-box-car might have driven them back for miles. But the hard-pressed Andrews was compelled to let it go on a level stretch. Fuller simply had reversed the Texas for a short distance, and, when the car slowed down, coupled it on and renewed the chase. When he came in sight of the bridge, Andrews was forced to flee, and, for the first time, a feeling that the fates were not on their side overtook the Union adventurers.

Certainly all the advantages of chance had gone against Andrews. Still, Fuller's pursuit had been intelligent and daring and he had made no mistakes. None can question the daring of Andrews, but he had made a grave mistake in not destroying the Yonah.

On the bridge the Texas picked up the smoking car that Andrews had tried to convert into a firebrand. Both cars were side-tracked at Reseca, a station a few hundred yards beyond the bridge.

Passing Reseca the General did not run very fast. It was plain that there was no eluding the Texas by speed alone. The Yankees tried wrecking her. As there was no time to stop and dismantle the track, a hole was rammed in the rear end of the remaining box-car, and ties and sticks of firewood were dropped out in the hope of obstructing a rail. The wood showed a maddening disposition to roll off the track, but now and then a piece stayed on and Fuller was forced by the protests of his men to slow up.

The desperate expedient was effective as long as the wood lasted, but presently it was all gone, except a few sticks which were crammed into the fire-box for a sprint to the next woodyard. There about half a load had been thrown aboard when the Texas hove in sight, but fuel was so precious that the men continued to pile it on and Fuller' had to check speed to avert a collision. Before the hard-pressed General pulled out, Andrews's men had made a barrier of ties across the track, and, while Fuller removed it, the fugitives gained a few minutes' headway in their race to the water tank a few miles farther, for the General's boilers were almost dry. When the General left the water tank, the Texas was again in view.

Andrews was now ten or twelve miles from Dalton which was a large town with a complicated arrangement of switches. Somehow the hard-pressed Yankees must gain a few minutes to take care of possible delays there. It was also equally important to cut the wires before a message could get into Dalton to raise enemies in his path. A tremendous spurt was made. Then a sudden stop by throwing the engine into reverse. Before the wheels had ceased to revolve, the diminutive Scott was out of the car and up a pole. Another party was building a barrier across the track. Another was frantically trying to wrench up a rail. Corporal Pittenger, a young law student who had got in the army with difficulty because of his thick spectacles, approached Mr. Andrews.

"We can capture that train if you are willing," he said.

"How?" asked Andrews.

Without hesitating for a word the Corporal outlined an excellent plan of attack. "Block the track and place our party in ambush. Run our engine out of sight to disarm suspicion. When they stop to remove the obstruction we'll seize their engine and reverse it against any other trains that may be in this pursuit."

Mr. Andrews said nothing for a moment. "It is a good plain," he conceded. "It is worth trying." He glanced about as if studying the landscape. His survey was interrupted by the inevitable whistle of the pursuers. His glance shifted to the men who were vainly straining to force the rail.

"All aboard, boys," he called, and the dash to Dalton began.

X

The Texas was not in sight when the General halted a hundred yards in front of the Dalton depot which was a large structure with a shed enclosing the track. Several local railwaymen came up. The powder story was useless now—what with one battered car which had been literally peeled for firewood and a company of correspondingly battered men. Andrews dropped from the cab to see if the switches were set for a clear track. They appeared to be. "I am running this train through to Corinth," he called out in general acknowledgment of a flood of inquiries, and, signalling Knight to proceed, caught on the engine step as it passed.

The General tore through the station shed and through the town to the great consternation of the citizens of Dalton. This consternation had not diminished when, five minutes later, Fuller's Texas rolled in merely slowing up to drop a man who bolted like a shot from a gun and literally fell upon the telegrapher's key.

At the same instant, a mile from Dalton, in plain sight of a Confederate regiment, John Scott was climbing a telegraph pole. One minute later the wire was cut, putting a period where no period was intended in Conductor Fuller's message from Dalton. But this much got through:

"GEN LEADBETTER COMMANDER AT CHATTANOOGA. MY TRAIN CAPTURED THIS A M AT BIG SHANTY EVIDENTLY BY FEDERAL SOLDIERS IN DISGUISE. THEY ARE MAKING FOR CHATTANOOGA POSSIBLY WITH THE IDEA OF BURNING . . ."

The Chattanooga commandant understood. What chance now for Andrews and his band? Every mile of flight from Fuller brought them a mile nearer to the open arms of the waiting Leadbetter.

Some distance from Dalton the road passed through a tunnel. Here was the place to turn and fight if they were ever to do it. But Andrews signalled to keep on. He meant to stake everything on the destruction of the Chickamauga River bridge. He ordered a fire built in the remaining box-car. This was hard to do. The car had been picked clean. Inside and out, it was wet and rain was still falling in torrents.

By drawing on the last quart of oil and almost the last stick of fire-wood a blaze was started. It crackled encouragingly and the spirits of the men rose with it. The little train stopped under the shelter of the bridge. As the oil burned from the surface of the wet wood the fire dropped a little. Still, the interior of the bridge shed was fairly dry and given time the flames in the car would do their work.

A fire always holds an attraction, and, as this fire meant so much to its guardians, they half forgot their peril, and tarried to watch it. It was midday and the strain since dawn had been great. It was worth the price to relax. If the fire failed a few minutes would not matter.

The blaze picked up again. It took possession of the car and tongues of flame licked the half-dry timbers of the bridge. No one had said a word for what might have been a full moment when the lookout called that the smoke of the Texas was in sight.

The burning car was uncoupled rather deliberately and one of Andrews's men, who was brave enough to tell the truth, said that his heart sank. The General limped through the village of Ringgold. Wood was gone and oil was gone, but Andrews dared not stop.

Fuller picked up the blazing car on the bridge and dropped it at Ringgold. A few miles from there he sighted the Yankees drilling along at fifteen miles an hour. They were burning their clothing to keep moving and the journals on their engine were melting from want of oil. Their last fragment of hope was a wood-yard several miles ahead.

Fuller guessed their straits and their plan, but he lagged back. He knew that he was dealing with men who would be desperate at bay. With the whole country behind him aroused and other engines in pursuit by now, Fuller felt no call to precipitate a battle.

The General's speed fell to eight miles an hour and Fuller slacked accordingly, keeping a good quarter to half a mile in the rear.

Knight said he could not make the wood-yard. Andrews did not delay his decision.

" Jump and scatter, men, and be quick."

The men began to jump, rolling over and over until they vanished in the dripping woods beside the right-of-way. When all were off Knight reversed the engine and jumped. The old General moved off toward the pursuers, but the steam was too low for it to obtain any speed. Fuller simply reversed, ran back away and let the General come up gradually and couple on.

A troop train which had joined the pursuit was soon on the spot and the country was smothered with searchers under orders to take the " train thieves," dead or alive.

XI

All were taken, the captures requiring from a few hours to ten days.

Nothing the soldiers of the North did during the war aroused the South to a greater pitch than the exploit of these twenty-one men. The newspaper *Southern Confederacy* of Atlanta declared the preservation of the railroad bridges a victory equal to Bull Run. " The mind and heart sink back at the bare contemplation of the consequences that would have followed the success " of the raid. It resulted in reorganisation of railroad administration in the South.

Mr. Andrews left his bones in Dixie. He was hanged in Atlanta, ten days before the date set for his wedding. When his Kentucky fiancée read an account of it in a newspaper, the shock killed her.

The following week seven others were executed, but the sudden thrust of a Federal column interrupted the court martial of their fourteen comrades, eight of whom eventually escaped and reached the Union pickets. By this time the cry for vengeance had modulated and a few southerners went so far as to show publicly their admiration for the Yankees' valour. A year later the six who remained in Confederate hands were exchanged for their weight in important political prisoners held by the North. President Lincoln received them at the White House and listened to an account of their adventures.

" A little luck with the battles now and the war will be over," he said.

WAR IS THE PROVINCE OF FRICTION

*Everything is very simple in War, but the simplest thing is
difficult. These difficulties accumulate and produce a friction
which no man can imagine exactly who has not seen War.*

THE TROJAN HORSE

Virgil

The Grecian leaders, now disheartened by the war, and baffled
by the Fates, after a revolution of so many years, build a
horse to the size of a mountain, and interweave its ribs
with planks of fir. This they pretend to be an offering, in
order to procure a safe return; which report spread. Hither
having secretly conveyed a select band, chosen by lot, they
shut them up into the dark sides, and fill its capacious caverns
and womb with armed soldiers. In sight of Troy lies Tenedos,
an island well known by fame, and flourishing while Priam's
kingdom stood : now only a bay, and a station unfaithful for
ships. Having made this island, they conceal themselves in that
desolate shore. We imagined they were gone, and that they
had set sail for Mycenae. In consequence of this, all Troy
is released from its long distress : the gates are thrown open;
with joy we issue forth, and view the Grecian camp, the
deserted plains, and the abandoned shore. Some view with
amazement that baleful offering of the virgin Minerva, and
wonder at the stupendous bulk of the horse; and Thymoetes
first advises that it be dragged within the walls and lodged
in the tower, whether with treacherous design, or that the
destiny of Troy now would have it so. But Capys, and all
whose minds had wiser sentiments, strenuously urge either
to throw into the sea the treacherous snare and suspected
oblation of the Greeks; or by applying flames consume it to
ashes; or to lay open and ransack the recesses of the hollow
womb. The fickle populace is split into opposite inclinations.
Upon this, Laocoön, accompanied with numerous troop, first
before all, with ardour hastens down from the top of the

From: *the Aeneid.*

citadel; and while yet a great way off cries out, "O, wretched countrymen, what desperate infatuation is this? Do you believe the enemy gone? or think you any gifts of the Greeks can be free from deceit? Is Ulysses thus known to you? Either the Greeks lie concealed within this wood, or it is an engine framed against our walls, to overlook our houses, and to come down upon our city; or some mischievous design lurks beneath it. Trojans, put no faith in this horse. Whatever it be, I dread the Greeks, even when they bring gifts." Thus said, with valiant strength he hurled his massive spear against the sides and belly of the monster, where it swelled out with its jointed timbers; the weapon stood quivering, and the womb being shaken, the hollow caverns rang, and sent forth a groan. And had not the decrees of heaven been adverse, if our minds had not been infatuated, he had prevailed on us to mutilate with the sword this dark recess of the Greeks; and thou, Troy, should still have stood, and thou, lofty tower of Priam, now remained!

In the meantime, behold, Trojan shepherds, with loud acclamations, came dragging to the king a youth, whose hands were bound behind him; who, to them a mere stranger, had voluntarily thrown himself in the way, to promote this same design, and open Troy to the Greeks; a resolute soul, and prepared for either event, whether to execute his perfidious purpose, or submit to inevitable death. The Trojan youth pour tumultuously around from every quarter, from eagerness to see him, and they vie with one another in insulting the captive. Now learn the treachery of the Greeks, and from one crime take a specimen of the whole nation. For as he stood among the gazing crowds perplexed, defenceless, and threw his eyes around the Trojan bans, "Ah!" says he, "what land, what seas can now receive me? or to what further extremity can I, a forlorn wretch, be reduced, for whom there is no shelter anywhere among the Greeks? and to complete my misery the Trojans too, incensed against me, sue for satisfaction with my blood." By which mournful accents our affections at once were moved towards him, and all our resentment suppressed.

At these tears we grant him his life, and pity him from our hearts. Priam himself first gives orders that the manacles and strait bonds be loosened from the man, then thus addresses him in the language of a friend: "Whoever you are, now henceforth forget the Greeks you have lost; ours you shall be: and give me an ingenuous reply to these questions: To what purpose raised they this stupendous bulk of a horse?

Who was the contriver? or what do they intend? what was the religious motive? or what warlike engine is it?" he said. The other, practised in fraud and Grecian artifice, lifted up to heaven his hands, loosed from the bonds: " Troy can never be razed by the Grecian sword, unless they repent the omens at Argos, and carry back the goddess whom they had conveyed in their curved ships. And now, that they have sailed for their native Mycenae with the wind, they are providing themselves with arms; and, they will come upon you unexpected." For he declared that " if your hands should violate this offering sacred to Minerva, then signal ruin awaited Priam's empire and the Trojans. But, if by your hands it mounted into the city, that Asia, without further provocation given, would advance with a formidable war to the very walls, and our posterity be doomed to the same fate." By such treachery and artifice of perjured Sinon, the story was believed: and we, whom neither Diomede, nor Achilles, nor a siege of ten years, nor a thousand ships, had subdued, were ensnared by guile and constrained tears.

Meanwhile they urge with general voice to convey the statue to its proper seat, and implore the favour of the goddess. We make a breach in the walls, and lay open the bulwarks of the city. All keenly ply the work; and under the feet apply smooth-rolling wheels; stretch hempen ropes from the neck. The fatal machine passes over our walls, pregnant with arms. It advances, and with menacing aspect slides into the heart of the city. O country, O Ilium, the habitation of gods, and ye walls of Troy by war renowned! Four times it stopped in the very threshold of the gate, and four times the arms resounded in its womb: yet we, heedless, and blind with frantic zeal, urge on, and plant the baneful monster in the sacred citadel. Unhappy we, to whom that day was to be the last, adorn the temples of the gods throughout the city with festive boughs. Meanwhile, the heavens change, and night advances rapidly from the ocean, wrapping in her extended shade both earth and heaven, and the wiles of the Myrmidons. The Trojans, dispersed about the walls, were hushed: deep sleep fast binds them weary in his embraces. And now the Grecian host, in their equipped vessels, set out for Tenedos, making towards the well-known shore, by the friendly silence of the quiet moonshine, as soon as the royal galley stern had exhibited the signal fire; and Sinon, preserved by the will of the adverse gods, in a stolen hour unlocks the wooden prison to the Greeks shut up in its tomb: the horse, from his expanded caverns, pours them forth to the open air. They assault the city buried in sleep, and wine. The sentinels are beaten down; and with opened gates they receive all their friends, and join the conquering bands.

Meanwhile the city is filled with mingled scenes of woe; and though my father's house stood retired and enclosed with trees, louder and louder the sounds rise on the ear, and the horrid din of arms assails. I start from sleep and, by hasty steps, gain the highest battlement of the palace, and stand with erect ears: as when a flame is driven by the furious south winds on standing corn; or as a torrent impetuously bursting in a mountain-flood desolates the fields, desolates the rich crops of corn and the labours of the ox.

Then, indeed, the truth is confirmed and the treachery of the Greeks disclosed. Now Deiphosus' spacious house tumbles down, overpowered by the conflagration; now, next to him, Ucalegon blazes: the straits of Sigaeum shine far and wide with the flames. The shouts of men and clangour of trumpets arise. My arms I snatch in mad haste: nor is there in arms enough of reason: but all my soul burns to collect a troop for the war and rush into the citadel with my fellows: fury and rage hurry on my mind, and it occurs to me how glorious it is to die in arms.

The towering horse, planted in the midst of our streets, pours forth armed troops; and Sinon victorious, with insolent triumph scatters the flames. Others are pressing at our wide-opened gates, as many thousands as ever came from populous Mycenae: others with arms have blocked up the lanes to oppose our passage; the edged sword, with glittering point, stands unsheathed, ready for dealing death: hardly the foremost wardens of the gates make an effort to fight and resist in the blind encounter. By the impulse of the gods, I hurry away into flames and arms, whither the grim Fury, whither the din and shrieks that rend the skies, urge me on. Ripheus and Iphitus, mighty in arms, join me; Hypanis and Dymas come up with us by the light of the moon, and closely adhere to my side. Whom, close united, soon as I saw resolute to engage, to animate them the more I thus begin: "Youths, souls magnanimous in vain! If it is your determined purpose to follow me in this last attempt, you see what is the situation of our affairs. All the gods, by whom this empire stood, have deserted their shrines and altars to the enemy: you come to the relief of the city in flames: let us meet death, and rush into the thickest of our armed foes. The only safety for the vanquished is to throw away all hopes of safety." Thus the courage of each youth is kindled into fury. Then, like ravenous wolves in a gloomy fog, whom the fell rage of hunger hath driven forth, blind to danger, and whose whelps left behind long for their return with thirsting jaws; through arms, through enemies, we march up to imminent death, and advance through the middle of the city: sable Night hovers around us with her hollow shade.

Who can describe in words the havoc, who the death of that night? or who can furnish tears equal to the disaster? Our ancient city, having borne sway for many years, falls to the ground: great numbers of sluggish carcasses are strewn up and down, both in the streets, in the houses, and the sacred thresholds of the gods. Nor do the Trojans alone pay the penalty with their blood: the vanquished too at times resume courage in their hearts, and the victorious Grecians fall: everywhere is cruel sorrow, everywhere terror and death in a thousand shapes.

We march on, mingling with the Greeks, but not with heaven on our side; and in many a skirmish we engage during the dark night: many of the Greeks we send down to Hades. Some fly to the ships, and hasten to the trusty shore; some through dishonest fear, scale once more the bulky horse, and lurk within the well-known womb.

Ye ashes of Troy, ye expiring flames of my country! witness, that in your fall I shunned neither darts nor any deadly chances of the Greeks. Thence we are forced away, forthwith to Priam's palace called by the outcries. Here, indeed, we beheld a dreadful fight, as though this had been the only seat of the war, as though none had been dying in all the city besides; with such ungoverned fury we see Mars raging and the Greeks rushing forward to the palace, and the gates besieged by an advancing testudo. Scaling ladders are fixed against the walls, and by their steps they mount to the very door-posts, and protecting themselves by their left arms, oppose their bucklers to the darts, while with their right hands they grasp the battlements. On the other hand, the Trojans tear down the turrets and roofs of their houses; with these weapons, since they see the extremity, they seek to defend themselves now in their last death-struggle, and tumble down the gilded rafters; others with drawn swords beset the gates below; these they guard in a firm, compact body. I mount up to the roof of the highest battlement, whence the distressed Trojans were hurling unavailing darts. With our swords assailing all around a turret, situated on a precipice, and shooting up its towering top to the stars, (whence we were wont to survey all Troy, the fleet of Greece, and all the

Grecian camp,) where the topmost story made the joints more apt to give way, we tear it from its deep foundation, and push it on our foes. Suddenly tumbling down, it brings thundering desolation with it, and falls with wide havoc on the Grecian troops. But others succeed: meanwhile, neither stones, nor any sort of missile weapons, cease to fly. Just before the vestibule, and at the outer gate, Pyrrhus exults, glittering in arms and gleamy brass. At the same time, all the youth from Scyros advance to the wall, and toss brands to the roof. Pyrrhus himself in the front, snatching up a battleaxe, beats through the stubborn gates, and labours to tear the brazen posts from the hinges; and now, having hewn away the bars, he dug through the firm boards, and made a large, wide-mouthed breach. The palace within is exposed to view, and the long galleries are discovered: the sacred recesses of Priam and the ancient kings are exposed to view; and they see armed men standing at the gate.

As for the inner palace, it is filled with mingled groans and doleful uproar, and the hollow rooms all throughout howl with female yells: their shrieks strike the golden stars. Then the trembling matrons roam through the spacious halls, and in embraces hug the door-posts, and cling to them with their lips. Pyrrhus presses on with all his father's violence: nor bolts, nor guards themselves, are able to sustain. The gate, by repeated battering blow, gives way, and the door-posts, torn from their hinges, tumble to the ground. The Greeks make their way by force, burst a passage, and, being admitted, butcher the first they meet, and fill the places all about with their troops. Those fifty bedchambers, those doors, that proudly shone with barbaric gold and spoils, were levelled to the ground: where the flames relent, the Greeks take their place.

Perhaps, too, you are curious to hear what was Priam's fate. As soon as he beheld the catastrophe of the taken city, and his palace gates broken down, and the enemy planted in the middle of his private apartments, the aged monarch, with unavailing aim, buckles on his shoulders (trembling with years) arms long disused, girds himself with his useless sword, and rushes into the thickest of the foes, resolute on death. And lo! Polites, one of Priam's sons, who had escaped from the sword of Pyrrhus, through darts, through foes, flies along the long galleries, and wounded traverses the waste halls. Pyrrhus, all afire, pursues him with the hostile weapon, is just grasping him with his hand, and presses on him with the spear. Soon as he at length got into the sight and presence of his parents, he dropped down, and poured out his life with a stream of blood. Upon this, Priam, though now held in the very midst of death, yet did not forbear, nor spared his tongue and passion; and, without any force, threw a feeble dart: which was instantly repelled by the hoarse brass, and hung on the highest boss of the buckler without any execution. Pyrrhus made answer and dragged him to the very altar, trembling and sliding in the streaming gore of his son: and with his left hand grasped his twisted hair, and with his right unsheathed his glittering sword, and plunged it into his side up to the hilt. Such was the end of Priam's fate: this was the final doom allotted to him, having before his eyes Troy consumed, and its towers laid in ruins; once the proud monarch over so many nations and countries of Asia: now his mighty trunk lies extended on the shore, the head torn from the shoulders, and a nameless corpse.

THE RETREAT FROM CAPORETTO

Ernest Hemingway

At noon we were stuck in a muddy road about, as nearly as we could figure, ten kilometres from Udine. The rain had stopped during the forenoon and three times we had heard planes coming, seen them pass overheard, watched them go far to the left and heard them bombing on the main highroad. We had worked through a network of secondary roads and had taken many roads that were blind, but had always, by backing up and finding another road, gotten closer to Udine. Now, Aymo's car, in backing so that we might get out of a blind road, had gotten into the soft earth at the side and the wheels, spinning, had dug deeper and deeper until the car rested on its differential. The thing to do now was to dig out in front of the wheels, put in brush so that the chains could grip, and then push until the car was on the road. We were all down on the road around the car. The two sergeants looked at the car and examined the wheels. Then they started off down the road without a word. I went after them.

" Come on," I said. " Cut some brush."

" We have to go," one said.

" Get busy," I said, " and cut brush."

" We have to go," one said. The other said nothing. They were in a hurry to start. They would not look at me.

" I order you to come back to the car and cut brush," I said. The one sergeant turned. " We have to go on. In a little while you will be cut off. You can't order us. You're not our officer."

" I order you to cut brush," I said. They turned and started down the road.

" Halt," I said. They kept on down the muddy road, the hedge on either side. " I order you to halt," I called. They went a little faster. I opened up my holster, took the pistol, aimed at the one who had talked the most, and fired. I missed and they both started to run. I shot three times and dropped one. The other went through the hedge and was out of sight. I fired at him through the hedge as he ran across the field. The pistol clicked empty and I put in another clip. I saw it was too far to shoot at the second sergeant. He was far across the field, running, his head held low. I commenced to reload the empty clip. Bonello came up.

" Let me go finish him," he said. I handed him the pistol and he walked down to where the sergeant of engineers lay face down across the road. Bonello leaned over, put the pistol against the man's head and pulled the trigger. The pistol did not fire.

" You have to cock it," I said. He cocked it and fired twice. He took hold of the sergeant's legs and pulled him to the side of the road so he lay beside the hedge. He came back and handed me the pistol.

" The son of a bitch," he said. He looked toward the sergeant. " You see me shoot him, Tenente?"

" We've got to get the brush quickly," I said. " Did I hit the other one at all?"

" I don't think so," Aymo said. " He was too far away to hit with a pistol."

" The dirty scum," Piani said. We were all cutting twigs and branches. Everything had been taken out of the car. Bonello was digging out in front of the wheels. When we were ready Aymo started the car and put it into gear. The wheels spun round throwing brush and mud. Bonello and I pushed until we could feel our joints crack. The car would not move.

" Rock her back and forth, Barto," I said.

He drove the engine in reverse, then forward. The wheels only dug in deeper. Then the car was resting on the differential again, and the wheels spun freely in the holes they had dug. I straightened up.

" We'll try her with a rope," I said.

" I don't think it's any use, Tenente. You can't get a straight pull."

" We have to try it," I said. " She won't come out any other way."

Piani's and Bonello's cars could only move straight ahead down the narrow road. We roped both cars together and pulled. The wheels only pulled sideways against the ruts.

" It's no good," I shouted. " Stop it."

Piani and Bonello got down from their cars and came back. Aymo got down. The girls were up the road about forty yards sitting on a stone wall.

" What do you say, Tenente?" Bonello asked.

" We'll dig out and try once more with the brush," I said. I looked down the road. It was my fault. I had led them up here. The sun was almost out from behind the clouds and the body of the sergeant lay beside the hedge.

"We'll put his coat and cape under," I said. Bonello went to get them. I cut brush and Aymo and Piani dug out in front and between the wheels. I cut the cape, then ripped it in two, and laid it under the wheel in the mud, then piled brush for the wheels to catch. We were ready to start and Aymo got up on the seat and started the car. The wheels spun and we pushed and pushed. But it wasn't any use.

"It's ——ed," I said. "Is there anything you want in the car, Barto?"

Aymo climbed up with Bonello, carrying the cheese and two bottles of wine and his cape. Bonello, sitting behind the wheel, was looking through the pockets of the sergeant's coat.

"Better throw the coat away," I said. "What about Barto's virgins?"

"They can get in the back," Piani said. "I don't think we are going far."

I opened the back door of the ambulance.

"Come on," I said. "Get in." The two girls climbed in and sat in the corner. They seemed to have taken no notice of the shooting. I looked back up the road. The sergeant lay in his dirty long-sleeved underwear. I got up with Piani and we started. We were going to try to cross the field. When the road entered the field I got down and walked ahead. If we could get across, there was a road on the other side. We could not get across. It was too soft and muddy for the cars. When they were finally and completely stalled, the wheels dug in to the hubs, we left them in the field and started on foot for Udine.

When we came to the road which led back toward the main highway I pointed down it to the two girls.

"Go down there," I said. "You'll meet people." They looked at me. I took out my pocket-book and gave them each a ten-lira note. "Go down there," I said, pointing. "Friends! Family!"

They did not understand but they held the money tightly and started down the road. They looked back as though they were afraid I might take the money back. I watched them go down the road, their shawls close around them, looking back apprehensively at us. The three drivers were laughing.

"How much will you give me to go in that direction, Tenente?" Bonello asked.

"They're better off in a bunch of people than alone if they catch them," I said.

"Give me two hundred lire and I'll walk straight back toward Austria," Bonello said.

"They'd take it away from you," Piani said.

"Maybe the war will be over," Aymo said. We were going up the road as fast as we could. The sun was trying to come through. Beside the road were mulberry trees. Through the trees I could see our two big moving-vans of cars stuck in the field. Piani looked back too.

"They'll have to build a road to get them out," he said.

"I wish to Christ we had bicycles," Bonello said.

"Do they ride bicycles in America?" Aymo asked.

"They used to."

"Here it is a great thing," Aymo said. "A bicycle is a splendid thing."

"I wish to Christ we had bicycles," Bonello said. "I'm no walker."

"Is that firing?" I asked. I thought I could hear firing a long way away.

"I don't know," Aymo said. He listened.

"I think so," I said.

"The first thing we will see will be the cavalry," Piani said.

"I don't think they've got any cavalry."

"I hope to Christ not," Bonello said. "I don't want to be stuck on a lance by any ——— cavalry."

"You certainly shot that sergeant, Tenente," Piani said. We were walking fast.

"I killed him," Bonello said. "I never killed anybody in this war, and all my life I've wanted to kill a sergeant."

"You killed him on the sit all right," Piani said. "He wasn't flying very fast when you killed him."

"Never mind. That's one thing I can always remember. I killed that ——— of a sergeant."

"What will you say in confession?" Aymo asked.

"I'll say, 'Bless me, father, I killed a sergeant.'" They all laughed.

"He's an anarchist," Piani said. "He doesn't go to church."

"Piani's an anarchist too," Bonello said.

"Are you really anarchists?" I asked.

"No, Tenente. We're socialists. We come from Imola."

"Haven't you ever been there?"

"No."

"By Christ it's a fine place, Tenente. You come there after the war and we'll show you something."

"Are you all socialists?"

"Everybody."

"Is it a fine town?"

"Wonderful. You never saw a town like that."

"How did you get to be socialists?"

"We're all socialists. Everybody is a socialist. We've always been socialists."

"You come, Tenente. We'll make you a socialist too."

Ahead the road turned off to the left and there was a little hill and, beyond a stone wall, an apple orchard. As the road went uphill they ceased talking. We walked along together all going fast against time.

We were on a road that led to a river. There was a long line of abandoned trucks and carts on the road leading to the bridge. No one was in sight. The river was high and the bridge had been blown up in the centre; the stone arch was fallen into the river and the brown water was going over it. We went on up the bank looking for a place to cross. Up ahead I knew there was a railway bridge and I thought we might be able to get across there. The path was wet and muddy. We did not see any troops; only abandoned trucks and stores. Along the river bank there was nothing and no one but the wet brush and muddy ground. We went up to the bank and finally we saw the railway bridge.

"What a beautiful bridge," Aymo said. It was a long plain iron bridge across what was usually a dry river-bed.

"We better hurry and get across before they blow it up," I said.

"There's nobody to blow it up," Piani said. "They're all gone."

"It's probably mined," Bonello said. "You cross first, Tenente."

"Listen to the anarchist," Aymo said. "Make him go first."

"I'll go," I said. "It won't be mined to blow up with one man."

"You see," Piani said. "That is brains. Why haven't you brains, anarchist?"

"If I had brains I wouldn't be here," Bonello said.

"That's pretty good, Tenente," Aymo said.

"That's pretty good," I said. We were close to the bridge now. The sky had clouded over again and it was raining a little. The bridge looked long and solid. We climbed up the embankment.

"Come one at a time," I said and started across the bridge. I watched the ties and the rails for any trip-wires or signs of explosive but I saw nothing. Down below the gaps in the ties the river ran muddy and fast. Ahead across the wet countryside I could see Udine in the rain. Across the bridge I looked back. Just up the river was another bridge. As I watched, a yellow mud-coloured motor car crossed it. The sides of the bridge were high and the body of the car, once on, was out of sight. But I saw the heads of the driver, the man on the seat with him, and the two men on the rear seat. They all wore German helmets. Then the car was over the bridge and out of sight behind the trees and the abandoned vehicles on the road. I waved to Aymo who was crossing and to the others to come on. I climbed down and crouched beside the railway embankment. Aymo came down with me.

" Did you see the car?" I asked.

" No. We were watching you."

" A German staff car crossed on the upper bridge."

" A staff car?"

" Yes."

" Holy Mary."

The others came and we all crouched in the mud behind the embankment, looking across the rails at the bridge, the line of trees, the ditch and the road.

" Do you think we're cut off then, Tenente?"

" I don't know. All I know is a German staff car went along that road."

" You don't feel funny, Tenente? You haven't got strange feelings in the head?"

" Don't be funny, Bonello."

" What about a drink?" Piani asked. " If we're cut off we might as well have a drink." He unhooked his canteen and uncorked it.

" Look! Look!" Aymo said and pointed toward the road. Along the top of the stone bridge we could see German helmets moving. They were bent forward and moved smoothly, almost supernaturally, along. As they came off the bridge we saw them. They were bicycle troops. I saw the faces of the first two. They were ruddy and healthy-looking. Their helmets came low down over their foreheads and the side of their faces. Their carbines were clipped to the frame of the bicycles. Stick bombs hung handle down from their belts. Their helmets and their grey uniforms were wet and they rode easily, looking ahead and to both sides. There were two—then four in line, then two, then almost a dozen; then another dozen— then one alone. They did not talk but we could not have heard them because of the noise from the river. They were gone out of sight up the road.

"Holy Mary," Aymo said.

"They were Germans," Piani said. "Those weren't Austrians."

"Why isn't there somebody here to stop them?" I said. "Why haven't they blown the bridge up? Why aren't there machine-guns along this embankment?"

"You tell us, Tenente," Bonello said.

I was very angry.

"The whole bloody thing is crazy. Down below they blow up a little bridge. Here they leave a bridge on the main road. Where is everybody? Don't they try and stop them at all?"

"You tell us, Tenente," Bonello said. I shut up. It was none of my business; all I had to do was to get to Pordenone with three ambulances. I had failed at that. All I had to do now was get to Pordenone. I probably could not even get to Udine. The hell I couldn't. The thing to do was to be calm and not get shot or captured.

"Didn't you have a canteen open?" I asked Piani. He handed it to me. I took a long drink. "We might as well start," I said. "There's no hurry though. Do you want to eat something?"

"This is no place to stay," Bonello said.

"All right. We'll start."

"Should we keep on this side—out of sight?"

"We'll be better off on top. They may come along this bridge too. We don't want them on top of us before we see them."

We walked along the railroad track. On both sides of us stretched the wet plain. Ahead across the plain was the hill of Udine. The roofs fell away from the castle on the hill. We could see the campanile and the clock-tower. There were many mulberry trees in the fields. Ahead I saw a place where the rails were torn up. The ties had been dug out too and thrown down the embankment.

"Down! Down!" Aymo said. We dropped down beside the embankment. There was another group of bicycles passing along the road. I looked over the edge and saw them go on.

"They saw us but they went on," Aymo said.

"We'll get killed up there, Tenente," Bonello said.

"They don't want us," I said. "They're after something else. We're in more danger if they should come on us suddenly."

"I'd rather walk here out of sight," Bonello said.

"All right. We'll walk along the tracks."

"Do you think we can get through?" Aymo asked.

"Sure. There aren't very many of them yet. We'll go through in the dark."

"What was that staff car doing?"

"Christ knows," I said. We kept on up the tracks. Bonello tired of walking in the mud of the embankment and came up with the rest of us. The railway moved south away from the highway now and we could see what passed along the road. A short bridge over a canal was blown up but we climbed across on what was left of the span. We heard firing ahead of us.

We came up on the railway beyond the canal. It went on straight toward the town across the low fields. We could see the line of the other railway ahead of us. To the north was the main road where we had seen the cyclists; to the south there was a small branch-road across the fields with thick trees on each side. I thought we had better cut to the south and work around the town that way and across country toward Campoformio and the main road to the Tagliamento. We could avoid the main line of the retreat by keeping to the secondary roads beyond Udine. I knew there were plenty of side-roads across the plain. I started down the embankment.

"Come on," I said. We would make for the side-road and work to the south of the town. We all started down the embankment. A shot was fired at us from the side-road. The bullet went into the mud of the embankment.

"Go on back," I shouted. I started up the embankment, slipping in the mud. The drivers were ahead of me. I went up the embankment as fast as I could go. Two more shots came from the thick brush and Aymo, as he was crossing the tracks, lurched, tripped and fell face down. We pulled him down on the other side and turned him over. "His head ought to be uphill," I said. Piani moved him around. He lay in the mud on the side of the embankment, his feet pointing downhill, breathing blood irregularly. The three of us squatted over him in the rain. He was hit low in the back of the neck and the bullet had ranged upward and come out under the right eye. He died while I was stopping up the two holes. Piani laid his head down, wiped at his face, with a piece of the emergency dressing, then let it alone.

"The ——," he said.

"They weren't Germans," I said. "There can't be any Germans over there."

"Italians," Piani said, using the word as an epithet, "Italiani!" Bonello said nothing. He was sitting beside Aymo, not looking at him. Piani picked up Aymo's cap where it had rolled down the embankment and put it over his face. He took out his canteen.

"Do you want a drink?" Piani handed Bonello the canteen.

"No," Bonello said. He turned to me. "That might have happened to us any time on the railway tracks."

"No," I said. "It was because we started across the field."

Bonello shook his head. "Aymo's dead," he said. "Who's dead next, Tenente? Where do we go now?"

"Those were Italians that shot," I said. "They weren't Germans."

"I suppose if they were Germans they'd have killed all of us," Bonello said.

"We are in more danger from Italians than Germans," I said. "The rear guard are afraid of everything. The Germans know what they're after."

"You reason it out, Tenente," Bonello said.

"Where do we go now?" Piani asked.

"We better lie up some place till it's dark. If we could get south we'd be all right."

"They'd have to shoot us all to prove they were right the first time," Bonello said. "I'm not going to try them."

"We'll find a place to lie up as near to Udine as we can get and then go through when it's dark."

"Let's go then," Bonello said. We went down the north side of the embankment. I looked back. Aymo lay in the mud with the angle of the embankment. He was quite small and his arms were by his side, his puttee-wrapped legs and muddy boots together, his cap over his face. He looked very dead. It was raining. I had liked him as well as any one I ever knew. I had his papers in my pocket and would write to his family. Ahead across the fields was a farmhouse. There were trees around it and the farm buildings were built against the house. There was a balcony along the second floor held up by columns.

"We better keep a little way apart," I said. "I'll go ahead." I started toward the farmhouse. There was a path across the field.

Crossing the field, I did not know but that some one would fire on us from the trees near the farmhouse or from the farmhouse itself. I walked toward it, seeing it very clearly. The balcony of the second floor merged into the barn and there was hay coming out between the columns. The courtyard was of stone blocks and all the trees were dripping with the rain. There was a big empty two-wheeled cart, the shafts tipped high up in the rain. I came to the courtyard, crossed it, and stood under the shelter of the balcony. The door of the house was open and I went in. Bonello and Piani came in after me. It was dark inside. I went back to the kitchen. There were ashes of a fire on the big open hearth. The pots hung over the ashes, but they were empty. I looked around but I could not find anything to eat.

"We ought to lie up in the barn," I said. "Do you think you could find anything to eat, Piani, and bring it up there?"

"I'll look," Piani said.

"I'll look too," Bonello said.

"All right," I said. "I'll go up and look at the barn." I found a stone stairway that went up from the stable underneath. The stable smelt dry and pleasant in the rain. The cattle were all gone, probably driven off when they left. The barn was half full of hay. There were two windows in the roof, one was blocked with boards, the other was a narrow dormer window on the north side. There was a chute so that hay might be pitched down to the cattle. Beams crossed the opening down into the main floor where the hay-carts drove in when the hay was hauled in to be pitched up. I heard the rain on the roof and smelled the hay and, when I went down, the clean smell of dried dung in the stable. We could pry a board loose and see out of the south window down into the courtyard. The other window looked out on the field toward the north. We could get out of either window onto the roof and down, or go down the hay chute if the stairs were impractical. It was a big barn and we could hide in the hay if we heard any one. It seemed like a good place. I was sure we could have gotten through to the south if they had not fired on us. It was impossible that there were Germans there. They were coming from the north and down the road from Cividale. They could not have come through from the south. The Italians were even more dangerous. They were frightened and firing on anything they saw. Last night on the retreat we had heard that there had been many Germans in Italian uniforms mixing with the retreat in the north. I did not believe it. That was one of the things you always heard in the war. It was one of the things the enemy always did to you. You did not know any one who went over in German uniform to confuse them. Maybe they did but it sounded difficult. I did not believe the Germans did it. I did not believe they had to. There was no need to confuse our retreat. The size of the army and the fewness of the roads did that. Nobody gave any orders, let alone Germans. Still, they would shoot us for Germans. They shot Aymo. The hay smelled good and lying in a barn in the hay took away all the years in between. We had lain in hay and talked and shot sparrows with an air-rifle when they perched in the triangle cut high up in the wall of the barn. The barn was gone now and one year they had cut the hemlock woods and there were only stumps, dried tree-tops, branches and fireweed where the woods had been. You could not go back. If you did not go forward what happened? You never got back to Milan. And if you got back to Milan what happened? I listened to the firing to the north toward Udine. I could hear machine-gun firing. There was no shelling. That was something. They must have gotten some troops along the road. I looked down in the half-light of the hay-barn and saw Piani standing on the hauling floor. He had a long sausage, a jar of something and two bottles of wine under his arm.

"Come up," I said. "There is the ladder." Then I realised that I should help him with the things and went down. I was vague in the head from lying in the hay. I had been nearly asleep.

"Where's Bonello?" I asked.

"I'll tell you," Piani said. We went up the ladder. Up on the hay we set the things down. Piani took out his knife with the corkscrew and drew the cork on a wine bottle.

"They have sealing-wax on it," he said: "It must be good." He smiled.

"Where's Bonello?" I asked.

Piani looked at me.

"He went away, Tenente," he said. "He wanted to be a prisoner."

I did not say anything.

"He was afraid we would get killed."

I held the bottle of wine and did not say anything.

"You see we don't believe in the war anyway, Tenente."

"Why didn't you go?" I asked.

"I did not want to leave you."

"Where did he go?"

"I don't know, Tenente. He went away."

"All right," I said. "Will you cut the sausage?"

Piani looked at me in the half-light.

"I cut it while we were talking," he said. We sat in the hay and ate the sausage and drank the wine. It must have been wine they had saved for a wedding. It was so old that it was losing its colour.

"You look out of this window, Luigi," I said. "I'll go look out the other window."

We had each been drinking out of one of the bottles and I took my bottle with me and went over and lay flat on the hay and looked out the narrow window at the wet country. I do not know what I expected to see but I did not see anything except the fields and the bare mulberry trees and the rain falling. I drank the wine and it did not make me feel good. They had kept it too long and it had gone to pieces and lost its quality and colour. I watched it get dark outside; the darkness came very quickly. It would be a black night with the rain. When it was dark there was no use watching any more, so I went over to Piani. He was lying asleep and I did not wake him but sat down beside him for a while. He was a big man and he slept heavily. After a while I woke him and we started.

That was a very strange night. I do not know what I had expected, death perhaps and shooting in the dark and running, but nothing happened. We waited, lying flat beyond the ditch along the main road while a German battalion passed, then when they were gone we crossed the road and went on to the north. We were very close to Germans twice in the rain but they did not see us. We got past the town to the north without seeing any Italians, then after a while came on the main channels of the retreat and walked all night toward the Tagliamento. I had not realised how gigantic the retreat was. The whole country was moving, as well as the army. We walked all night, making better time than the vehicles. My leg ached and I was tired but we made good time. It seemed so silly for Bonello to have decided to be taken prisoner. There was no danger. We had walked through two armies without incident. If Aymo had not been killed there would never have seemed to be any danger. No one had bothered us when we were in plain sight along the railway. The killing came suddenly and unreasonably. I wondered where Bonello was.

"How do you feel, Tenente?" Piani asked. We were going along the side of a road crowded with vehicles and troops.

"Fine."

"I'm tired of this walking."

"Well, all we have to do is walk now. We don't have to worry."

"Bonello was a fool."

"He was a fool all right."

"What will you do about him, Tenente?"

"I don't know."

"Can't you just put him down as taken prisoner?"

"I don't know."

"You see if the war went on they would make bad trouble for his family."

"The war won't go on," a soldier said. "We're going home. The war is over."

"Everybody's going home."

"We're all going home."

"Come on, Tenente," Piani said. He wanted to get past them.

"Tenente? Who's a Tenente? *A basso gli ufficiali!* Down with the officers!"

Piani took me by the arm. "I better call you by your name," he said. "They might try and make trouble. They've shot some officers." We worked up past them.

"I won't make a report that will make trouble for his family." I went on with our conversation.

"If the war is over it makes no difference," Piani said. "But I don't believe it's over. It's too good that it should be over."

"We'll know pretty soon," I said.

"I don't believe it's over. They all think it's over but I don't believe it."

"*Viva la Pace!*" a soldier shouted out. "We're going home!"

"It would be fine if we all went home," Piani said. "Wouldn't you like to go home?"

"Yes."

"We'll never go. I don't think it's over."

"*Andiamo a casa!*" a soldier shouted.

"They throw away their rifles," Piani said. "They take them off and drop them down while they're marching. Then they shout."

"They ought to keep their rifles."

"They think if they throw away their rifles they can't make them fight."

In the dark and the rain, making our way along the side of the road I could see that many of the troops still had their rifles. They stuck up above the capes.

"What brigade are you?" an officer called out.

"*Brigata di Pace,*" someone shouted. "Peace Brigade!" The officer said nothing.

"What does he say? What does the officer say?"

"Down with the officer. *Viva la Pace!*"

"Come on," Piani said. We passed two British ambulances, abandoned in the block of vehicles.

"They're from Gorizia," Piani said. "I know the cars."

"They got farther than we did."

"They started earlier."

"I wonder where the drivers are?"

"Up ahead probably."

"The Germans have stopped outside Udine," I said. "These people will all get across the river."

"Yes," Piani said. "That's why I think the war will go on."

"The Germans could come on," I said. "I wonder why they don't come on."

"I don't know. I don't know anything about this kind of war."

"They have to wait for their transport, I suppose."

"I don't know," Piani said. Alone he was much gentler. When he was with the others he was a very rough talker.

"Are you married, Luigi?"

"You know I am married."

"Is that why you did not want to be a prisoner?"

"That is one reason. Are you married, Tenente?"

"No."

"Neither is Bonello."

"You can't tell anything by a man's being married. But I should think a married man would want to get back to his wife," I said. I would be glad to talk about wives.

"Yes."

"How are your feet?"

"They're sore enough."

Before daylight we reached the bank of the Tagliamento and followed down along the flooded river to the bridge where all the traffic was crossing.

"They ought to be able to hold at this river," Piani said. In the dark the flood looked high. The water swirled and it was wide. The wooden bridge was nearly three-quarters of a mile across, and the river, that usually ran in narrow channels in the wide stony bed far below the bridge, was close under the wooden planking. We went along the bank and then worked our way into the crowd that were crossing the bridge. Crossing slowly in the rain a few feet above the flood, pressed tight in the crowd, the box of an artillery caisson just ahead, I looked over the side and watched the river. Now that we could not go our own pace I felt very tired. There was no exhilaration in crossing the bridge. I wondered what it would be like if a plane bombed it in the daytime.

"Piani," I said.

"Here I am, Tenente." He was a little ahead in the jam. No one was talking. They were all trying to get across as soon as they could: thinking only of that. We were almost across. At the far end of the bridge there were officers and carabinieri standing on both sides flashing lights. I saw them silhouetted against the sky-line. As we came close to them I saw one of the officers point to a man in the column. A carabiniere went in after him and came out holding the man by the arm. He took him away from the road. We came almost opposite them. The officers were scrutinising every one in the column, sometimes speaking to each other, going forward to flash a light in some one's face. They took some one else out just before we came opposite. I saw the man. He was a lieutenant-colonel. I saw the stars in the box on his sleeve as they flashed a light on him. His hair was grey and he was short and fat. The carabiniere pulled him in behind the line of officers. As we came opposite I saw one or two of them look at me. Then one pointed at me and spoke to a carabiniere. I saw the carabiniere start for me, come through the edge of the column toward me, then felt him take me by the collar.

"What's the matter with you?" I said and hit him in the face. I saw his face under the hat, upturned moustaches and blood coming down his cheek. Another one dove in toward us.

"What's the matter with you?" I said. He did not answer. He was watching a chance to grab me. I put my arm behind me to loosen my pistol.

"Don't you know you can't touch an officer?"

The other one grabbed me from behind and pulled my arm up so that it twisted in the socket. I turned with him and the other one grabbed me around the neck. I kicked his shins and got my left knee into his groin.

"Shoot him if he resists," I heard someone say.

"What's the meaning of this?" I tried to shout but my voice was not very loud. They had me at the side of the road now.

"Shoot him if he resists," an officer said. "Take him over back."

"Who are you?"

"You'll find out."

258

"Who are you?"

"Battle police," another officer said.

"Why don't you ask me to step over instead of having one of these airplanes grab me?"

They did not answer. They did not have to answer. They were battle police.

"Take him back there with the others," the first officer said. "You see. He speaks Italian with an accent."

"So do you, you——," I said.

"Take him back with the others," the first officer said. They took me down behind the line of officers below the road toward a group of people in a field by the river bank. As we walked toward them shots were fired. I saw flashes of the rifles and heard the reports. We came up to the group. There were four officers standing together, with a man in front of them with a carabiniere on each side of him. A group of men were standing guarded by carabinieri. Four other carabinieri stood near the questioning officers, leaning on their carbines. They were wide-hatted carabinieri. The two who had me shoved me in with the group waiting to be questioned. I looked at the man the officers were questioning. He was the fat grey-haired little lieutenant-colonel they had taken out of the column. The questioners had all the efficiency, coldness and command of themselves of Italians who are firing and are not being fired on.

"Your brigade?"

He told them.

"Why are you not with your regiment?"

He told them.

"Do you not know that an officer should be with his troops?"

He did.

That was all. Another officer spoke.

"It is you and such as you that have let the barbarians onto the sacred soil of the fatherland."

"I beg your pardon," said the lieutenant-colonel.

"It is because of treachery such as yours that we have lost the fruits of victory."

"Have you ever been in a retreat?" the lieutenant-colonel asked.

"Italy should never retreat."

We stood there in the rain and listened to this. We were facing the officers and the prisoner stood in front and a little to one side of us.

"If you are going to shoot me," the lieutenant-colonel

259

said, " please shoot me at once without further questioning. The questioning is stupid." He made the sign of the cross. The officers spoke together. One wrote something on a pad of paper.

" Abandoned his troops, ordered to be shot," he said.

Two carabinieri took the lieutenant-colonel to the river bank. He walked in the rain, an old man with his hat off, a carabiniere on either side. I did not watch them shoot him but I heard the shots. They were questioning some one else. This officer too was separated from his troops. He was not allowed to make an explanation. He cried when they read the sentence from the pad of paper, and they were questioning another when they shot him. They made a point of being intent on questioning the next man while the man who had been questioned before was being shot. In this way there was obviously nothing they could do about it. I did not know whether I should wait to be questioned or make a break now. I was obviously a German in Italian uniform. I saw how their minds worked; if they had minds and if they worked. They were all young men and they were saving their country. The second army was being re-formed beyond the Tagliamento. They were executing officers of the rank of major and above who were separated from their troops. They were also dealing summarily with German agitators in Italian uniform. They wore steel helmets. Only two of us had steel helmets. Some of the carabinieri had them. The other carabinieri wore the wide hat. Airplanes we called them. We stood in the rain and were taken out one at a time to be questioned and shot. So far they had shot every one they had questioned. The questioners had that beautiful detachment and devotion to stern justice of men dealing in death without being in any danger of it. They were questioning a full colonel of a line regiment. Three more officers had just been put in with us.

" Where was his regiment?"

I looked at the carabinieri. They were looking at the new-comers. The others were looking at the colonel. I ducked down, pushed between two men, and ran for the river, my head down. I tripped at the edge and went in with a splash. The water was very cold and I stayed under as long as I could. I could feel the current swirl me and I stayed under until I thought I could never come up. The minute I came up I took a breath and went down again. It was easy to stay under with so much clothing and my boots. When I came up the second time I saw a piece of timber ahead of me and reached it and held on with one hand. I kept my head behind it and did not even look over it. I did not want to see the bank. There were shots when I ran and shots when I came up the first time. I heard them when I was almost above water. There were no shots now. The piece of timber swung in the current and I held it with one hand. I looked at the bank. It seemed to be going by very fast. There was much wood in the stream. The water was very cold. We passed the brush of an island above the water. I held onto the timber with both hands and let it take me along. The shore was out of sight now.

WAR DEMANDS RESOLUTION, FIRMNESS AND STAUNCHNESS

Resolution is an act of courage in single instances, and if it becomes a characteristic trait, it is a habit of the mind. But here we do not mean courage in face of bodily danger but in face of responsibility; therefore to a certain extent against moral danger . . . mere intelligence is still not courage, for we often see the cleverest people devoid of resolution. The man must, therefore, first awaken the feeling of courage, and then be guided and supported by it because in momentary emergencies the man is swayed more by his feelings than his thoughts.

Firmness denotes the resistance of the will in relation to the force of a single blow. Staunchness in relation to a continuance of blows. Close as is the analogy between the two, and often as the one is used in the place of the other, still there is a notable difference between them which can not be mistaken. Inasmuch as firmness against a single powerful impression may have its root in the mere strength of a feeling, but staunchness must be supported rather by the understanding, for the greater the duration of an action the more systematic deliberation is connected with it, and from this staunchness partly derives its power.

Force of character leads us to a spurious variety of it— obstinacy.

HER PRIVATES WE

Private 19022

*By my troth, I care not; a man can die but once; we
owe God a death . . . and let it go which way it will,
he that dies this year is quit for the next.*

The darkness was increasing rapidly, as the whole sky had
clouded, and threatened thunder. There was still some desultory shelling. When the relief had taken over from them,
they set off to return to their original line as best they could.
Bourne, who was beaten to the wide, gradually dropped behind,
and in trying to keep the others in sight missed his footing
and fell into a shell-hole. By the time he had picked himself
up again the rest of the party had vanished; and, uncertain of
his direction, he stumbled on alone. He neither hurried nor
slackened his pace; he was light-headed, almost exalted, and
driven only by the desire to find an end. Somewhere,
eventually, he would sleep. He almost fell into the wrecked
trench and after a moment's hesitation turned left, caring little
where it led him. The world seemed extraordinarily empty
of men, though he knew the ground was alive with them. He
was breathing with difficulty, his mouth and throat seemed
to be cracking with dryness, and his water-bottle was empty.
Coming to a dug-out, he groped his way down, feeling for
the steps with his feet; a piece of Wilson canvas, hung across
the passage but twisted aside, rasped his cheek; and a few
steps lower his face was enveloped suddenly in the musty folds
of a blanket. The dug-out was empty. For the moment
he collapsed there, indifferent to everything. Then with shaking
hands he felt for his cigarettes, and putting one between his
lips struck a match. The light revealed a candle-end stuck
by its own grease to the oval lid of a tobacco-tin, and he lit
it; it was scarcely thicker than a shilling, but it would last
his time. He would finish his cigarette, and then move on
to find his company.

There was a kind of bank or seat excavated in the wall
of the dug-out, and he noticed first the tattered remains of a
blanket lying on it, and then, gleaming faintly in its folds
a small metal disk reflecting the light. It was the cap on

From: *Her Privates We.* Courtesy of G. P. Putnam's Sons.

the cork of a water-bottle. Sprawling sideways he reached it, the feel of the bottle told him it was full, and uncorking it he put it to his lips and took a great gulp before discovering that he was swallowing neat whiskey. The fiery spirit almost choked him for the moment, in his surprise he even spat some of it out; then recovering, he drank again, discreetly but sufficiently, and was meditating a more prolonged appreciation when he heard men groping their way down the steps. He recorked the bottle, hid it quickly under the blanket, and removed himself to what might seem an innocent distance from temptation.

Three Scotsmen came in; they were almost as spent and broken as he was, that he knew by their uneven voices; but they put up a show of indifference, and were able to tell him that some of his mob were on the left, in a dug-out about fifty yards away. They, too, had lost their way, and asked him questions in their turn; but he could not help them, and they developed among themselves an incoherent debate, on the question of what was the best thing for them to do in the circumstances. Their dialect only allowed him to follow their arguments imperfectly, but under the talk it was easy enough to see the irresolution of weary men seeking in their difficulties some reasonable pretext for doing nothing. It touched his own conscience, and throwing away the butt of his cigarette he decided to go. The candle was flickering feebly on the verge of extinction, and presently the dug-out would be in darkness again. Prudence stifled in him an impulse to tell them of the whiskey; perhaps they would find it for themselves; it was a matter which might be left for providence or chance to decide. He was moving towards the stairs, when a voice, muffled by the blanket, came from outside.

"Who are down there?"

There was no mistaking the note of authority and Bourne answered promptly. There was a pause, and then the blanket was waved aside, and an officer entered. He was Mr. Clinton, with whom Bourne had fired his course at Tregelly.

"Hullo, Bourne," he began, and then seeing the other men he turned and questioned them in his soft kindly voice. His face had the greenish pallor of crude beeswax, his eyes were red and tired, his hands were as nervous as theirs, and his voice had the same note of over-excitement, but he listened to them without a sign of impatience.

"Well, I don't want to hurry you men off," he said at last, "but your battalion will be moving out before we do. The

264

best thing you can do is to cut along to it. They're about a hundred yards down the trench. You don't want to straggle back to camp by yourselves; it doesn't look well either. So you had better get moving right away. What you really want is twelve hours solid sleep, and I am only telling you the shortest road to it."

They accepted his view of the matter quietly, they were willing enough; but, like all tired men in similar conditions, they were glad to have their action determined for them; so they thanked him and wished him good-night, if not cheerfully, at least with the air of being reasonable men, who appreciated his kindliness. Bourne made as though to follow them out, but Mr. Clinton stopped him.

"Wait a minute, Bourne, and we shall go together," he said as the last Scotsman groped his way up the steeply-pitched stairs. " It is indecent to follow a kilted Highlander too closely out of a dug-out. Besides I left something here."

He looked about him, went straight to the blanket, and took up the water-bottle. It must have seemed lighter than he expected, for he shook it a little suspiciously before uncorking it. He took a long steady drink and paused.

" I left this bottle full of whiskey," he said, "but those bloody Jocks must have smelt it. You know, Bourne, I don't go over with a skinful, as some of them do; but, by God, when I come back I want it. Here, take a pull yourself; you look as though you could do with one."

Bourne took the bottle without any hesitation; his case was much the same. One had lived instantaneously during that timeless interval, for in the shock and violence of the attack, the perilous instant, on which he stood perched so precariously, was all that the half-stunned consciousness of man could grasp; and, if he lost his grip on it, he fell back among the grotesque terrors and nightmare creatures of his own mind. Afterwards, when the strain had been finally released, in the physical exhaustion which followed, there was a collapse, in which one's emotional nature was no longer under control.

"We're in the next dug-out, those who are left of us," Mr. Clinton continued. " I am glad you came through all right, Bourne. You were in the last show, weren't you? It seems to me the old Hun has brought up a lot more stuff, and doesn't mean to shift, if he can help it. Anyway we should get a spell out of the line now. I don't believe there are more than a hundred of us left."

A quickening in his speech showed that the whiskey was beginning to play on frayed nerves: it had steadied Bourne for the time being. The flame of the candle gave one leap and went out. Mr. Clinton switched on his torch, and shoved the water-bottle into the pocket of his raincoat.

"Come on," he said, making for the steps, "you and I are two of the lucky ones, Bourne; we've come through without a scratch; and if our luck holds we'll keep moving out of one bloody misery into another, until we break, see, until we break."

Bourne felt a kind of suffocation in his throat: there was nothing weak or complaining in Mr. Clinton's voice, it was full of angry soreness. He switched off the light as he came to the Wilson canvas.

"Don't talk so bloody wet," Bourne said to him through the darkness. "You'll never break."

The officer gave no sign of having heard the sympathetic but indecorous rebuke. They moved along the battered trench silently. The sky flickered with the flash of guns, and an occasional star-shell flooded their path with light. As one fell slowly, Bourne saw a dead man in field grey popped up in a corner of a traverse; probably he had surrendered, wounded, and reached the trench only to die there. He looked indifferently at this piece of wreckage. The grey face was senseless and empty. As they turned the corner they were challenged by a sentry over the dug-out.

"Good-night, Bourne," said Mr. Clinton quietly.

"Good-night, sir," said Bourne, saluting; and he exchanged a few words with the sentry.

"Wish to Christ they'd get a move on," said the sentry, as Bourne turned to go down.

The dug-out was full of men, and all the drawn, pitiless faces turned to see who it was as he entered, and after that flicker of interest relapsed into apathy and stupour again. The air was thick with smoke and the reek of guttering candles. He saw Shem lift a hand to attract his attention, and he managed to squeeze in beside him. They didn't speak after each had asked the other if he were all right; some kind of oppression weighed on them all, they sat like men condemned to death.

"Wonder if they'll keep us up in support?" whispered Shem.

Probably that was the question they were all asking, as they sat there in their bitter resignation, with brooding enigmatic faces, hopeless, but undefeated; even the faces of boys seeming curiously old; and then it changed suddenly: there were quick hurried movements, belts were buckled, rifles taken up, and stooping, they crawled up into the air. Shem and Bourne were among the first out. They moved off at once. Shells travelled overhead; they heard one or two bump fairly close, but they saw nothing except the sides of the trench, whitish with chalk in places, and the steel helmet and lifting swaying shoulders of the man in front, or the frantic uplifted arms of shattered trees, and the sky with the clouds broken in places, through which opened the inaccessible peace of the stars. They seemed to hurry, as though the sense of escape filled them. The walls of the communication trench became gradually lower, the track sloping upward to the surface of the ground, and at last they emerged, the officer standing aside, to watch what was left of his men file out, and form up in two ranks before him. There was little light, but under the brims of the helmets one could see living eyes moving restlessly in blank faces. His face, too, was a blank from weariness, but he stood erect, an ash-stick under his arm, as the dun-coloured shadows shuffled into some sort of order. The words of command that came from him were no more than whispers, his voice was cracked and not quite under control, though there was still some harshness in it. Then they moved off in fours, away from the crest of the ridge, towards the place they called Happy Valley.

They had not far to go. As they were approaching the tents a crump dropped by the mule-lines, and that set them swaying a little, but not much. Captain Malet called them to attention a little later; and from the tents, camp-details, cooks, snobs, and a few unfit men, gathered in groups to watch them, with a sympathy genuine enough, but tactfully aloof; for there is a gulf between men just returned from action, and those who have not been in the show as unbridgeable as that between the sober and the drunk. Captain Malet halted his men by the orderly-room tent. There was even a pretence to dress ranks. Then he looked at them, and they at him for a few seconds which seemed long. They were only shadows in the darkness.

"Dismiss!"

His voice was still pitched low, but they turned almost with the precision of troops on the square, each rifle was struck smartly, the officer saluting; and then the will which bound them together dissolved, the enervated muscles relaxed, and they lurched off to their tents as silent and as dispirited as beaten men. One of the tailors took his pipe out of his mouth and spat on the ground.

"They can say what they like," he said appreciatively, "but we're a bloody fine mob."

Once during the night Bourne started up in an access of inexplicable horror, and after a moment of bewildered recollection, turned over and tried to sleep again. He remembered nothing of the nightmare which had roused him, if it were a nightmare, but gradually his awakened sense felt a vague restlessness troubling equally the other men. He noticed it first in Shem, whose body, almost touching his own, gave a quick, convulsive jump, and continued twitching for a moment, while he muttered unintelligibly, and worked his lips as though he were trying to moisten them. The obscure disquiet passed fitfully from one to another, lips parted with the sound of a bubble bursting, teeth met grinding as the jaws worked, there were little whimperings which quickened into sobs, passed into long shuddering moans, or culminated in angry, half-articulate obscenities, and then relapsed, with fretful, uneasy movements and heavy breathing, into a more profound sleep. Even though Bourne tried to persuade himself that these convulsive agonies were merely reflex actions, part of an unconscious physical process, through which the disordered nerves sought to readjust themselves, or to perform belatedly some instinctive movement which an over-riding will had thwarted at its original inception, his own conscious mind now filled itself with the passions, of which the mutterings and twitchings heard in the darkness were only the unconscious mimicry. The senses certainly have, in some measure, an independent activity of their own, and remain vigilant even in the mind's eclipse. The darkness seemed to him to be filled with the shuddering of tormented flesh, as though something diabolically evil probed curiously to find a quick sensitive nerve and wring from it a reluctant cry of pain. At last, unable to ignore the sense of misery which filled him, he sat up and lit the inevitable cigarette. The formless terrors haunting their sleep took shape for him. His mind reached back into the past day, groping among obscure and broken memories, for it seemed to him now that for the greater part of the time he had been stunned and blinded, and that what he had seen, he had seen in sudden, vivid flashes, instantaneously: he felt again the tension of waiting, that became impatience, and then the immense effort to move, and the momentary relief which came with movement, the sense of unreality and dread which descended on one, and some restoration of balance as one saw other men moving forward in a way that seemed commonplace, mechanical, as though at some moment of ordinary routine; the restraint, and the haste that fought against it with every voice in one's being crying out to hurry. Hurry? One cannot hurry, alone, into nowhere, into nothing. Every impulse created immediately its own violent contradiction. The confusion and tumult in his own mind was inseparable from the senseless fury about him, each reinforcing the other. He saw great chunks of the German line blown up, as the artillery blasted a way for them; clouds of dust and smoke screened their advance, but the Hun searched for them scrupulously; the air was alive with the rush and flutter of wings; it was ripped by screaming shells, hissing like tons of molten metal plunging suddenly into water, there was the blast and concussion of their explosion men smashed, obliterated in sudden eruptions of earth, rent and strewn in bloody fragments, shells that were like hell-cats humped and spitting, little sounds, unpleasantly close, like the plucking of tense strings, and something tangling his feet, tearing at his trousers and puttees as he stumbled over it, and then a face suddenly, an inconceivably distorted face, which raved and sobbed at him as he fell with it into a shell-hole. He saw with astonishment the bare stern of a Scotsman who had gone into action wearing only a kilt-apron; and then they righted themselves and looked at each other, bewildered and humiliated. There followed a moment of perfect lucidity, while they took a breather; and he found himself, though unwounded, wondering with an insane prudence where the nearest dressing-station was. Other men came up; two more Gordons joined them, and then Mr. Halliday, who flung himself on top of them and, keeping his head well down, called them a lot of bloody skullers. He had a slight wound in the fore-arm. They made a rush forward again, the dust and smoke clearing a little, and they heard the elastic twang of Mills bombs as they reached an empty trench, very narrow where shelling had not wrecked or levelled it. Mr. Halliday was hit again, in the knee, before they reached the trench, and Bourne felt something pluck the front of his tunic at the same time. They pulled Mr. Halliday into the trench and left him with one of the Gordons who had also been hit. Men were converging then, and he went forward with some of his own company again. From the moment he had thrown himself into the shell-hole with the

Scotsman something had changed in him; the conflict and tumult of his mind had gone, his mind itself seemed to have gone, to have contracted and hardened within him, fear remained, an implacable and restless fear, but that, too, seemed to have been beaten and forged into a point of exquisite sensibility and to have become indistinguishable from hate. Only the instincts of the beast survived in him, every sense was alert and in that tension was some poignancy. He neither knew where he was nor whither he was going, he could have no plan because he could foresee nothing, everything happening was inevitable and unexpected, he was an act in a whole chain of acts; and, though his movements had to conform to those of others, spontaneously, as part of some infinitely flexible plan, which he could not comprehend very clearly even in regard to its immediate object, he could rely on no one but himself. They worked round a point still held by machine-guns, through a rather intricate system of trenches linking up shell-craters. The trenches were little more than bolt-holes, through which the machine-gunners, after they had held up the advancing infantry as long as possible, might hope to escape to some other appointed position further back, and resume their work, thus gaining time for the troops behind to recover from the effect of the bombardment, and emerge from their hiding-places. They were singularly brave men, these Prussian machine-gunners, but the extreme heroism, alike in foe or friend, is indistinguishable from despair. Bourne found himself playing again a game of his childhood, though not now among rocks from which reverberated heat quivered in wavy films, but in made fissures too chalky and unweathered for adequate concealment. One has not, perhaps, at thirty years the same zest in the game as one had at thirteen, but the sense of danger brought into play a latent experience which had become a kind of instinct with him, and he moved in those tortuous ways with the furtive cunning of a stoat or weasel. Stooping low at an angle in the trench he saw the next comparatively straight length empty, and when the man behind was close to him, ran forward still stooping. The advancing line, hung up at one point, inevitably tended to surround it, and it was suddenly abandoned by the few men holding it. Bourne, running, checked as a running Hun rounded the further angle precipitately, saw him prop, shrink back into a defensive posture, and fired without lifting the butt of his rifle quite level with his right breast. The man fell shot in the face, and someone screamed at Bourne to go on; the body choked the narrow angle, and when he put his foot on it, squirmed or moved, making him check again, fortunately, as a bomb exploded a couple yards round the corner. He turned, dismayed, on the man behind him, but behind the bomber he saw the grim bulk of Captain Malet, and his strangely exultant face; and Bourne, incapable of articulate speech, could only wave a hand to indicate the way he divined the Huns to have gone. Captain Malet swung himself above the ground, and the men, following, overflowed the narrow channel of the trench; but the two waves, which had swept round the machine-gun post, were now on the point of meeting; men bunched together, and there were some casualties among them before they went to ground again. Captain Malet gave him a word in passing, and Bourne, looking at him with dull uncomprehending eyes, lagged a little to let others intervene between them. He had found himself immediately afterwards next to Company-Sergeant-Major Glasspool, who nodded to him swiftly and appreciatively; and then Bourne understood. He was doing the right thing. In that last rush he had gone on and got into the lead, somehow, for a brief moment; but he realised himself that he had only gone on because he had been unable to stand still. The sense of being one in a crowd did not give him the same confidence as at the start, the present stage seemed to call for a little more personal freedom. Presently, just because they were together they would rush something in a hurry instead of stalking it. Two men of another regiment, who had presumably got lost, broke back momentarily demoralised, and Sergeant-Major Glasspool confronted them.

" Where the bloody hell do you reckon you're going?"

He rapped out the question with the staccato of a machine-gun; facing their hysterical disorder, he was the living embodiment of a threat.

" We were ordered back," one said, shamefaced and fearful.

" Yes. You take your bloody orders from Fritz," Glasspool, whitelipped and with heaving chest, shot sneering at them. They came to heel quietly enough, but all the rage and hatred in their hearts found an object in him, now. He forgot them as soon as he found them in hand.

" You're all right, chum," whispered Bourne, to the one who had spoken. " Get among your own mob again as soon as there's a chance."

The man only looked at him stonily. In the next rush forward something struck Bourne's helmet, knocking it back over the nape of his neck so that the chin-strap tore his ears. For the moment he thought he had been knocked out, he had bitten his tongue, too, and his mouth was salt with blood. The blow had left a deep dent in the helmet, just fracturing the steel. He was still dazed and shaken when they reached some building-ruins, which he seemed to remember. They were near the railway-station.

He wished he could sleep, he was heavy with it; but his restless memory made sleep seem something to be resisted as too like death. He closed his eyes and had a vision of men advancing under a rain of shells. They had seemed so toylike, so trivial and ineffective when opposed to that overwhelming wrath, and yet they had moved forward mechanically as though they were hynotised or fascinated by some superior will. That had been one of Bourne's most vivid impressions in action, a man close to him moving forward with the jerky motion a clockwork toy has when it is running down; and it had been vivid to him because of the relief with which he had turned to it and away from the confusion and tumult of his own mind. It had seemed impossible to relate that petty, common-place, unheroic figure, in ill-fitting khaki and a helmet like the barber's basin with which Don Quixote made shift on his adventures, to the moral and spiritual conflict, almost super-human in its agony, within him. Power is measured by the amount of resistance which it overcomes, and, in the last resort, the moral power of men was greater than any purely material force, which could be brought to bear on it. It took the chance of death, as one of the chances it was bound to take; though, paradoxically enough, the function of our moral nature consists solely in the assertion of one's own individual will against anything which may be opposed to it, and death, therefore, would imply its extinction in the particular and individual case. The true inwardness of tragedy lies in the fact that its failure is only apparent, and as in the case of the martyr also, the moral conscience of man has made its own deliberate choice, and asserted the freedom of its being. The sense of wasted effort is only true for meaner and more material natures. It took the more horrible chance of mutilation. But as far as Bourne himself, and probably also, since the moral impulse is not necessarily an intellectual act, as far as the majority of his comrades were concerned, its strength and its weakness were inseparably entangled in each other. Whether a man be killed by a rifle-bullet through the brain, or blown into fragments by a high-explosive shell, may seem a matter of indifference to the conscientious objector, or to any other equally well-placed observer, who in point of fact is probably right; but to the poor fool who is a candidate for posthumous honours, and necessarily takes a more directly interested view, it is a question of importance. He is, perhaps, the victim of an illusion, like all who, in the words of Paul, are fools for Christ's sake; but he has seen one man shot cleanly in his tracks and left face downwards, dead, and he has seen another torn into bloody tatters as by some invisible beast, and these experiences had nothing illusory about them: they were actual facts. Death, of course, like chastity, admits of no degree; a man is dead or not dead, and a man is just as dead by one means as by another; but it is infinitely more horrible and revolting to see a man shattered and eviscerated, than to see him shot. And one sees such things; and one suffers vicariously, with the inalienable sympathy of man for man. One forgets quickly. The mind is averted as well as the eyes. It reassures itself after that first despairing cry: "It is I!"

"No, it is not I. I shall not be like that."

And one moves on, leaving the mauled and bloody thing behind: gambling, in fact, on that implicit assurance each one of us has of his own immortality. One forgets, but he will remember again later, if only in his sleep.

After all, the dead are quiet. Nothing in the world is more still than a dead man. One sees living men living, living, as it were, desperately, and then suddenly emptied of life. A man dies and stiffens into something like a wooden dummy, at which one glances for a second with a furtive curiosity. Suddenly he remembered the dead in Trones Wood, the unburied dead with whom one lived, he might say, cheek by jowl, Briton and Hun impartially confounded, festering, fly-blown corruption, the pasture of rats, blackening in the heat, swollen with distended bellies, or shrivelling away within their mouldering rags; and even when night covered them, one vented in the wind the stench of death. Out of one bloody misery into another, until we break. One must not break. He took in his breath suddenly in a shaken sob, and the mind relinquished its hopeless business. The warm smelly darkness of the tent seemed almost luxurious ease. He drowsed heavily; dreaming of womanly softness, sweetness; but their faces slipped away from him like the reflections in water when the wind shakes it, and his soul sank deeply and more deeply into the healing of oblivion.

LISETTE AT EYLAU

General Marbot

To enable you to understand my story, I must go back to the autumn of 1805, when the officers of the Grand Army, among their preparations for the battle of Austerlitz, were completing their outfits. I had two good horses, the third, for whom I was looking, my charger, was to be better still. It was a difficult thing to find, for though horses were far less dear than now, their price was pretty high, and I had not very much money; but chance served me admirably. I met a learned German, Herr von Aister, whom I had known when he was a professor at Sorèze. He had become tutor to the children of a rich Swiss banker, M. Scherer, established at Paris in partnership with M. Finguerlin. He informed me that M. Finguerlin, a wealthy man, living in fine style, had a large stud, in the first rank of which figured a lovely mare, called Lisette, easy in her paces, as light as a deer, and so well broken that a child could lead her. But this mare, when she was ridden, had a terrible fault, and fortunately a rare one: she bit like a bulldog, and furiously attacked people whom she disliked, which decided M. Finguerlin to sell her. She was bought for Mme. de Lauriston, whose husband, one of the Emperor's aides-de-camp, had written to her to get his campaigning outfit ready. When selling the mare, M. Finguerlin had forgotten to mention her fault, and that very evening a groom was found disembowelled at her feet. Mme. de Lauriston, reasonably alarmed, brought an action to cancel the bargain; not only did she get her verdict, but in order to prevent further disasters, the police ordered that a written statement should be placed in Lisette's stall to inform purchasers of her ferocity, and that any bargain with regard to her should be void unless the purchaser declared in writing that his attention had been called to the notice. You may suppose that with such a character as this the mare was not easy to dispose of, and thus Herr von Aister informed me that her owner had decided to let her go for what any one would give. I offered 1,000 francs, and M. Finguerlin delivered Lisette to me, though she had cost him 5,000. This animal gave me a good deal of trouble for some months. It took four or five men to saddle her, and you could only

From: *The Adventures of General Marbot.* Scribners.

bridle her by covering her eyes and fastening all four legs; but once you were on her back, you found her a really incomparable mount.

However, since while in my possession she had already bitten several people, and had not spared me, I was thinking of parting with her. But I had meanwhile engaged in my service Francis Woirland, a man who was afraid of nothing, and he, before going near Lisette, whose bad character had been mentioned to him, armed himself with a good hot roast leg of mutton. When the animal flew at him to bite him, he held out the mutton; she seized it in her teeth, and burning her gums, palate, and tongue, gave a scream, let the mutton drop, and from that moment was perfectly submissive to Woirland, and did not venture to attack him again. I employed the same method with a like result. Lisette became as docile as a dog, and allowed me and my servant to approach her freely. She even became a little more tractable towards the stablemen of the staff, whom she saw every day, but woe to the strangers who passed near her! I could quote twenty instances of her ferocity, but I will confine myself to one. While Marshal Augereau was staying at the château of Bellevue, near Berlin, the servants of the staff, having observed that when they went to dinner some cow stole the sacks of corn that were left in the stable, got Woirland to unfasten Lisette and leave her near the door. The thief arrived, slipped into the stable, and was in the act of carrying off a sack, when the mare seized him by the nape of the neck, dragged him into the middle of the yard and trampled on him till she broke two of his ribs. At the shrieks of the thief, people ran up, but Lisette would not let him go till my servant and I compelled her, for in her fury she would have flown at any one else. She had become still more vicious ever since the Saxon hussar officer, of whom I have told you, had treacherously laid open her shoulder with a sabre-cut on the battlefield of Jena.

Such was the mare which I was riding at Eylau at the moment when the fragments of Augereau's army corps, shattered by a hail of musketry and cannon-balls, were trying to rally near the great cemetery. You will remember how the 14th of the line had remained alone on a hillock, which it could not quit except by the Emperor's order. The snow had ceased for the moment; we could see how the intrepid regiment, surrounded by the enemy, was waving its eagle in the air to show that it still held its ground and asked for support. The Emperor, touched by the grand devotion of these brave men, resolved to try to save them, and ordered Augereau to send an officer to them with orders to leave the hillock, form a small square, and make their way towards us, while a brigade of cavalry should march in their direction and assist their efforts. This was before Murat's great charge. It was almost impossible to carry out the Emperor's wishes, because a swarm of Cossacks was between us and the 14th, and it was clear that any officer who was sent towards the unfortunate regiment would be killed or captured before he could get to it. But the order was positive, and the marshal had to comply.

It was customary in the Imperial army for the aides-de-camp to place themselves in file a few paces from their general, and for the one who was in front to go on duty first; then, when he had performed his mission, to return and place himself last, in order that each might carry orders in his turn, and dangers might be shared equally. A brave captain of engineers, named Froissard, who, though not an aide-de-camp, was on the marshal's staff, happened to be nearest to him, and was bidden to carry the order to the 14th. M. Froissard galloped off; we lost sight of him in the midst of the Cossacks, and never saw him again nor heard what had become of him. The marshal, seeing that the 14th did not move, sent an officer named David; he had the same fate as Froissard: we never heard of him again. Probably both were killed and stripped, and could not be recognised among the many corpses which covered the ground. For the third time the marshal called, " The officer for duty." It was my turn.

Seeing the son of his old friend, and I venture to say his favourite aide-de-camp, come up, the kind marshal's face changed, and his eyes filled with tears, for he could not hide from himself that he was sending me to almost certain death. But the Emperor must be obeyed. I was a soldier; it was impossible to make one of my comrades go in my place, nor would I have allowed it; it would have been disgracing me. So I dashed off. But though ready to sacrifice my life I felt bound to take all necessary precautions to save it. I had observed that the two officers who went before me had gone with swords drawn, which led me to think that they had purposed to defend themselves against any Cossacks who might attack them on the way. Such defence, I thought, was ill-considered, since it must have compelled them to halt in order to fight a multitude of enemies, who would overwhelm them in the end. So I went otherwise to work, and leaving my sword in the scabbard, I regarded myself as a horseman who is trying to win a steeplechase, and goes as quickly as possible and by the shortest line toward the appointed goal, without troubling himself with what is to right or left of his path. Now, as my goal was the hillock occupied by the 14th, I resolved to get there without taking any notice of the Cossacks, whom in thought I abolished. This plan answered perfectly. Lisette, lighter than a swallow and flying rather than running, devoured the intervening space, leaping the piles of dead men and horses, the ditches, the broken gun-carriages, the half-extinguished bivouac fires. Thousands of Cossacks swarmed over the plain. The first who saw me acted like sportsmen who, when beating, start a hare, and announce its presence to each other by shouts of "Your side! Your side!" but none of the Cossacks tried to stop me, first, on account of the extreme rapidity of my pace, and also probably because, their numbers being so great, each thought that I could not avoid his comrades farther on; so that I escaped them all, and reached the 14th regiment without either myself or my excellent mare having received the slightest scratch.

I found the 14th formed in square on the top of the hillock, but as the slope was very slight the enemy's cavalry had been able to deliver several charges. These had been vigorously repulsed, and the French regiment was surrounded by a circle of dead horses and dragoons, which formed a kind of rampart, making the position by this time almost inaccessible to cavalry; as I found, for in spite of the aid of our men, I had much difficulty in passing over this horrible entrenchment. At last I was in the square. Since Colonel Savary's death at the passage of the Wkra, the 14th had been commanded by a major. While I imparted to this officer, under a hail of balls, the order to quit his position and try to rejoin his corps, he pointed out to me that the enemy's artillery had been firing on the 14th for an hour, and had caused it such loss that the handful of soldiers which remained would inevitably be exterminated if they went down into the plain, and that, moreover, there would not be time to prepare to execute such a movement, since a Russian column was marching on him, and was not more than a hundred paces away. " I see no means of saving the regiment," said the major; " return to the Emperor, bid him farewell from the 14th of the line, which has faithfully executed his orders, and bear to him the eagle which he gave us, and which we can defend no longer: it would add too much to the pain of death to see it fall into the hands of the enemy." Then the major handed me his eagle.

Saluted for the last time by the glorious fragment of the intrepid regiment with cries of " Vive l'Empereur!" they were going to die for him. It was the *Cæsar morituri te salutant* of Tacitus, but in this case the cry was uttered by heroes. The infantry eagles were very heavy, and their weight was increased by a stout oak pole on the top of which they were fixed. The length of the pole embarrassed me much, and as the stick without the eagle could not constitute a trophy for the enemy, I resolved with the major's consent to break it and only carry off the eagle. But at the moment when I was leaning forward from my saddle in order to get a better purchase to separate the eagle from the pole, one of the numerous cannon-balls which the Russians were sending at us went through the hinder peak of my hat, less than an inch from my head. The shock was all the more terrible since my hat, being fastened on by a strong leather strap under the chin, offered more resistance to the blow. I seemed to be blotted out of existence, but I did not fall from my horse; blood flowed from my nose, my ears, and even my eyes; nevertheless I still could hear and see, and I preserved all my intellectual faculties, although my limbs were paralysed to such an extent that I could not move a single finger.

Meanwhile the column of Russian infantry which we had just perceived was mounting the hill; they were grenadiers wearing mitre-shaped caps with metal ornaments. Soaked with spirits, and in vastly superior numbers, these men hurled themselves furiously on the feeble remains of the unfortunate 14th, whose soldiers had for several days been living only on potatoes and melted snow; that day they had not had time to prepare even this wretched meal. Still our brave Frenchmen made a valiant defence with their bayonets, and when the square had been broken, they held together in groups and sustained the unequal fight for a long time.

During this terrible struggle several of our men, in order not to be struck from behind, set their backs against my mare's flanks, she contrary to her practice, remained perfectly quiet. If I had been able to move I should have urged her forward to get away from this field of slaughter. But it was absolutely impossible for me to press my legs so as to make the animal I rode understand my wish. My position was the more frightful since, as I have said, I retained the power of sight and thought. Not only were they fighting all round me, which exposed me to bayonet-thrusts, but a Russian officer with a hideous countenance kept making efforts to run me through.

As the crowd of combatants prevented him from reaching me, he pointed me out to the soldiers around him, and they, taking me for the commander of the French, as I was the only mounted man, kept firing at me over their comrades' heads, so that bullets were constantly whistling past my ear. One of them would certainly have taken away the small amount of life that was still in me had not a terrible incident led to my escape from the mêlée.

Among the Frenchmen who had got their backs against my mare's near flank was a quartermaster-sergeant, whom I knew from having frequently seen him at the marshal's, making copies for him of the " morning states." This man, having been attacked and wounded by several of the enemy, fell under Lisette's belly, and was seizing my leg to pull himself up, when a Russian grenadier, too drunk to stand steady, wishing to finish him by a thrust in the breast, lost his balance, and the point of his bayonet went astray into my cloak, which at that moment was puffed out by the wind. Seeing that I did not fall, the Russian left the sergeant and aimed a great number of blows at me. These were at first fruitless, but one at last reached me, piercing my left arm, and I felt with a kind of horrible pleasure my blood flowing hot. The Russian grenadier with redoubled fury made another thrust at me, but, stumbling with the force which he put into it, drove his bayonet into my mare's thigh. Her ferocious instincts being restored by the pain, she sprang at the Russian, and at one mouthful tore off his nose, lips, eyebrows, and all the skin of his face, making of him a living death's-head, dripping with blood. Then hurling herself with fury among the combatants kicking and biting, Lisette upset everything that she met on her road. The officer who had made so many attempts to strike me tried to hold her by the bridle; she seized him by his belly, and carrying him off with ease, she bore him out of the crush to the foot of the hillock, where, having torn out his entrails and mashed his body under her feet, she left him dying on the snow. Then, taking the road by which she had come, she made her way at full gallop towards the cemetery of Eylau. Thanks to the hussar's saddle on which I was sitting I kept my seat. But a new danger awaited me. The snow had begun to fall again, and great flakes obscured the daylight when, having arrived close to Eylau, I found myself in front of a battalion of the Old Guard, who, unable to see clearly at a distance, took me for an enemy's officer leading a charge of cavalry. The whole battalion at once opened fire on me;

my cloak and my saddle were riddled, but I was not wounded nor was my mare. She continued her rapid course, and went through the three ranks of the battalion as easily as a snake through a hedge. But this last spurt had exhausted Lisette's strength; she had lost much blood, for one of the large veins in her thigh had been divided, and the poor animal collapsed suddenly and fell on one side, rolling me over on the other.

Stretched on the snow among the piles of dead and dying, unable to move in any way, I gradually and without pain lost consciousness. I felt as if I was being gently rocked to sleep. At last I fainted quite away without being revived by the mighty clatter which Murat's ninety squadrons advancing to the charge must have made in passing close to me and perhaps over me. I judge that my swoon lasted four hours, and when I came to my senses I found myself in this horrible position. I was completely naked, having nothing on but my hat and my right boot. A man of the transport corps, thinking me dead, had stripped me in the usual fashion, and wishing to pull off the only boot that remained, was dragging me by one leg with his foot against my body. The jerks which the man gave me no doubt restored me to my senses. I succeeded in sitting up and spitting out the clots of blood from my throat. The shock caused by the wind of the ball had produced such an extravasation of blood, that my face, shoulders, and chest were black, while the rest of my body was stained red by the blood from my wound. My hat and my hair were full of bloodstained snow, and as I rolled my haggard eyes I must have been horrible to see. Anyhow, the transport man looked the other way, and went off with my property without my being able to say a single word to him, so utterly prostrate was I. But I had recovered my mental faculties, and my thoughts turned towards God and my mother.

The setting sun cast some feeble rays through the clouds. I took what I believed to be a last farewell of it. "If," thought I, "I had only not been stripped, some one of the numerous people who pass near me would notice the gold lace on my pelisse, and, recognising that I am a marshal's aide-de-camp, would perhaps have carried me to the ambulance. But seeing me naked, they do not distinguish me from the corpses with which I am surrounded, and, indeed, there soon will be no difference between them and me. I cannot call help, and the approaching night will take away all hope of succour. The cold is increasing: shall I be able to bear it till tomorrow, seeing that I feel my naked limbs stiffening already?" So I made up my mind to die, for if I had been saved by a miracle in the midst of the terrible mêlée between the Russians and the 14th, could I expect that there would be a second miracle to extract me from my present horrible position? The second miracle did take place in the following manner. Marshal Augereau had a valet named Pierre Dannel, a very intelligent and very faithful fellow, but somewhat given to arguing. Now it happened during our stay at La Houssaye that Dannel, having answered his master, got dismissed. In despair, he begged me to plead for him. This I did so zealously that I succeeded in getting him taken back into favour. From that time the valet had been devotedly attached to me. The outfit having been all left behind at Landsberg, he had started all out of his own head on the day of battle to bring provisions to his master. He had placed these in a very light wagon which could go everywhere, and contained the articles which the marshal most frequently required. This little wagon was driven by a soldier belonging to the same company of the transport corps as the man who had just stripped me. This latter, with my property in his hands, passed near the wagon, which was standing at the side of the cemetery, and, recognising the driver, his old comrade, he hailed him, and showed him the splendid booty which he had just taken from a dead man.

Now you must know that when we were in cantonments on the Vistula the marshal happened to send Dannel to Warsaw for provisions, and I commissioned him to get the trimming of black astrachan taken from my pelisse, and have it replaced by grey, this having recently been adopted by Prince Berthier's aides-de-camp, who set the fashion in the army. Up to now, I was the only one of Augereau's officers who had grey astrachan. Dannel, who was present when the transport man made his display, quickly recognised my pelisse, which made him look more closely at the other effects of the alleged dead man. Among these he found my watch, which had belonged to my father and was marked with his cypher. The valet had no longer any doubt that I had been killed, and while deploring my loss, he wished to see me for the last time. Guided by the transport man he reached me and found me living. Great was the joy of this worthy man, to whom I certainly owed my life. He made haste to fetch my servant and some orderlies, and had me carried to a barn, where he rubbed my body with rum. Meanwhile some one went to fetch Dr. Raymond, who came at length, dressed the wound in my arm, and declared that the release of blood due to it would be the saving of me.

My brother and my comrades were quickly round me; something was given to the transport soldier who had taken my clothes, which he returned very willingly, but as they were saturated with water and with blood, Marshal Augereau had me wrapped in things belonging to himself. The Emperor had given the marshal leave to go to Landsberg, but as his wound forbade him to ride, his aides-de-camp had procured a sledge, on which the body of a carriage had been placed. The marshal, who could not make up his mind to leave me, had me fastened up beside him, for I was too weak to sit upright.

Before I was removed from the field of battle I had seen my poor Lisette near me. The cold had caused the blood from her wound to clot, and prevented the loss from being too great. The creature had got on to her legs and was eating the straw which the soldiers had used the night before for their bivouacs. My servant, who was very fond of Lisette, had noticed her when he was helping to remove me, and cutting up into bandages the shirt and hood of a dead soldier, he wrapped her leg with them, and thus made her able to walk to Landsberg. The officer in command of the small garrison there had had the forethought to get quarters ready for the wounded, so the staff found places in a large and good inn.

In this way, instead of passing the night without help, stretched naked on the snow, I lay on a good bed surrounded by the attention of my brother, my comrades, and the kind Dr. Raymond. The doctor had been obliged to cut off the boot which the transport man had not been able to pull off, and which had become all the more difficult to remove owing to the swelling of my foot. You will see presently that this very nearly cost me my leg, and perhaps my life.

We stayed thirty-six hours at Landsberg. This rest, and the good care taken of me, restored me to the use of speech and senses, and when on the second day after the battle Marshal Augereau started for Warsaw I was able to be carried in the sledge. The journey lasted eight days. Gradually I recovered strength, but as strength returned I began to feel a sensation of icy cold in my right foot. At Warsaw I was lodged in the house that had been taken for the marshal, which suited me the better that I was not able to leave my bed. Yet the wound in my arm was doing well, the extravasated blood was becoming absorbed, my skin was recovering its natural colour. The doctor knew not to what he could ascribe my inability to rise, till, hearing me complaining of my leg, he examined it, and found that my foot was gangrened.

An accident of my early days was the cause of this new trouble. At Sorèze I had my right foot wounded by the unbuttoned foil of a schoolfellow with whom I was fencing. It seemed that the muscles of the part had become sensitive, and had suffered much from cold while I was lying unconscious on the field of Eylau; thence had resulted a swelling which explained the difficulty experienced by the soldier in dragging off my right boot. The foot was frostbitten, and as it had not been treated in time gangrene had appeared in the site of the old wound from the foil. The place was covered with an eschar as large as a five-franc piece. The doctor turned pale when he saw the foot: then, making four servants hold me, and taking his knife, he lifted the eschar, and dug the mortified flesh from my foot just as one cuts the damaged part out of an apple. The pain was great, but I did not complain. It was otherwise, however, when the knife reached the living flesh, and laid bare the muscles and bones till one could see them moving. Then the doctor, standing on a chair, soaked a sponge in hot sweetened wine, and let it fall drop by drop into the hole which he had just dug in my foot. The pain became unbearable. Still, for eight days I had to undergo this torture morning and evening, but my leg was saved.

Nowadays, when promotions and decorations are bestowed so lavishly, some reward would certainly be given to an officer who had braved danger as I had done in reaching the 14th regiment; but under the Empire a devoted act of that kind was thought so natural that I did not receive the cross, nor did it ever occur to me to ask for it. A long rest having been ordered for the cure of Marshal Augereau's wound, the Emperor wrote to bid him return for treatment to France, and sent to Italy for Masséna, to whom my brother, Bro, and several of my comrades were attached. Augereau took me with him, as well as Dr. Raymond and his secretary. I had to be lifted in and out of the carriage; otherwise I found my health coming back as I got away from those icy regions towards a milder climate. My mare passed the winter in the stables of M. de Launay, head of the forage department. Our road lay through Silesia. So long as we were in that horrible Poland, it required twelve, sometimes sixteen, horses to draw the carriage at a walk through the bogs and quagmires; but in Germany we found at length civilisation and real roads.

After a halt at Dresden, and ten or twelve days' stay at Frankfort, we reached Paris about March 15. I walked very lame, wore my arm in a sling, and still felt the terrible shaking caused by the wind of the cannon-ball; but the joy of seeing my mother again, and her kind care of me, together with the sweet influences of the spring, completed my cure. Before leaving Warsaw I had meant to throw away the hat which the ball had pierced, but the marshal kept it as a curiosity and gave it to my mother. It still exists in my possession, and should be kept as a family relic.

TRAFALGAR

Robert Southey

The station which Nelson had chosen was some fifty or sixty miles to the west of Cadiz, near Cape St. Mary. At this distance he hoped to decoy the enemy out, while he guarded against the danger of being caught with a westerly wind near Cadiz, and driven within the Straits. The blockade of the port was rigorously enforced, in hopes that the combined fleets might be forced to sea by want. The Danish vessels therefore, which were carrying provisions from the French ports in the bay, under the name of Danish property, to all the little ports from Ayamonte to Algeziras, from whence they were conveyed in coasting boats to Cadiz, were seized. Without this proper exertion of power the blockade would have been rendered nugatory by the advantage thus taken of the neutral flag. The supplies from France were thus effectually cut off. There was now every indication that the enemy would speedily venture out; officers and men were in the highest spirits at the prospect of giving them a decisive blow—such, indeed, as would put an end to all further contests upon the seas.

On the 9th Nelson sent Collingwood what he called in his diary the " Nelson touch." " I send you," said he, " my plan of attack, as far as a man dare venture to guess at the very uncertain position the enemy may be found in; but it is to place you perfectly at ease respecting my intentions, and to give full scope to your judgment for carrying them into effect. We can, my dear Coll, have no little jealousies. We have only one great object in view, that of annihilating our enemies, and getting a glorious peace for our country. No man has more confidence in another than I have in you, and no man will render your services more justice than your very old friend, Nelson and Bronte."

The order of sailing was to be the order of battle—the fleet in two lines, with an advanced squadron of eight of the fastest sailing two-deckers. The second in command, having the entire direction of his line, was to break through the enemy, about the twelfth ship from their rear; he would lead through the centre, and the advanced squadron was to cut off three or four ahead of the centre. This plan was to be adapted to the

From: *The Life of Nelson.*

strength of the enemy, so that they should always be one-fourth superior to those whom they cut off. Nelson said that " his admirals and captains, knowing his precise object to be that of a close and decisive action, would supply any deficiency of signals and act accordingly. In case signals cannot be seen or clearly understood, no captain can do wrong if he places his ship alongside that of an enemy."

About half-past nine in the morning of the 19th the *Mars*, being the nearest to the fleet of the ships which formed the line of communication with the frigates inshore, repeated the signal that the enemy were coming out of port. The wind was at this time very light, with partial breezes, mostly from the S. S. W. Nelson ordered the signal to be made for a chase in the south-east quarter. About two, the repeating ships announced that the enemy were at sea. All night the British fleet continued under all sail, steering to the south-east. At daybreak they were in the entrance of the Straits, but the enemy were not in sight. About seven, one of the frigates made signal that the enemy was bearing north. Upon this the *Victory* hove to, and shortly afterwards Nelson made sail again to the northward. In the afternoon the wind blew fresh from the southwest, and the English began to fear that the foe might be forced to return to port.

A little before sunset, however, Blackwood, in the *Euryalus*, telegraphed that they appeared determined to go to the westward. " And that," said the Admiral in his diary, " they shall not do, if it is in the power of Nelson and Bronte to prevent them." Nelson had signified to Blackwood that he depended upon him to keep sight of the enemy. They were observed so well that all their motions were made known to him, and as they wore twice, he inferred that they were aiming to keep the port of Cadiz open, and would retreat there as soon as they saw the British fleet; for this reason he was very careful not to approach near enough to be seen by them during the night. At daybreak the combined fleets were distinctly seen from the *Victory*'s deck, formed in a close line of battle ahead, on the starboard tack, about twelve miles to leeward, and standing to the south. Our fleet consisted of twenty-seven sail of the line and four frigates; theirs of thirty-three and seven large frigates. Their superiority was greater in size and weight of metal than in numbers. They had four thousand troops on board, and the best riflemen that could be procured, many of them Tyrolese, were dispersed through the ships.

Soon after daylight Nelson came upon deck. The 21st of

October was a festival in his family, because on that day his uncle, Captain Suckling, in the *Dreadnought,* with two other line-of-battle ships, had beaten off a French squadron of four sail of the line and three frigates. Nelson, with that sort of superstition from which few persons are entirely exempt, had more than once expressed his persuasion that this was to be the day of his battle also, and he was well pleased at seeing his prediction about to be verified. The wind was now from the west—light breezes, with a long heavy swell. Signal was made to bear down upon the enemy in two lines, and the fleet set all sail. Collingwood, in the *Royal Sovereign,* led the lee line of thirteen ships; the *Victory* led the weather line of fourteen. Having seen that all was as it should be, Nelson retired to his cabin, and wrote the following prayer—

" May the great God whom I worship, grant to my country, and for the benefit of Europe in general, a great and glorious victory, and may no misconduct in any one tarnish it, and may humanity after victory be the predominant feature in the British fleet! For myself individually, I commit my life to Him that made me, and may His blessing alight on my endeavours for serving my country faithfully! To Him I resign myself, and the just cause which is entrusted to me to defend. Amen, Amen, Amen."

Blackwood went on board the *Victory* about six. He found him in good spirits, but very calm; not in that exhilaration which he felt upon entering into battle at Aboukir and Copenhagen; he knew that his own life would be particularly aimed at, and seems to have looked for death with almost as sure an expectation as for victory. His whole attention was fixed upon the enemy. They tacked to the northward, and formed their line on the larboard tack; thus bringing the shoals of Trafalgar and St. Pedro under the lee of the British, and keeping the port of Cadiz open for themselves. This was judiciously done; and Nelson, aware of all the advantages which he gave them, made signal to prepare to anchor.

Villeneuve was a skilful seaman, worthy of serving a better master and a better cause. His plan of defence was as well conceived and as original as the plan of attack. He formed the fleet in a double line, every alternate ship being about a cable's length to windward of her second ahead and astern. Nelson, certain of a triumphant issue to the day, asked Blackwood what he should consider as a victory. That officer answered that, considering the handsome way in which battle was offered by the enemy, their apparent determination for a fair trial of strength, and the situation of the land, he thought it would be a glorious result if fourteen were captured. He replied: " I shall not be satisfied with less than twenty." Soon afterwards he asked him if he did not think there was a signal wanting. Captain Blackwood made answer that he thought the whole fleet seemed very clearly to understand what they were about. These words were scarcely spoken before that signal was made which will be remembered as long as the language or even the memory of England shall endure— " ENGLAND EXPECTS EVERY MAN WILL DO HIS DUTY! " It was received throughout the fleet with a shout of answering acclamation, made sublime by the spirit which it breathed and the feeling which it expressed. " Now," said Lord Nelson, " I can do no more. We must trust to the great disposer of all events and the justice of our cause. I thank God for this great opportunity of doing my duty."

He wore that day, as usual, his admiral's frock-coat, bearing on the left breast four stars of the different orders with which he was invested. Ornaments which rendered him so conspicuous a mark for the enemy were beheld with ominous apprehension by his officers. It was known that there were riflemen on board the French ships, and it could not be doubted but that his life would be particularly aimed at. They communicated their fears to each other, and the surgeon, Mr. Beatty, spoke to the chaplain, Dr. Scott, and to Mr. Scott, the public secretary, desiring that some person would entreat him to change his dress or cover the stars; but they knew that such a request would highly displease him. " In honour I gained them," he had said when such a thing had been hinted to him formerly, " and in honour I will die with them." Mr. Beatty, however, would not have been deterred by any fear of exciting his displeasure from speaking to him himself upon a subject in which the weal of England, as well as the life of Nelson, was concerned; but he was ordered from the deck before he could find an opportunity. This was a point upon which Nelson's officers knew that it was hopeless to remonstrate or reason with him; but both Blackwood and his own captain, Hardy, represented to him how advantageous to the fleet it would be for him to keep out of action as long as possible, and he consented at last to let the *Leviathan* and the *Temeraire*, which were sailing abreast of the *Victory* be ordered to pass ahead.

Yet even here the last infirmity of this noble mind was indulged, for these ships could not pass ahead if the *Victory* continued to carry all her sail; and so far was Nelson from shortening sail, that it was evident he took pleasure in pressing on, and rendering it impossible for them to obey his own orders. A long swell was setting into the Bay of Cadiz. Our ships, crowding all sail, moved majestically before it, with light winds from the south-west. The sun shone on the sails of the enemy, but their well-formed line, with their numerous three-deckers, made an appearance which any other assailants would have thought formidable, but the British sailors only admired the beauty and the splendour of the spectacle, and in full confidence of winning what they saw, remarked to each other what a fine sight yonder ships would make at Spithead!

The French admiral, from the *Bucentaure,* beheld the new manner in which his enemy was advancing—Nelson and Collingwood, each leading his line; and pointing them out to his officers, he is said to have exclaimed that such conduct could not fail to be successful. Yet Villeneuve had made his own dispositions with the utmost skill, and the fleets under his command waited for the attack with perfect coolness. Ten minutes before twelve they opened their fire. Eight or nine of the ships immediately ahead of the *Victory,* and across her bows, fired single guns at her to ascertain whether she was yet within their range. As soon as Nelson perceived that their shot passed over him, he desired Blackwood and Captain Prowse, of the *Sirius,* to repair to their respective frigates, and on their way to tell all the captains of the line-of-battle ships that he depended on their exertions, and that, if by the prescribed mode of attack they found it impracticable to get into action immediately, they might adopt whatever they thought best, provided it led them quickly and closely alongside an enemy. As they were standing on the poop, Blackwood took him by the hand, saying he hoped soon to return and find him in possession of twenty prizes. He replied, " God bless, you, Blackwood; I shall never see you again."

Nelson's column was steered about two points more to the north than Collingwood's, in order to cut off the enemy's escape into Cadiz. The lee line, therefore, was first engaged. " See," cried Nelson, pointing to the *Royal Sovereign,* as she steered right for the centre of the enemy's line, cut through it astern of the *Santa Anna,* three-decker, and engaged her at the muzzle of her guns on the starboard side; " see how that noble fellow Collingwood carries his ship into action!" Collingwood, delighted at being first in the heat of the fire, and knowing the feelings of his commander and old friend, turned to his captain and exclaimed: " Rotherham, what would Nelson give to be here!" Both these brave officers, perhaps, at this moment thought of Nelson with gratitude for a circumstance which had occurred on the preceding day. Admiral Collingwood, with some of the captains, having gone on board the *Victory* to receive instructions, Nelson inquired of him where his captain was, and was told in reply that they were not upon good terms with each other. "Terms!" said Nelson; "good terms with each other!" Immediately he sent a boat for Captain Rotherham, led him, so soon as he arrived, to Collingwood, and saying, "Look, yonder are the enemy!" bade them shake hands like Englishmen.

The enemy continued to fire a gun at a time at the *Victory* till they saw that a shot had passed through her main-top-gallant sail; then they opened their broadsides, aiming chiefly at her rigging, in the hope of disabling her before she could close with them. Nelson as usual had hoisted several flags, lest one should be shot away. The enemy showed no colours till late in the action, when they began to feel the necessity of having them to strike. For this reason the *Santissima Trinidad*, Nelson's old acquaintance, as he used to call her, was distinguishable only by her four decks, and to the bow of this opponent he ordered the *Victory* to be steered. Meantime an incessant raking fire was kept up upon the *Victory*. The Admiral's secretary was one of the first who fell; he was killed by a cannon shot while conversing with Hardy. Captain Adair, of the marines, with the help of a sailor, endeavoured to remove the body from Nelson's sight, who had a great regard for Mr. Scott, but he anxiously asked, "Is that poor Scott that's gone?" and being informed that it was indeed so, exclaimed, "Poor fellow!"

Presently a double-headed shot struck a party of marines who were drawn up on the poop, and killed eight of them, upon which Nelson immediately desired Captain Adair to disperse his men round the ship, that they might not suffer so much from being together. A few minutes afterwards a shot struck the fore-brace bits on the quarter-deck, and passed between Nelson and Hardy, a splinter from the bit tearing off Hardy's buckle and bruising his foot. Both stopped, and looked anxiously at each other: each supposed the other to be wounded. Nelson then smiled, and said: "This is too warm work, Hardy, to last long."

The *Victory* had not yet returned a single gun; fifty of her men had by this time been killed or wounded, and her main-topmast, with all her studding sails and their booms, shot away. Nelson declared that in all his battles he had seen nothing which surpassed the cool courage of his crew on this occasion. At four minutes after twelve she opened her fire from both sides of her deck. It was not possible to break the enemy's lines without running on board one of their ships; Hardy informed him of this, and asked him which he would prefer. Nelson replied: "Take your choice, Hardy; it does not signify much." The master was ordered to put the helm to port, and the *Victory* ran on board the *Redoubtable* just as her tiller-ropes were shot away. The French ship received her with a broadside, then instantly let down her lower-deck ports for fear of being boarded through them, and never afterwards fired a great gun during the action. Her tops, like those of all the enemy's ships, were filled with riflemen. Nelson never placed musketry in his tops; he had a strong dislike to the practice, not merely because it endangers setting fire to the sails, but also because it is a murderous sort of warfare, by which individuals may suffer and a commander now and then be picked off, but which never can decide the fate of a general engagement.

Captain Harvey, in the *Temeraire,* fell on board the *Redoubtable* on the side; another enemy was in like manner on board the *Temeraire*; so that these four ships formed as compact a tier as if they had been moored together, their heads all lying the same way. The lieutenants of the *Victory* seeing this, depressed their guns of the middle and lower decks, and fired with a diminished charge, lest the shot should pass through and injure the *Temeraire*; and because there was danger that the *Redoubtable* might take fire from the lower deck guns, the muzzles of which touched her side when they were run out, the fireman of each gun stood ready with a bucket of water, which, as soon as the gun was discharged, he dashed into the hole made by the shot. An incessant fire was kept up from the *Victory* from both sides, her larboard guns playing upon the *Bucentaure* and the huge *Santissima Trinidad.*

It had been part of Nelson's prayer that the British fleet should be distinguished by humanity in the victory he expected. Setting an example himself, he twice gave orders to cease firing upon the *Redoubtable,* supposing that she had struck, because her great guns were silent; for, as she carried no flag, there was no means of instantly ascertaining the fact. From this ship, which he had thus twice spared, he received his death. A ball fired from her mizzen-top, which in the then situation of the two vessels was not more than fifteen yards from that part of the deck where he was standing, struck the epaulette on his left shoulder, about a quarter after one, just in the heat of action. He fell upon his face, on the spot which was covered with his poor secretary's blood.

Hardy, who was a few steps from him, turning round saw three men raising him up. "They have done for me at last, Hardy!" said he. "I hope not!" cried Hardy. "Yes," he replied, "my backbone is shot through!"

Yet even now, not for a moment losing his presence of mind, he observed as they were carrying him down the ladder, that the tiller-ropes, which had been shot away, were not yet replaced, and ordered that new ones should be rove immediately. Then, that he might not be seen by the crew, he took out his handkerchief and covered his face and his stars. Had he but concealed these badges of honour from the enemy, England perhaps would not have had cause to receive with sorrow the news of the battle of Trafalgar. The cockpit was crowded with wounded and dying men, over whose bodies he was with some difficulty conveyed, and laid upon a pallet in the midshipmen's berth. It was soon perceived, upon examination, that the wound was mortal. This, however, was concealed from all except Captain Hardy, the chaplain, and the medical attendants. He himself being certain, from the sensation in his back and the gush of blood he felt momently within his breast, that no human care could avail him, insisted that the surgeon should leave him, and attend to those to whom he might be useful, "for," said he, "you can do nothing for me."

All that could be done was to fan him with paper, and frequently give him lemonade to alleviate his intense thirst. He was in great pain, and expressed much anxiety for the event of the action, which now began to declare itself. As often as a ship struck, the crew of the *Victory* hurrahed, and at every hurrah a visible expression of joy gleamed in the eyes and marked the countenance of the dying hero. But he became impatient to see Captain Hardy, and as that officer, though often sent for, could not leave the deck, Nelson feared that some fatal cause prevented him, and repeatedly cried, "Will no one bring Hardy to me? He must be killed! He is surely dead!"

An hour and ten minutes elapsed from the time when Nelson received his wound before Hardy could come to him. They shook hands in silence; Hardy in vain struggling to express the feelings of that most painful and yet sublimest moment. "Well, Hardy," said Nelson, "how goes the day with us?" —"Very well," replied Hardy; "ten ships have struck, but five of the van have tacked, and show an intention to bear down upon the *Victory*. I have called two or three of our fresh ships round, and have no doubt of giving them a drubbing." —"I hope," said Nelson, "none of our ships have struck." Hardy answered, "There was no fear of that." Then, and not till then, Nelson spoke of himself. "I am a dead man, Hardy," said he; "I am going fast; it will be all over with me soon. Come nearer to me." Hardy observed that he hoped Mr. Beatty could yet hold out some prospect of life. "Oh no!" he replied, "it is impossible; my back is shot through. Beatty will tell you so." Captain Hardy then once more shook hands with him, and with a heart almost bursting hastened upon deck.

By this time, all feeling below the breast was gone; and Nelson, having made the surgeon ascertain this, said to him: "You know I am gone. I know it. I feel something rising in my breast"—putting his hand on his left side—"which tells me so." And upon Beatty's inquiring whether his pain was very great, he replied, "So great that he wished he was dead." "Yet," said he in a lower voice, "one would like to live a little longer too!" Captain Hardy, some fifty minutes after he had left the cockpit, returned, and again taking the hand of his dying friend and commander, congratulated him on having gained a complete victory. How many of the enemy were taken he did not know, as it was impossible to perceive them distinctly; but fourteen or fifteen at least. "That's well!" cried Nelson; "but I bargained for twenty." And then in a stronger voice he said, "Anchor, Hardy, anchor." Hardy upon this hinted that Admiral Collingwood would take upon himself the direction of affairs. "Not while I live, Hardy," said the dying Nelson, ineffectually endeavouring to raise himself from the bed; "Do you anchor."

His previous order for preparing to anchor had shown how clearly he foresaw the necessity of this. Presently calling Hardy back, he said to him in a low voice: "Don't throw me overboard"; and he desired that he might be buried by his parents, unless it should please the king to order otherwise. Then turning to Hardy: "Kiss me, Hardy," said he. Hardy knelt down and kissed his cheek, and Nelson said: "Now I am satisfied. Thank God, I have done my duty!" Hardy stood over him in silence for a moment or two, then knelt again and kissed his forehead. "Who is that?" said Nelson; and being informed, he replied: "God bless you, Hardy." And Hardy then left him for ever.

Nelson now desired to be turned upon his right side, and said: "I wish I had not left the deck, for I shall soon be gone." Death was indeed rapidly approaching. He had said to the chaplain: "Doctor, I have *not* been a *great* sinner." His articulation now became difficult, but he was distinctly heard to say: "Thank God, I have done my duty!" These words he repeatedly pronounced. And they were the last words that he uttered. He expired at thirty minutes after four, three hours and a quarter after he had received his wound!

THE BATTLE OF YPRES

Frank Richards

The first week in October we left the Aisne to march north, and were issued with topcoats but no packs. We folded our topcoats and tied them on our shoulder-straps with string. We marched by night and rested by day. My gambling money came in very handy: we could buy food in the villages where we rested. There were three of us mucking in and we lived like fighting cocks. Our clothes were beginning to show signs of wear, though, and some of the men were wearing civilian trousers which they had scrounged. A lot of us had no caps: I was wearing a handkerchief knotted at the four corners —the only headgear I was to wear for some time. We looked a ragtime lot, but in good spirits and ready for anything that turned up. About eighty per cent of us were Birmingham men: I never saw better soldiers or wished for better pals. Our Colonel was very strict but a good soldier: the Adjutant likewise. We all admired the Adjutant very much: he could give us all chalks on at swearing and beat the lot of us easily.

Our Company Commander had left us on the Retirement, and during the last day's march from the Aisne a new one took over the company: he was a First Battalion officer and the majority of us had never seen him before. We were loading a train when he first appeared on the scene and he commenced to rave and storm, saying that everything was being loaded up wrong and that we were a lot of ruddy idiots. Company-Sergeant-Major Stanway and Sergeant Fox, who was my platoon sergeant, were directing the loading of the train, and what they didn't know about loading trains was not worth knowing. Stanway had about fifteen years service and Fox about twelve, the greater part of which they had spent abroad. They were the two best non-commissioned officers I ever soldiered under. In any battalion of men there were always a number of bullies, and it's natural to expect one or two among the officers: our new Company Commander was agreed to be a first-class bully. Bullies as a rule are bad soldiers, but he was an exception to the rule.

We entrained that evening and arrived at St. Omer. We were on the move next morning, and a couple of days later we had a brush-up with some German Uhlans who were

From: *Old Soldiers Never Die.*

fine cavalrymen and excellent raiders; there were bands of them operating around the Bailleul area. One lot had done a good deal of damage to Steenwerk railway station, between Armentières and Bailleul, blowing up the points. We were advancing by platoons in extended order over open country when rifle-fire opened out from somewhere in front. We judged it to come from a fair sized wood about six hundred yards away, and laying down opened out with rapid fire at it. A few more shots were fired at us and then the firing ceased. We advanced again and through the wood but saw no one. No doubt the Uhlans had seen us advancing and opened fire with their carbines from inside the wood, then mounting their horses and using the wood as a screen had galloped safely out of sight. My platoon had no casualties, but Number 2 and Number 3 platoons had about half a dozen during the day. The men of Number 3 told us later in the day that they had killed four Uhlans and their horses as they had galloped out of a small wood on their right front about five hundred yards away.

One of our badly wounded men was taken to a lone farmhouse; McGregor, a stretcher-bearer, volunteered to stay the night with him. The next morning he told us that he had been through a bit of torture: the wounded man had been carried upstairs and during the night six Uhlans had rode up to the farm, tied their horses up outside and entered. They had made the old lady of the farm put them out food and drink. McGregor was wondering whether they would have a scrounge through the house after they had finished their meal. The wounded man was delirious too and might easily have given the show away. The Uhlans left as soon as they had finished their meal but McGregor reckoned that he had lost a stone in weight during that short time they were in the house.

We entered Bailleul in the afternoon and the people there were very glad to see us. The place had been in possession of the enemy for a few days and the Uhlans had intended to billet there that night. At this place Stevens rejoined the Battalion. His wanderings on the retirement had been similar to my own: he had also been to Le Mans and had been in hospital a week with fever and ague, after which he had been sent up country and had been serving with another unit for a fortnight. The next morning as we left Bailleul on our way to Vlamertinghe we saw about a dozen Uhlans galloping for all they were worth back from the outskirts. We fired a few shots but they were too far away for us to do any damage. The sight of one Uhlan would frighten the French people more than if half a dozen large shells were exploding in their villages. They told us that the Uhlans were brigands of the first water and would pinch anything they could carry with them. Although the French were our allies we used to do much the same. But we had to be careful: at this early date in the War the penalty for looting was death. We were at Vlamertinghe a few days and then marched for thirteen hours, arriving at a place named Laventie the following morning; we must have come a roundabout way to have taken that time. We moved off again at daybreak and relieved some French troops the farther side of Fromelles on the Belgian frontier: two days later we retired back through Fromelles and dug our trenches about four hundred yards this side of that village.

Little did we think when we were digging those trenches that we were digging our future homes; but they were the beginnings of the long stretch that soon went all the way from the North Sea to Switzerland and they were our homes for the next four years. Each platoon dug in on its own, with gaps of about forty yards between each platoon. B Company were in support, but one platoon of B were on the extreme right of the Battalion's front line. On our left were the 1st Middlesex, and on our right was a battalion of Indian native infantry. Our Company Commander used to visit the other three platoons at night; he, the Second-in-Command of the Company and the platoon officer stayed on the extreme right of our trench. We dug those trenches simply for fighting; they were breast-high with the front parapet on ground level and in each bay we stood shoulder to shoulder. We were so squeezed for room that whenever an officer passed along the trench one man would get behind the traverse if the officer wanted to stay awhile in that bay. No man was allowed to fire from behind the traverse: because the least deflection of his rifle would put a bullet through someone in the bay in front of him. Traverses were made to counteract enfilade rifle-fire. Sandbags were unknown at that time.

A part of our trench crossed a willow ditch and about forty yards in front of us we blocked this ditch with a little bank which was to be our listening post at night. The ditch was dry at present. Every order was passed up the trench by word of mouth, and we found in many instances that by the time an order reached the last man it was entirely different from what the first man had passed along. When our Company Commander passed along the trench we had to squeeze our bodies into the front parapet to allow him to pass. If a man did not move smart enough, out would come his revolver and he would threaten to blow the man's ruddy brains out. During this time he had a perfect mania for pulling his gun and threatening us one and all for the least trifling thing we did. Our platoon officer followed his example but he used to pull his gun in a half ashamed manner. The platoon nicknamed them Buffalo Bill and Deadwood Dick. I got on very well with Deadwood Dick and he was a decent platoon officer. We always numbered off at night: one, two, one, two—odd numbers up, even numbers down, and change every hour. It made no difference whether we were down or up: we could only lay over the parapet by our rifles and with our heads resting on the wet ground try and snatch an hour's sleep.

About the third day we were there Buffalo Bill came up to our part of the trench: I got behind the traverse to allow him to get in the bay. He ordered us to keep a sharp look-out, as the enemy were attacking on our extreme right, and said that it was quite possible the attack would develop all along the front. About four hundred yards in front of us was a road leading into Fromelles. Just behind the road were some trees. I spotted a few of the enemy advancing among the trees and, forgetting for a moment that I was behind a traverse, I rose my rifle to fire, but recollected in time and put it down again. At the same time a man in the next bay below me opened fire. Buffalo Bill turned around. He was red in the face, the veins in his neck had swelled, and he looked for all the world like a cobra ready to strike. "You dog!" he shouted. "You fired!" I replied that I hadn't. He did not go for his gun but picked up a big clod of earth and threw it at me, hitting me on the chest. All my discipline vanished at that moment. "You dirty swine!" I said. By a bit of luck he didn't hear me, for at that moment the enemy's artillery happened to open out and shells began bursting all along our front; but I could hear *him* all right. "Get in that next bay," he roared. I squeezed myself in the next bay.

Some of the enemy had now come out of the trees and no doubt intended to advance a little way under cover of their barrage. But the shelling was not severe enough to prevent us opening out rapid fire at them. I don't think any one of them ran twenty yards before he was dropped. To good, trained, pre-War soldiers who kept their nerve, ten men holding a trench could easily stop fifty who were trying to take it, advancing from a distance of four hundred yards. The enemy now put up a tremendous barrage on our trench, but fortunately for us the shells were dropping short. Some more of the enemy had advanced at the run under cover of this barrage and had dropped down behind some little tumps of ground about two hundred and fifty yards away. I was watching the ground in front but it was very difficult to make anything out through the smoke and showers of dirt being blown up by the exploding shells. Buffalo Bill came into the bay I was in: he had his glasses out and was peering through them but seemed unable to see more than we had done. Most of us now had our heads well below the parapet, waiting for the barrage to lift. The enemy opened out with rifle-fire, and although they could not see us their bullets were kicking up the dirt all around. Buffalo Bill was as cool as a cucumber: he had plenty of guts, I'll say that for him. He passed down the trench warning us as soon as the barrage lifted to be prepared to stop an attack.

At last the barrage lifted: the shells were now exploding about a hundred yards behind us. We were all on the alert and stood to. The enemy rose up and started to advance. They were stopped at once: with the parapet as a rest for our rifles it was impossible to miss. The attack was over before it had hardly commenced. From somewhere under cover by the trees the enemy then opened out with rifle-fire on our trench and a couple of men in the next bay to me were shot through the head. We directed our fire in that direction. Stevens shouted to me to look at one of the men in our bay: he had his head well below the parapet and was firing in the air. We made him put his head well up and fire properly. The whole of the men in the bay threatened to shoot him dead if he did it again. If Buffalo Bill had seen him he wouldn't have given him that chance, but soon put daylight through him.

The left platoon of Indian native infantry on the extreme right of the Battalion had lost their white officer and the enemy's shelling had put the wind up them properly. While the enemy was advancing toward them our men on their left noticed that none of the Germans were falling; so they got a cross fire on them which soon held the attack up. The Indians were firing all the time as if they were mad, but they must have had their heads well below the parapet, like the man in our bay, and been firing up in the air. Every evening after, until the native infantry were relieved by a British battalion, twelve of our men were sent over to their trench with orders to stay the night there; they went over at dusk and returned at dawn. Every man of the twelve had served in India. One of the men told me later that the first night they went over they found the natives wailing and weeping; no one was on sentry and they hadn't attempted to remove their dead out of the trench. Our fellows cursed the natives in Hindustani and finding that of no avail commenced to kick and hit them about and also threatened to shoot or bayonet the lot of them if they did not put their heads over the parapet: in fact they put the wind up them more thoroughly than what the German shells had. It was quite possible that the natives might have hopped it in the dark, but if they had attempted to in the day they would have been mowed down by our own men as well as by the enemy. Native infantry were no good in France. Some writers in the papers wrote at the time they couldn't stand the cold weather; but the truth was that they suffered from cold feet, and a few enemy shells exploding round their trenches were enough to demoralise the majority of them. But there was one thing about them: over three years later the Battalion passed through a village they had been billeted in, and I saw several half-caste mites playing in the street. One old Expeditionary Force man remarked to me that if the bloody niggers were no good at fighting they were good at something else that sounded much the same.

That night we heard the enemy working on our front, but we didn't know whether they were entrenching themselves or not. The next morning a heavy mist hung over everywhere and it was impossible to see ten yards ahead. Buffalo Bill decided to send a patrol out, consisting of a corporal and two men; in my battalion throughout the whole of the War no privates were ever warned to go out on patrol—volunteers were always called for. Corporal Pardoe, Private Miles and I went out on that patrol; our orders were simply to proceed as far as we could up the willow ditch and to discover what we could. We had gone a considerable way past our listening-post when we halted. Pardoe said: "How far do you think we have come?" "Over two hundred yards," said Miles, and I agreed with him. The mist was still heavy and we were listening intently. Presently we heard voices not far off and the sounds of men working. We were wondering whether to work up closer or to go back and report, when all of a sudden the mist blew away, and there, a little over a hundred yards in front of us, were new enemy trenches. The enemy were taking advantage of the mist and working on the parapet: some were a good thirty yards from their trench —they had been levelling some corn-stacks so as to have a clear line of fire. Pardoe got on one side of the ditch, and Miles and I on the other, and opened out with rapid fire. We had our rifles resting on the banks. The three of us had been marksmen all through our soldiering: each of us could get off twenty-five aimed rounds a minute and it was impossible to miss at that distance. We had downed half a dozen men before they realised what was happening; then they commenced to jump back in the trench. Those that were out in front started to run, but we bowled them over like rabbits. It put me in mind of firing at the " running man " on a peace-time course of musketry. Against we had expended our magazines which held ten rounds there wasn't a live enemy to be seen, and the whole affair had not lasted half a minute. We quickly reloaded our magazines, which took us a couple of seconds, turned around, and ran towards our trench, each of us in turn halting to fire five rounds covering fire at the enemy's trench.

The mist had now lifted everywhere: we could see our own trench quite plainly and bullets were zipping around us. Our men on the extreme left of the platoon had opened fire on the enemy's trench, but the men in line with the ditch were not allowed to fire for fear of hitting us (we learned this when we got back). We arrived at our listening-post, jumped the little bank and laid down, properly winded. We were not out of the soup yet: we still had forty yards to travel before we got back in our trench. We were safe from rifle-fire as long as we crawled on our bellies to the parapet but when we got to the end of the ditch we would have to jump out in the open before getting into the trench, and we knew full well that the enemy would be waiting for that move. We arrived at the end of the ditch and there we heard Buffalo Bill shouting over for us to remain where we were for a couple of minutes, and then to get back in the trench one by one. He passed word up the trench for the whole platoon to open out with rapid fire which would make the enemy keep their heads down and give us a decent chance to get home without being hit. We got back safely; I never knew how well I could jump until that morning. I was out of the ditch and into the trench in the twinkling of an eye: Duffy said that I cleared the parapet like a Grand National winner. The corporal made his report to Buffalo Bill who was delighted at our brush-up. Miles and I did not know what narrow squeaks we had had until someone noticed a bullet-hole through Miles's trousers and two more through the right sleeve of my tunic.

About an hour later Miles was busy sniping. In those early

days of trench-warfare both sides were pretty reckless, and it was no uncommon sight on our front, and especially on our right front, to see a German pop up out of his trench and make a dart for the village. He did not always get there, and as time went on both sides respected the marksmanship of each other so much so that no one dared to show a finger. Miles had just claimed to have popped a German over when he got a bullet through the head himself. That same evening Corporal Pardoe also got killed in the same way, after getting away with that stunt in the morning it was tough luck on the both of them.

Our dead we used to put on the back of the paparet and we carried them at night to a place just behind the line and buried them there. All companies carried their dead to the same place. If a dead man's clothes or boots were in good condition we never hesitated to take them off him, especially when they would fit a man. My own puttees were in ribbons, so I took the Corporal's, which were in good condition. In a belt that Corporal Pardoe wore next to his skin they found about sixty English sovereigns, besides French money. None of it went back to his next-of-kin. I could have had some but I didn't want to touch it: I was satisfied with his puttees. We began to sap out to our left and right platoons and dug a trench from the officers' bay back to a dip in the ground about twenty yards from a farmhouse. We used to fill our water-bottles at the farm at night, and each man's water-bottle had to last him twenty-four hours.

There was no such thing as cooked food or hot tea at this stage of the War, and rations were very scarce: we were lucky if we got our four biscuits a man daily, a pound tin of bully between two, a tin of jam between six, and the rum ration which was about a tablespoonful and a half. Even at this early period the jam was rotten and one firm that supplied it must have made hundreds of thousands of pounds profit out of it—the stuff they put in instead of fruit and sugar! One man swore that if ever he got back to England he would make it his first duty to shoot up the managing director and all the other heads of that particular firm. Tobacco, cigarettes and matches were also very scarce. We had plenty of small-arm ammunition but no rifle-oil or rifle-rag to clean our rifles with. We used to cut pieces off our shirts for use as rifle-rags, and some of us who had bought small tins of Vaseline (in villages we passed through during our Aisne advance) for use on sore heels or chafed legs, used to grease our rifles with that. A rifle soon got done up without oil in these conditions. Our sanitary arrangements were very bad: we used empty bully-beef tins for urinating in, throwing it over the back of the parapet. If a man was taken short during the day he had to use the trench he was in and then throw it over the back of the trench and throw earth after it.

One night there was an enemy attack which we beat off and the next morning some corpses were to be seen lying just out in front of us: they were wearing spiked helmets. We crawled out the next night and went through their packs, taking anything they had of value from them. The spiked helmets we intended to keep as souvenirs, but we soon came to the conclusion that it was no good keeping souvenirs of that sort when any moment we may be dancing a two-step in another world. So we used them as latrine buckets, throwing them over the parapet at the back when we had used them. A few days later we had completed a trench back to a dip in the ground where we dug a square pit which we used as a latrine: we could go back in the day to it and be quite safe from rifle-fire.

The only artillery covering our front were two eighteen-pounders which had a limited number of shells to fire each day. They were so hard up for shells that they couldn't spare a shell to fire at a large straw rick on our right from which some enemy snipers were causing us casualties. The young artillery officer with the guns often used to come up to our trench during the night, and sometimes bring us tobacco and cigarettes: he was a very cheery soul. Two companies of Argyll and Sutherland Highlanders were in reserve to the whole of the Brigade front.

The 29th October, 1914, was a miserable rainy day. One young soldier remarked that he did not believe anyone was in support or reserve to us. Big Duffy said, "What the hell does it matter about supports or reserves? We have plenty of small-arm ammunition, and as long as our rifles hold out we can stop any attack, especially if they make it during the day." The night before a party of Engineers had come up to our trench and had driven some posts in the ground about fifteen yards in front with one strand of barbed wire stretching across them. It looked like a clothes line during the day. We had put a covering party about thirty yards in front of them while they were doing the work. The Old Soldier of the platoon remarked that the British Government must be terribly hard up, what with short rations, no rifle-oil, no shells, and now sending Engineers up to the front line to stretch one single bloody strand of barbed wire out, which he had no doubt was the only single bloody strand in the whole of France, and which a bloody giraffe could rise up and walk under. It was enough to make good soldiers weep tears of blood, he said, the way things were going on. This was the first and last time Engineers put out wire in front of the Battalion: after this we always put out our own, no matter where we were.

Well, it was still raining on the night of the 29th when heavy rifle-fire broke out on the extreme right of our front. At the same time our listening-post sent back to say that the enemy were getting out of their trenches, so the post was called in at once, and presently we could see dim forms in front of us. Then our right platoon opened out with rapid fire. We opened out with rapid fire too. We were firing as fast as we could pull the trigger: no man can take a sight in the dark so we were firing direct in front of us. One of our eighteen-pounders had fired a star shell which enabled us to see the enemy dropping down on their stomachs. Five or six ordinary shells were fired too, and one of them set fire to the straw-rick on our right front which was soon burning merrily. The enemy in front of us were held up for the time being, so we opened fire on our right front where we cou see some more of them quite clearly by the light of the burning rick. On the left of our left platoon the enemy had captured one platoon-frontage of trench from the Middlesex, but a company of the Argylls had been rushed up and soon re-captured it. The platoon of Middlesex holding that trench had lost a lot of men a few days before, and the trench was thinly manned.

One of our chaps in turning to get another bandolier of ammunition out of the box, noticed three men coming towards our trench from the back. " Halt! Hands up! Who are you?" he challenged. We turned around. We knew it was quite possible for some of the enemy to have got through the gap between us and our left platoon and come around the back of us. Instead of answering the challenge two of the men dropped on their stomachs and the other mumbled something which we did not understand. Two men opened fire at him and he dropped; then one of the men on the ground shouted: " You bloody fools! We're artillery signallers and you've shot our officer." We asked them why they did not answer when challenged. They said that they had left it to the officer to answer, and that they were running a telephone line out to our trench. He was the young officer who used to visit us: one bullet had gone through his jaw and the other through his right side. The two men carried him back and we hoped that he would recover from his wounds; but we never heard any more news of him.

The attack was still going on: we kept up a continuous fire on our front, but one by one our rifles began to jam. Word was passed up the trench for Richards and Smith to go down to the officers' bay. When we two arrived there we were warned to stay in that bay for the night. In a short time mine and Smith's rifles were about the only two that were firing in the whole of the platoon. Then ours were done up too: the fact was that continual rain had made the parapet very muddy and the mud had got into the rifle mechanism, which needed oiling in any case, and continual firing had heated the metal so that between the one thing and the other it was impossible to open and close the bolts. The same thing had happened all along the Battalion front.

About a couple of hours before dawn, word was passed along the trench for every man to get out and lay down five paces in front of the parapet and be prepared to meet the enemy with the bayonet. When everyone was out Buffalo Bill walked up and down the platoon and told us all that we would have to fight to the last man. He had his sword in one hand and his revolver in the other; officers carried their swords in action at this time. We were all dead-beat, and if any man had slept two hours during the last seven days without being disturbed he had been a very lucky man. Smith said to me: " I expect this is our last time around, Dick, but I hope we take a few of them on the long journey with us." I replied that I was going to do my level best in that way. The straw-rick had practically burned itself out, but it had now stopped raining and we could see more clearly in front of us. The enemy were about thirty yards away. They had halted and begun talking together. One of them fired a rocket; it was a very poor one, it spluttered into sparks and fell only a few paces in front of them.

There was no firing all along our front. The enemy were not firing either; perhaps their rifles were done up the same as our own. In spite of the danger I had great difficulty in keeping my eyes open, and the man on the left of Smith had commenced to snore. Smith drove his elbow into his ribs. The Second-in-Command of the company had dozed off too. Buffalo Bill spoke to him sharply a few times before he answered; even the knowledge that it might be their last minute on earth did not prevent some of the men from dozing off. Sleep will beat any man and under any conditions. It was passed along for us to get up on our feet to receive the charge. But no charge came. It was getting a little lighter, and just before dawn broke the enemy turned around and hurried back to their trench; and we didn't have a single good rifle to fire a round at them. We had two machine-guns in the Battalion at this time, one in the centre and the other on the extreme right, and both had done good work during the night; but they were done up too, the same as our rifles.

We got back in our trench wet through to the skin (but we were getting used to that) and commenced to clean our rifles. This proved a difficult job; but the metal had cooled now and some of us who still had some Vaseline left handed it around and we got them all in working order again. A sentry was posted in each bay and we snatched a few hours' sleep, the best way we could. Our rations that day, October 30th, were three biscuits, a tin of bully between four, a spoonful of jam and our rum ration. To hungry, half-starved men it was a flea-bite. The Old Soldier remarked that the Government was trying to make us as fierce as Bengal tigers so that all the Germans we killed in future we would also devour as well. We could now see the effects of our night's work: a lot of the enemy dead lay out in front. One of the men in our left platoon threw his equipment off, jumped on the parapet with his hands above his head and then pointed to a wounded German who was trying to crawl to our lines. He then went forward, got hold of the wounded man and carried him in, the enemy clapping their hands and cheering until he had disappeared into our trench.

We were constantly sapping out to our left and right platoons whenever we had the chance and now had plenty of room in the trench. There was a decent orchard in the farm at the back of our trench, and Stevens and I used to slip over in the night and fill his pack full of apples—Stevens was the only man in the whole platoon with a pack. We had to fill our bellies with *something*. There was one cow and one pig left in the farm. Buffalo Bill had the pig killed and sent back to the company cooks with instructions to melt a lot of the fat down and cook the remainder; the pork came up the following night and we enjoyed it greatly although we had no bread to eat with it. The fat that was melted down we used for greasing our rifles with. With the exception of one dicksee of tea, which was stone-cold against it reached us, this was the only occasion that the cooks had to do anything for us the whole of the time we were there.

One morning the officers were about to have breakfast at the end of the trench leading to their bay, from where it was possible by stooping low in a ditch to get into the farm by daylight. One of the officers' servants, whose duty it was to milk the cow so that the officers could have milk in their tea, reported that the cow had broken loose and that they would have to do without milk that morning. Buffalo Bill jumped to his feet, revolver out, and roared at the man: "My God, you'll catch that cow and milk her or I'll blow your ruddy brains out!" The cow was grazing about twenty yards away where there was a dip in the ground. The man ran after her, the cow ran up the slope in the rear, the man following; if they kept on they would soon be in full view of the enemy. Buffalo Bill saw the danger the man would soon be in. He shouted: "Come back, you ruddy fool, and never mind the cow!" The man evidently did not hear him, but kept on. One or two bullets hit up the dirt around him. The enemy had been sending over a few light shells that morning, and now they sent over one or two more. One burst quite close to the cow. The cow got killed and the man received a nice wound in the leg which took him back to Blighty. I expect when he got home he blessed Buffalo Bill, also the cow and the German who shot him: even at this time we used to reckon that anyone who got a clean wound through the leg or arm was an extremely fortunate man.

One night some of the men in the company on our right were pinching chickens out of the farm when Buffalo Bill appeared on the scene. He roared like a lion and threatened to blow their ruddy brains out if he caught them again and told them that everything on the farm belonged to *him*. Not many hours later there wasn't a feathered fowl left on that farm: the men had pinched the lot. His favourite punishment from now on was forty-eight hours continual digging in a support trench. Yet he never troubled himself to see whether the punishment was being done or not, and in some instances that punishment was a blessing in disguise because we took things far easier behind than in the front trench. I never remembered him having any favourites: he treated all the men in the same way—like dirt.

The enemy made a half-hearted attack on us a few nights after the 29th, but we stopped them before they had come far. After this we settled down to ordinary trench-warfare, and were finally relieved on the night of the 15th November.

By this time we were as lousy as rooks. No man had washed or shaved for nearly a month, and with our beards and mud we looked a proper ragtime band of brigands.

Twenty-four hours later, after a wash, shave and sleep we were different men, and in another twenty-four hours we had marched through Armentières and relieved some troops in trenches on the right of Houplines. We were relieved eight days later and billeted in a cotton factory in that place. We thought we were going to have a rest, but we were wrong: every night we had to go up the line digging communication trenches leading back from the front line. During this time we were issued with caps and packs. It was the first cap I had worn since August.

About one hundred of us were sent to a village outside Armentières, where the King inspected some of his Army. I hadn't seen the King since he was Prince of Wales, when early in 1905 he held a garden party in the grounds of Sikundra Taj, about six miles from Agra in India. I was present as a signaller at that party, and although over nine years had elapsed he did not look a day older. No king in the history of England ever reviewed more loyal or lousier troops than what His Majesty did that day. To look at us we were as clean as new pins, but in our shirts, pants and trousers were whole platoons of crawlers. His Majesty decorated one of our sergeants with the Distinguished Conduct Medal, who had won it at Fromelles.

There were fifty-eight Number One Field Punishment prisoners in the Battalion at this time. When out of action they were locked up and had to do all the dirty jobs that wanted doing, and were tied up two hours a day (by the ankles and wrists, generally) to the carts and wagons in the transport lines. Outside the factory on the one side of the street was a wall with some iron railings sunk in. One afternoon the fifty-eight prisoners were tied up to the railings and I should think three parts of the female population of Houplines and Armentières paraded that street in the afternoon. Some were sympathetic and some were laughing. The prisoners resented this very much, and one remarked that he didn't mind being tied up but he didn't want a bloody lot of frog-eating bastards gaping at him. There were some hard cases among the Number One's and the majority were continually in trouble, but these on the whole were the finest soldiers, in action, that I ever saw. During the first four months of the War, if a man was sentenced to imprisonment he left the Battalion to serve his sentence, but afterwards it was only an isolated case that was sent away. I have known men who were sentenced to five or ten years imprisonment stay with the Battalion, and in less than a month's time have their sentences washed out for gallant conduct in the field.

One man in my company whom we called Broncho was the hardest case of the lot. Whenever we were out of action he was always up in front of the Colonel for some crime or other. He was a grand front-line soldier, and most of his crimes were caused by overbearing non-commissioned officers. There was an old saying that in the Army they tamed lions; but Broncho was never tamed. I was one of the escort to him one morning when he was in front of the Colonel. His crime was too serious for the Company Commander to deal with. It was insubordination to an N.C.O.—he had told a corporal that he was no bloody good. The Colonel gave Broncho the usual twenty-eight days Number One and warned him that he would be put up against the wall and shot if he did not alter. Broncho then reminded the Colonel that it was the third time he had given him that warning and that he didn't care a damn whether he was shot or not. "March him out!" shouted the Colonel. He was brought up again next morning and sentenced to another twenty-eight days Number One for insubordination to his Commanding Officer.

But he got the whole lot washed out a fortnight later in the following manner. The enemy had been shelling so badly in the rear of us that all communication had broken down, and Buffalo Bill called for a volunteer to take a message back to Battalion Headquarters. Anyone who took the message back would have to make his way through the barrage and the communication trench had not yet been dug. Broncho shouted out: "I'll take the bloody message," and it was handed to him. It was a hundred to one he would be blown to bits before he had gone sixty yards—he not only arrived at Battalion Headquarters with the message but also came back with an answer. He was recommended for a decoration for this. A week previous when returning from a night-patrol one of the patrol had got badly wounded by unaimed fire; and it was Broncho who carried him back safely to the trench. For these two acts he had a term of imprisonment washed out and about six months accumulated Number Ones; but he got no decoration.

The third Battle of Ypres commenced on July 31st and our Division were sent to the Belgian coast. We travelled by train and barge and arrived at Dunkirk. A little higher up the coast was a place named Bray Dunes, where we stayed about a week, and the architect and I went for many a long swim in the sea. We moved closer to the line along the coast and arrived at a place which the majority of inhabitants had only just evacuated. In July a British division had relieved the Belgian troops around this part. Ever since November 1914 the people had been living in peace and security in the towns and villages in this area, but as soon as the British troops took over the enemy began shelling these places and the people cleared out. In one place we were in the people were in the act of leaving and complaining very bitterly because the arrival of British troops had caused a lot of shelling and forced them to leave their homes. In one pretty village by the sea there hadn't been enough of shells exploded in it to have frightened a poll parrot away, yet there wasn't a soul left there now. They were evidently not such good stickers as the French people who worried less about their lives than about their property and hung on to the last possible minute.

At Bray Dunes I got in conversation with a Canadian officer who was in charge of some men building a light railway. He said it was a good job that the States came in the War as the French were ready to throw the sponge up. A few days later two of our signallers overheard a full colonel of the Staff telling our Colonel that he did not know what would have happened if the United States had not come in when they did. It was common knowledge among the Staff that the whole of the French Army were more or less demoralised, and the States coming in had to a great extent been the means of restoring their morale. We got wind that our Division and another had been sent up the coast to try and break through the German Front and capture Ostend. This was freely discussed by the officers, but no break through was attempted owing to so little progress being made on the Ypres front.

One of the largest concentration prison camps I ever saw was erected in this area. It was estimated to hold between ten and fifteen thousand prisoners, but all I saw in it were two solitary prisoners who must have been very lonely in so large a place.

On the night the Battalion went in the line I went on leave. It was eighteen months since I had the last one and as usual I made the most of it. I didn't spend the whole of it in pubs: I spent two days going for long tramps in the mountains, which I thoroughly enjoyed after being so long in a flat country. I was presented with a gold watch, in recognition of winning the D.C.M., which I still have, but it has been touch-and-go with it several times since the War. Probably if there hadn't been an inscription on it I should have parted with it. This time every man of military age that I met wanted to shake hands with me and also ask my advice on how to evade military service, or, if they were forced to go, which would be the best corps to join that would keep them away from the firing line. They were wonderfully patriotic at smoking concerts given in honour of soldiers returning from the Front, but their patriotism never extended beyond that.

When I landed back at Boulogne I came across the man who had been shot through his cheeks at Bois Grenier in April 1915. If anything, that bullet had improved his appearance. He now had a nice little dimple on each side of his face. We had a chat. I asked what he was doing now and he said that he had a Staff job, as a military policeman around the Docks. He told me very seriously that if it was possible, and he had the name and address of the German that shot him, he would send him the largest parcel he could pack and a hundred-franc note as well. He was having the time of his life on his present job and had one of the smartest fillies in Boulogne, who was the goods in every way. As I left him I could not help thinking how lucky some men were and how unlucky were others.

When I arrived back I found that the Division had left the coastal area on short notice. All returning leave men of the Division were in a little camp outside Dunkirk. One night some German planes came over bombing and one of our searchlights kept a plane in its rays for some time. Anti-aircraft guns, machine-guns and Lewis guns, and we with our rifles were all banging at him, but he got away with it. Whilst everyone was busy firing at that one, his friends were busy dropping their bombs on Dunkirk. It was very rare that a plane flying at any height was brought down by anti-aircraft guns or rifle-fire but we lost a lot of planes on the Somme by rifle-fire when they came down very low, machine-gunning the enemy before our troops attacks. German planes used to do the same thing and seldom got away with it either.

I rejoined the Battalion in a village near Ypres and guessed that we would soon be in the blood tub. Ricco and Paddy had been made full corporals but Paddy had taken a lot of persuading before he consented to be made an N.C.O. He was sent back to Division Headquarters for a special course of signalling and was lucky enough to miss the next show we were in. Our Colonel went on leave and missed the show too. The name of our Acting-Colonel was Major Poore. He was not an old regimental officer but had been posted to us some six months before from the Yeomanry, I believe. He was a very big man, about fifty years of age, slightly deaf, and his favourite expression was " What, what! " He was a very decent officer. A tall, slender young lieutenant who had just returned from leave was made Assistant-Adjutant for the show. I believe he was given that job because he was an excellent map-reader. As we were marching along the road, Sealyham asked him if he had come across Mr. Sassoon during his leave. He replied that he hadn't and that he had spent a good part of his leave trying to find out where he was but had failed to get any news at all. This young officer had joined the Battalion about the same time as Mr. Sassoon and we old hands thought he was a man and a half to spend his leave looking for a pal. His name was Casson. I wrote it down first here as Carson, but an old soldiering pal tells me that I had it wrong. Mr. Casson was said to be a first-class pianist, but trench warfare did not give him much opportunity to show his skill at that. If he was as good a pianist as he was a cool soldier he must have been a treat to hear.

During the night we passed through a wood where a Very-light dump had been exploded by a German shell. It was like witnessing a fireworks display at home. We stayed in the wood for the night. Our Brigade were in reserve and ready to be called upon at any moment. Orders were given that no fires were to be lit. September 26th, 1917, was a glorious day from the weather point of view and when dawn was breaking Ricco and I who were crack hands at making smokeless fires had found a dump of pickhandles which when cut up in thin strips answered very well. We soon cooked our bacon and made tea for ourselves and the bank clerk and architect, and made no more smoke than a man would have done smoking a cigarette. We had at least made sure of our breakfast which might be the last we would ever have.

At 8 a.m. orders arrived that the Battalion would move off to the assistance of the Australians who had made an attack early in the morning on Polygon Wood. Although the attack was successful they had received heavy casualties and were now hard pressed themselves. Young Mr. Casson led the way, as cool as a cucumber. One part of the ground we travelled over was nothing but lakes and boggy ground and the whole of the Battalion were strung out in Indian file walking along a track about eighteen inches wide. We had just got out of this bad ground but were still travelling in file when the enemy opened out with a fierce bombardment. Just in front of me half a dozen men fell on the side of the track: it was like as if a Giant Hand had suddenly swept them to one side. The Battalion had close on a hundred casualties before they were out of that valley. If a man's best pal was wounded he could not stop to dress his wounds for him.

We arrived on some rising ground and joined forces with the Australians. I expected to find a wood but it was undulating land with a tree dotted here and there and little banks running in different directions. About half a mile in front of us was a ridge of trees, and a few concrete pillboxes of different sizes. The ground that we were now on and some of the pillboxes had only been taken some hours previously. I entered one pillbox during the day and found eighteen dead Germans inside. There was not a mark on one of them; one of our heavy shells had made a direct hit on the top of it and they were killed by concussion, but very little damage had been done to the pillbox. They were all constructed with reinforced concrete and shells could explode all round them but the flying pieces would never penetrate the concrete. There were small windows in the sides and by jumping in and out of shell holes attacking troops could get in bombing range: if a bomb was thrown through one of the windows the pillbox was as good as captured.

There was a strong point called Black Watch Corner which was a trench facing north, south, east and west. A few yards outside the trench was a pillbox which was Battalion Headquarters. The bank clerk, architect and I got in the trench facing our front, and I was soon on friendly terms with an Australian officer, whom his men called Mr. Diamond. He was wearing the ribbon of the D.C.M., which he told me he had won in Gallipoli while serving in the ranks and had been granted a commission some time later. About a hundred yards in front of us was a bank which extended for hundreds of yards across the ground behind which the Australians were. Our chaps charged through them to take a position in front and Captain Mann, our Adjutant, who was following close behind, fell with a bullet through his head. The enemy now began to heavily bombard our position and Major Poore and Mr. Casson left the pillbox and got in a large shell hole which had a deep narrow trench dug in the bottom of it. They were safer there than in the pillbox, yet in less than fifteen minutes an howitzer shell had pitched clean in it, killing the both of them.

During the day shells fell all around the pillbox but not one made a direct hit on it. The ground rocked and heaved with the bursting shells. The enemy were doing their best to obliterate the strong points that they had lost. Mr. Diamond and I were mucking-in with a tin of Maconochies when a dud shell landed clean in the trench, killing the man behind me, and burying itself in the side of the trench by me. Our Maconochie was spoilt but I opened another one and we had the luck to eat that one without a clod of earth being thrown over it. If that shell had not been a dud we should have needed no more Maconochies in this world. I had found eight of them in a sandbag before I left the wood and brought them along with me. I passed the other six along our trench, but no one seemed to want them with the exception of the bank clerk and architect who had got into my way of thinking that it was better to enter the next world with a full belly than an empty one.

The bombardment lasted until the afternoon and then ceased. Not one of us had hardly moved a yard for some hours but we had been lucky in our part of the trench, having only two casualties. In two other parts of the strong point every man had been killed or wounded. The shells had been bursting right on the parapets and in the trenches, blowing them to pieces. One part of the trench was completely obliterated. The fourth part of the strong point had also been lucky, having only three casualties. Mr. Diamond said that we could expect a counter attack at any minute. He lined us up on the parapet in extended order outside the trench and told us to lie down. Suddenly a German plane swooped very low, machine-gunning us. We brought him down not before he had done some damage, several being killed including our Aid Post Sergeant.

A few minutes later Dr. Dunn temporarily resigned from the Royal Army Medical Corps. He told me to get him a rifle and bayonet and a bandolier of ammunition. I told him that he had better have a revolver but he insisted on having what he had asked me to get. I found them for him and slinging the rifle over his shoulder he commenced to make his way over to the troops behind the bank. I accompanied him. Just before we reached there our chaps who were hanging on to a position in front of it started to retire back. The doctor barked at them to line up with the others. Only Captain Radford and four platoon officers were left in the Battalion and the Doctor unofficially took command.

We and the Australians were all mixed up in extended order. Everyone had now left the strong point and were lined up behind the bank, which was about three feet high. We had lent a Lewis-gun team to the 5th Scottish Rifles on our right, and when it began to get dark the Doctor sent me with a verbal message to bring them back with me, if they were still in the land of the living. When I arrived at the extreme right of our line I asked the right-hand man if he was in touch with the 5th Scottish. He replied that he had no more idea than a crow where they were, but guessed that they were somewhere in front and to the right of him. I now made my way very carefully over the ground. After I had walked some way I began to crawl. I was liable any moment to come in contact with a German post or trench. I thought I saw someone moving in front of me, so I slid into a shell hole and landed on a dead German. I waited in that shell hole for a while trying to pierce the darkness in front. I resumed my journey and skirting one shell hole, a wounded German was shrieking aloud in agony; he must have been hit low down but I could not stop for no wounded man. I saw the forms of two men in a shallow trench and did not know whether they were the 5th Scottish or the Germans until I was sharply challenged in good Glasgow English. When I got in their trench they told me that they had only just spotted me when they challenged. The Lewis-gun team were still kicking and my journey back with them was a lot easier than the outgoing one.

I reported to the Doctor that there was a gap of about one hundred yards between the 5th Scottish Rifles and we; and he went himself to remedy it. The whole of the British Front that night seemed to be in a semi-circle. We had sent up some S O S rockets and no matter where we looked we could see our S O S rockets going up in the air: they were only used when the situation was deemed critical and everybody seemed to be in the same plight as ourselves. The bank clerk and I got into a shell hole to snatch a couple of hours rest, and although there were two dead Germans in it we were soon fast asleep. I was woke up to guide a ration party to us who were on their way. Dawn was now breaking and I made my way back about six hundred yards, where I met them. We landed safely with the rations.

Major Kearsley had just arrived from B Echelon to take command of the Battalion. The Brigadier-General of the

Australians had also arrived and was sorting his men out. It was the only time during the whole of the War that I saw a brigadier with the first line of attacking troops. Some brigadiers that I knew never moved from Brigade Headquarters. It was also the first time I had been in action with the Australians and I found them very brave men. There was also an excellent spirit of comradeship between officers and men.

We were moving about quite freely in the open but we did not know that a large pillbox a little over an hundred yards in front of us was still held by the enemy. They must have all been having a snooze, otherwise some of us would have been riddled. Major Kearsley, the Doctor and I went out reconnoitring. We were jumping in and out of shell holes when a machine-gun opened out from somewhere in front, the bullets knocking up the dust around the shell holes we had just jumped into. They both agreed that the machine-gun had been fired from the pillbox about a hundred yards in front of us. We did some wonderful jumping and hopping, making our way back to the bank. The enemy's artillery had also opened out and an hour later shells were bursting all over our front and in the rear of us.

A sapping platoon of one sergeant and twenty men under the command of The Athlete were on the extreme left of the bank, and the Major and I made our way towards them. We found the men but not the officer and sergeant, and when the Major inquired where they were they replied that they were both down the dug-out. There was a concrete dug-out at this spot which had been taken the day before. I shouted down for them to come up, and the Major gave the young officer a severe reprimand for being in the dug-out, especially as he knew our men had just started another attack. Our chaps and the 5th Scottish Rifles had attacked on our right about fifteen minutes previously. The Major gave The Athlete orders that if the pillbox in front was not taken in fifteen minutes he was to take his platoon and capture it and then dig a trench around it. If the pillbox was captured during that time he was still to take his platoon and sap around it. I felt very sorry for The Athlete. This was the first real action he had been in and he had the most windy sergeant in the Battalion with him. Although The Athlete did not know it, this sergeant had been extremely lucky after one of his Arras stunts that he had not been court-martialled and tried on the charge of cowardice in face of the enemy.

We arrived back at our position behind the bank. We and the Australians were in telephone communication with no one; all messages went by runners. Ricco, the bank clerk and the architect were running messages, the majority of our Battalion runners being casualties. Sealyham was still kicking and Lane was back in B Echelon; it was the first time for over two years he had been left out of the line. The Sapping-Sergeant came running along the track by the bank and informed the Major that The Athlete had sent him for further instructions as he was not quite certain what he had to do. The Major very nearly lost his temper and told me to go back with the Sergeant and tell him what he had to do. Just as we arrived at the sapping-platoon we saw some of our chaps rushing towards the pillbox, which surrendered, one officer and twenty men being inside it.

C and D Companies were now merged into one company. They advanced and took up a position behind a little bank about a hundred yards in front of the pillbox. I informed The Athlete that he had to take his platoon and sap around the pillbox, and that this was a verbal message which Major Kearsley had given me for him. I left him and the Sergeant conferring together and made my way back by a different route.

The enemy were now shelling very heavily and occasionally the track was being sprayed by machine-gun bullets. I met a man of one of our companies with six German prisoners whom he told me he had to take back to a place called Clapham Junction, where he would hand them over. He then had to return and rejoin his company. The shelling was worse behind us than where we were and it happened more than once that escort and prisoners had been killed making their way back. I had known this man about eighteen months and he said, " Look here, Dick. About an hour ago I lost the best pal I ever had, and he was worth all these six Jerries put together. I'm not going to take them far before I put them out of mess." Just after they passed me I saw the six dive in one large shell hole and he had a job to drive them out. I expect being under their own shelling would make them more nervous than under ours. Some little time later I saw him coming back and I knew it was impossible for him to have reached Clapham Junction and returned in the time, especially by the way his prisoners had been ducking and jumping into shell holes. As he passed me again he said: " I done them in as I said, about two hundred yards back. Two bombs did the trick." He had not walked twenty yards beyond me when he fell himself: a shell-splinter had gone clean through him. I had often heard some of our chaps say that they had done their prisoners in whilst taking them back but this was the only case I could vouch for, and no doubt the loss of his pal had upset him very much.

During the afternoon the Major handed me a message to take to A Company, which consisted of the survivors of two companies now merged into one under the command of a young platoon officer. They had to advance and take up a position about two hundred yards in front of them. The ground over which I had to travel had been occupied by the enemy a little while before and the Company were behind a little bank which was being heavily shelled. I slung my rifle, and after I had proceeded some way I pulled my revolver out for safety. Shells were falling here and there and I was jumping in and out of shell holes. When I was about fifty yards from the Company, in getting out of a large shell hole I saw a German pop up from another shell hole in front of me and rest his rifle on the lip of the shell hole. He was about to fire at our chaps in front who had passed him by without noticing him. He could never have heard me amidst all the din around: I expect it was some instinct made him turn around with the rifle at his shoulder. I fired first and as the rifle fell out of his hands I fired again. I made sure he was dead before I left him. If he hadn't popped his head up when he did no doubt I would have passed the shell hole he was in. I expect he had been shamming death and every now and then popping up and sniping at our chaps in front. If I hadn't spotted him he would have soon put my lights out after I had passed him and if any of his bullets had found their mark it would not have been noticed among the Company, who were getting men knocked out now and then by the shells that were bursting around them. This little affair was nothing out of the ordinary in a runner's work when in attacks.

The shelling was very severe around here and when I arrived I shouted for the officer. A man pointed along the bank. When I found him and delivered the message he shouted above the noise that he had not been given much time; I had delivered the message only three minutes before they were timed to advance. During the short time they had been behind the bank one-third of the Company had become casualties. When I arrived back I could only see the Major. All the signallers had gone somewhere on messages and the Doctor was some distance away attending wounded men whom he came across. He seemed to be temporarily back in the R.A.M.C.

The Major asked me how my leg was. I replied that it was

all right when I was moving about, but it became very stiff after I had been resting. During the two days many pieces and flying splinters of shells and bullets must have missed me by inches. But when a small piece of spent shrapnel had hit me on the calf of the leg I knew all about it. I thought at the time that someone had hit me with a coal hammer. I had the bottom of my trousers doubled inside the sock on the calf and also my puttee doubled in the same place which, no doubt, had helped to minimise the blow. If it had not been a spent piece it would have gone clean through the calf and given me a beautiful blighty wound, which I don't mind admitting I was still hoping for.

Ricco in returning from running a message to Brigade had come across the ration party of another battalion who had all been killed, and he had brought back with him a lovely sandbag full of officers' rations. There were several kinds of tinned stuffs and three loaves of bread. The bank clerk, architect and Sealyham had also arrived back and we all had a muck in. The way the bank clerk and architect got a tin of cooked sausages across their chests made me wonder whether their forefathers had not been pure-bred Germans. The officers who the bag of rations were intended for could never have enjoyed them better than we did.

Just as we finished our feed Major Kearsley called me and told me to follow him. I could see we were making our way towards where we had visited the sapping-platoon, but I could not see any men sapping around the pillbox and was wondering if they had been knocked out. When we arrived at the concrete dug-out some of the sapping-platoons were still outside it and some had become casualties, but The Athlete and the Sergeant were still down in the dug-out. I shouted down and told them to come up and the Major asked The Athlete the reason why he had not carried out his orders. He replied that the shelling had been so intense around the pillbox after it was taken that he decided to stop where he was until it slackened. Then he had seen our troops advance again and he was under the impression that the trench would not be needed. The Major again gave him a severe reprimand and told him to take what men he had left and sap around the pillbox as he had been ordered at first.

Shortly after, the Major said he was going to visit the positions our companies had lately taken. We set off on our journey and when we passed through the Australians they started shouting, " Come back, you bloody fools! They've got everything in line with machine-gun fire." We took no notice and by jumping in shell holes now and again we reached halfway there. We had only advanced a few yards further when in jumping into a large shell hole an enemy machine-gun opened out and the ground around us was sprayed with bullets. The Major was shot clean through the leg just above the ankle. As I dressed his wound we discussed the possibility of returning to the bank. I said that it would be dusk in two hours' time and that we had better wait until then. He replied that he could not do that as he would have to hand over the command of the Battalion, and also wanted to discuss matters with the Commanding Officer of the 5th Scottish Rifles, and that we would make our way back at once. He clambered out of the shell hole and I followed. He hopped back to the bank, taking a zig-zag course and I the same. How we were not riddled was a mystery: the machine-gun had been playing a pretty tune behind us.

We met the Doctor and Captain Radford, who had been sent for some time before, advancing along the bank. They had decided to shift Battalion Headquarters more on the left of the bank and they had just shifted in time. The spot where Battalion Headquarters had been was now being blown to pieces. Shells were bursting right along the bank and for a considerable way back and men were being blowed yards in the air. The Major said that the Battalion would be relieved at dusk and he would try to stick it until then; but the Doctor warned him, if he did, that it might be the cause of him losing his leg.

He then handed over the command to Captain Radford, who said that he would much prefer the Doctor taking command, as he seemed to have a better grip of the situation than what he had. But the Major said he could not do that as the Doctor was a non-combatant, but that they could make any arrangements they liked when he had left. We made our way to the 5th Scottish Rifles and met their colonel outside a little dug-out. He mentioned that only three young platoon-officers were left in his battalion. They went in the dug-out to discuss matters and when we left the Major had a difficult job to walk. The Casualty Clearing Station was at Clapham Junction and all along the track leading down to it lay stretcher-bearers and bandaged men who had been killed making their way back. Many men who had received what they thought were nice blighty wounds had been killed along this track. The previous day the track, in addition to being heavily shelled had also been under machine-gun fire. As we were moving along I counted over twenty of our tanks which had been put out of action. Mr. Diamond, whom I had not seen since the previous day, passed us with his arm in a sling and said, " Hello. I'm glad to see you alive." He had been hit through the muscle of his arm. Shells were bursting here and there and we could sniff gas. We put our gas helmets on for a little while and it was twilight when we reached Clapham Junction.

The Major told me that the Battalion was going back to Dickiebusch after it was relieved and that I had no need to return. He wrote me out a note to take back to the transport. He then said that he would have liked to have remained with the Battalion until they were relieved but he thought it best to follow the Doctor's advice, especially when he said that he might lose his leg. I told him not to take too much notice of the Doctor, who would have made a better general than a doctor, and that I had seen worse bullet-wounds than what he had which had healed up in a fortnight's time. I hoped he would be back with the Battalion inside a couple of months. We shook hands and wished one another the best of luck and I had made my way back to the transport.

The enemy bombed Dickiebusch that night but it was such a common occurrence around this area and I was so dead-beat that I took no notice of it. The following morning I rejoined the remnants of the Battalion and found that Ricco, the bank clerk, the architect and Sealyham were still kicking. They thought I had gone West and were as delighted to see me as I was them. We had lost heavily in signallers, but Tich was still hale and hearty.

We were back in a village many miles from the Front, and one dark evening when I was standing outside my billet The Athlete came up to me and asked me if I would mind going for a walk with him. I thought it was a strange request for an officer to make to a private, especially when out of action, but I accompanied him. If he had been seen by a senior officer he might easily have been brought up for a breach of discipline. The Peer who had been back with Minimum Reserve had rejoined us, and also the Colonel from leave. When we were out of the village he said : " Richards, I'm in a fix, and what I am going to tell you is in confidence." He then told me that the previous day he had been sent for to appear in front of the Colonel, who informed him that he had received a very bad report on the way he had conducted himself in action on September 26th and 27th, and then read out the charges that had been made against him. He was then asked what explanation he could give in answer to the charges. He had explained to the best of his ability, and the Colonel had then dismissed him. He did not know whether he would be court-martialled or not. In case he was, he thought about calling upon me as a witness. I told him I was very sorry, but if he called upon me as a witness I was afraid I would do him more harm than good. I said that the sergeant he had with him was the most windy man in France and didn't care a damn who else got in the soup as long as he didn't, and that he should never have listened to his advice. The Athlete said that a young officer who had been left out in Minimum Reserve had since told him the same, and he wished he had realised it before. We then parted. When I arrived back at my billet the boys wanted to know where I had been, and when I told them I had picked up with a fair young maid they called me a scrounging old hound.

Two days later I called at the transport lines and an old soldier asked me if I thought The Athlete would be stuck against the wall and shot. I inquired what for. He then gave me full details of the case and said it was now stale news on the transport and was surprised I knew nothing about it. Our transport men were marvels; they knew everything that was happening on the Western Front. The Old Soldier when he was with the Battalion often used to say that they had a private telephone line to the Commander-in-Chief's bedroom.

The Athlete was not court-martialled, however, and later proved himself a very brave and capable officer, winning the Military Cross. In July 1918 he was wounded in a night raid on Beaumont-Hamel. I don't remember what became of the windy sergeant in the end; if he had had his just deserts he should have been given a couple of severe reprimands and then put against the wall and shot. All I know is that he later was with one of our new service battalions as a company-sergeant-major. It was only natural that a young inexperienced lieutenant would look for guidance from an experienced sergeant, but in this case it very nearly proved the undoing of what turned out to be a brave and capable officer.

THE TAKING OF LUNGTUNGPEN

Rudyard Kipling

So we loosed a bloomin' volley,
 An' we made the beggars cut,
An' when our pouch was emptied out,
 We used the bloomin' butt,
  Ho! My!
  Don't yer come anigh,
When Tommy is a playin' with the
  bayonit an' the butt.

Barrack Room Ballad

My friend Private Mulvaney told me this, sitting on the parapet of the road to Dagshai, when we were hunting butter- flies together. He had theories about the Army, and coloured clay pipes perfectly. He said that the young soldier is the best to work with, " on account av the surpassing innocinse av the child."

" Now, listen!" said Mulvaney, throwing himself full length on the wall in the sun. " I'm a born scutt av the barrick room! The Army's mate an' dhrink to me, bekaze I'm wan av the few that can't quit ut. I've put in sivinteen years, an' the pipe- clay's in the marrow av me. Av I cud have kept out av wan big dhrink a month, I wud have been a Hon'ry Lift'nint by this time—a nuisance to my betthers, a laughin' shtock to my equils, an' a curse to meself. Bein' fwhat I am, I'm Privit Mulvaney, wid no good-conduc' pay an' a devourin' thirst. Always barrin' me little frind Bobs Bahadur, I know as much about the Army as most men."

I said something here.

" Wolseley be shot! Betune you an' me an' that butterfly net, he's a ramblin', incoherent sort av a divil, wid wan oi on the Quane an' the Coort, an' the other on his blessed silf— everlastin'ly playing Saysar an' Alexandrier rowled into a lump. Now Bobs is a sinsible little man. Wid Bobs an' a

From: *Soldiers Three.*

few three-year-olds, I'd swape any army av the earth into a towel, an' throw it away afthterward. Faith, I'm not jokin'! 'Tis the bhoys—the raw bhoys—that don't know fwhat a bullet manes, an' wudn't care av they did—that dhu the work. They're crammed wid bull-mate till they fairly *ramps* wid good livin'; and thin, av they don't fight, they blow each other's hids off. 'Tis the trut' I'm tellin' you. They shud be kept on water an' rice in the hot weather; but there'd be a mut'ny av 'twas done.

"Did ye iver hear how Privit Mulvaney tuk the town av Lungtungpen? I thought not! 'Twas the Lift'nint got the credit; but 'twas me planned the schame. A little before I was inviladed from Burma, me an' four-an'-twenty young wans undher a Lift'nint Brazenose, was ruinin' our dijeshins thryin' to catch dacoits. An' such double-ended divils I niver knew! 'Tis only a *dah* an' a Snider that makes a dacoit. Widout thim, he's a paceful cultivator, an' felony for to shoot. We hunted, an' we hunted, an' tuk fever an' elephints now an' again; but no dacoits. Evenshually, we *puckarowed* wan man. 'Trate him tinderly,' sez the Lift'nint. So I tuk him away into the jungle, wid the Burmese Interprut'r an' my clanin'-rod. Sez I to the man, 'My paceful squireen,' sez I, 'you shquot on your hungers an' dimonstrate to *my* frind here, where *your* frinds are whin they're at home?' Wid that I introjuced him to the clanin'-rod, an' he comminst to jabber; the Interprut'r interprutin' in betweens, an' me helpin' the Intilligence Departmint wid my clanin'-rod whin the man misremembered.

"Prisintly, I learn that, acrost the river, about nine miles away, was a town just dhrippin' wid *dahs,* an' bohs an' arrows, an' dacoits, an' elephints, an' *jingles*. 'Good!' sez I; 'this office will now close!'

"That night, I went to the Lift'nint an' communicates my information. I never thought much of Lift'nint Brazenose till that night. He was shtiff wid books an' the-ouries, an' all manner av thrimmin's no manner av use. 'Town did ye say?' sez he. 'Accordin' to the the-ouries av War, we shud wait for reinforcemints.'—'Faith!' thinks I, 'we'd betther dig our graves thin;' for the nearest throops was up to their shtocks in the marshes out Mimbu way. 'But,' says the Lift'nint, 'since 'tis a speshil case, I'll make an excepshin. We'll visit this Lungtungpen tonight.'

"The bhoys was fairly woild wid deloight whin I tould 'em; an', by this an' that, they wint through the jungle like buck-rabbits. About midnight we come to the shtrame which had clane forgot to minshin to my orficer. I was on, ahead, wid four bhoys, an' I thought that the Lift'nint might want to the-ourise. 'Shtrip bhoys!' sez I. 'Shtrip to the buff, an' shwim in where glory waits!'—'But I *can't* shwim!' sez two of thim. 'To think I should live to hear that from a bhoy wid a board-school edukashin!' sez I. 'Take a lump av timber, an' me an' Conolly here will ferry ye over, ye young ladies!'

" We got an ould tree-trunk, an' pushed off wid the kits an' the rifles on it. The night was chokin' dhark, an' just as we was fairly embarked, I heard the Lift'nint behind av me callin' out. 'There's a bit av a *nullah* here, sorr,' sez I, 'but I can feel the bottom already.' So I cud, for I was not a yard from the bank.

" ' Bit av a *nullah*! Bit av an eshtuary!' sez the Liftn'nint. Go on, ye mad Irishman! Shtrip bhoys!' I heard him laugh; an' the bhoys begun shtrippin' an' rollin' a log into the wather to put their kits on. So me an' Conolly shtruck out through the warm wather wid our log, an' the rest come on behind.

" That shtrame was miles woide! Orth'ris, on the rear-rank log, whispers we had got into the Thames below Sheerness by mistake. 'Kape on shwimmin', ye little blayguard,' sez I, 'an' Irriwaddy.'—'Silence, men!' sings out the Lift'nint. So we shwum on into the black dhark, wid our chests on the logs, trustin' in the Saints an' the luck av the British Army.

" Evenshually, we hit ground—a bit av sand—an' a man. I put my heel on the back av him. He skreeched an' ran.

" ' *Now* we've done it!' sez Lift'nint Brazenose. 'Where the Divil *is* Lungtungpen?' There was about a minute and a half to wait. The bhoys laid a hould av their rifles an' some thried to put their belts on; we was marchin' wid fixed baynits av coorse. Thin we knew where Lungtungpen was; for we had hit the river-wall av it in the dhark, an' the whole town blazed wid thim messin' *jingles* an' Sniders like a cat's back on a frosty night. They was firin' all ways at wanst; but over our heads into the shtrame.

" ' Have you got your rifles?' sez Brazenose. 'Got 'em!' sez Orth'ris. 'I've got that thief Mulvaney's for all my back-pay, an' she'll kick my heart sick wid that blunderin' long shtock av hers.'—'Go on!' yells Brazenose, whippin' his sword out. 'Go on an' take the town! An' the Lord have mercy on our sowls!'

" Thin the bhoys gave wan divastatin' howl, an' pranced into the dhark, feelin' for the town, an' blindin' an' stiffin' like Cavalry Ridin' Masters whin the grass pricked their bare legs. I hammered wid the butt at some bamboo-thing that felt wake, an' the rest come an' hammered contagious, while the *jingles* was jingling, an' feroshus yells from inside was shplittin' our ears. We was too close under the wall for thim to hurt us.

"Evenshually, the thing, whatever ut was, bruk; an' the six-an'-twenty av us tumbled, wan after the other, naked as we was borrun, into the town of Lungtungpen. There was a *melly* av a sumpshus kind for a whoile; but whether they tuk us, all white an' wet, for a new breed av divil, or a new kind of dacoit, I don't know. They ran as though we was both, an' we wint into thim, baynit an' butt, shriekin' wid laughin'. There was torches in the shtreets, an' I saw little Orth'ris rubbin' his showlther ivry time he loosed my long-shtock Martini; an' Brazenose walkin' into the gang wid his sword, like Diarmid av the Gowlden Collar—barring he hadn't a stitch av clothin' on him. We diskivered elephints wid dacoits under their bellies, an', what wid wan thing an' other, we was busy till mornin' takin' possession av the town of Lungtungpen.

"Then we halted an' formed up, the wimmen howlin' in the houses an' the Lift'nint blushin' pink in the light av the mornin' sun. 'Twas the most ondasint p'rade I iver tuk a hand in. Foive-an'-twinty privits an' a orficer av the Line in review ordher, an' not as much as wud dust a fife betune 'em all in the way of clothin'! Eight av us had their belts an' pouches on; but the rest had gone in wid a handful av cart-ridges an' the skin God gave them. *They* was as nakid as Vanus.

"'Number off from the right!' sez the Lift'nint. 'Odd numbers fall out to dress; even numbers pathrol the town till relieved by the dressing party.' Let me tell you, pathrollin' a town wid nothin' on is an ex*pay*rience. I pathrolled for tin minutes, an' begad, before 'twas over, I blushed. The women laughed so. I niver blushed before or since; but I blushed all over my carkiss thin. Orth'ris didn't pathrol. He sez only, 'Portsmouth Barricks an' the 'Ard av a Sunday!' Thin he lay down an' rolled any ways wid laughin'.

"Whin we was all dhressed, we counted the dead—sivinty-foive dacoits besides the wounded. We tuk five elephints, a hunder' an' sivinty Sniders, two hunder' dahs, and a lot of other burglarious thruck. Not a man av us was hurt—excep' maybe the Lift'nint, an' he from the shock of his dasincy.

"The Headman av Lungtungpen, who surrinder'd himself asked the Interprut'r—'Av the English fight like that wid their clo'es off, what in the wurruld do they do wid their clo'es on?' Orth'ris began rowlin' his eyes an' crackin' his fingers an' dancin' a step-dance for to impress the Headman. He ran to his house; an' we spint the rest av the day carryin' the Lift'nint on our showlthers round the town, an' playin' wid the Burmese babies—fat, little, brown little divils, as pretty as picturs.

"Whin I was inviladed for the dysent'ry to India, I sez to the Lift'nint, 'Sorr,' sez I, 'you've the makin' in you av a great man; but, av you'll let an ould sodger spake, you're too fond of the-ourisin'.' He shuk hands wid me and sez, 'Hit high, hit low, there's no plazin' you, Mulvaney. You've seen me waltzin' through Lungtungpen like a Red Injin widout the warpaint, an' you say I'm too fond av the-ourisin'?'— 'Sorr,' sez I, for I loved the bhoy; 'I wud waltz wid you in that condishin through *Hell*, an' so wud the rest av the men!' Thin I went downshtrame in the flat an' left him my blessin'. May the Saints carry ut where ut shud go, for he was a fine upstandin' young orficer.

"To reshume. Fwhat I've said jist shows the use av three-year-olds. Wud fifty seasoned sodgers have taken Lungtungpen in the dhark that way? No! They'd know the risk av fever an' chill. Let alone the shootin'. Two hunder' might have done ut. But the three-year-olds know little an' care less; an' where there's no fear, there's no danger. Catch thim young, feed thim high, an' by the honour av that great, little man Bobs, behind a good orficer, 'tisn't only dacoits they'd smash wid their clo'es off—'tis Con-ti-nental Ar-r-r-mies! They tuk Lungtungpen nakid; an' they'd take St. Pethersburg in their dhrawers! Begad, they would that!"

So saying, Mulvaney took up his butterfly-net, and returned to the barracks.

SQUADRON SCRAMBLE!

Byron Kennerly

as told to Graham Berry

After a week of being confined to the ground by bad weather, we were awakened one night by the blasts of high-explosive bombs and the "whap! whap!" percussion of anti-aircraft fire. Our brick officers' quarters rocked and shook with the crescendo. This meant that the storms which had grounded the Nazis were breaking, that Jerry probably would be back during the daylight hours to make up for lost time, and that we would see action after a week of restless waiting.

The thunderous pounding stopped shortly after midnight and we snatched a bit of sleep.

An hour before dawn the batman brought in the cup of tea, now our "official" getting up drink. Luke climbed out of bed and we began the cumbersome ritual of getting into our flying togs.

I stuck my head out the window and discovered it wasn't cold enough for the fur-lined Irving suit. We dressed in thick silk teddy bears and fireproof sidkas. Pulling on our boots, into which we stuffed maps, and carrying helmets, Mae Wests and gloves and mittens, we headed downstairs for breakfast. We found most of the boys unusually voluble, keyed up at the prospect of action.

Breakfast done we hurried out into the approaching dawn to check the aircraft and see if the bombing had harmed the airdrome. It hadn't, although my sergeant pilot informed me that a near-by dummy airfield, on which were four dummy planes made of old wooden boxes, had been blasted to bits.

As I crawled into the Hurricane's cockpit, my mechanic sang out his customary, "She's hot and ready, sir." Since Jerry was afraid to send over bomber formations during the day, I set the gunsights for thirty-two and one-half feet the wing span of an Me. 109. We were more apt to run into them than any other type of Nazi aircraft.

Laying the parachute on the wing where it could be grabbed quickly, I hurried—you do everything in a hurry over here excepting the waiting—to the airdrome office and signed the

From: *The Eagles Roar!* Copyright 1941, 1942. By permission of Harper & Brothers.

"700 sheet," first making sure that every member of my ground crew had his name down. Luke and Flight Lieutenant B., the other two pilots of Red Section, signed up. B., as section leader, telephoned operations, "Red Section now in readiness."

We went into the dispersal hut; nothing to do but wait expectantly. For awhile the favourite between-flight diversion was teaching the British pilots how to shoot dice. They were too lucky so we dropped this game for dominoes or cards.

About two hours passed. Suddenly the long-expected metallic voice—the one we'd waited a week to hear—snapped over the Tannoy loud-speaker:

"Squadron ———, Red Section. Scramble!"

That was us! I caught Luke's triumphant grin as he jumped up. He and I ran out to our aircraft, pulling on helmets and gloves. I grabbed my 'chute and climbed into its harness. My big Merlin Rolls-Royce motor already was ticking beautifully.

I got aboard and adjusted the Sutton harness, fastening it loosely so I could lean forward to fight off blackouts. I revved up the motor, holding the brakes on. Attaching the oxygen tube to the tank and plugging the radio cord to the R.T. set, I eased off the brakes.

Like a long-caked bird anxious for the sky's freedom, the big hurricane rolled down the runway, gathering speed with each revolution of the propellor. Flipping the magneto switches to test them, I adjusted the propellor at full fine and set the carburettor boost. The motor was only about two-thirds open on the take-off. B. was ahead and Luke beside me. In a vic we hopped off, boosting the planes into a steep climb. Luke and I were concentrating so intensely on B.'s wing tips that he could have flown us into a mountain and we'd never have seen it.

B. called operations by its code name of the day, Battle Control, and reported we were air-borne.

Later operations asked, "Hello, Red Leader. Battle Control calling. Are you receiving me?"

"Hello, Battle Control, Red Leader answering. Receiving you loud and clear. Over."

"Hello, Red Leader. Vector 110. Is that understood?"

"Hello, Battle Control, Red Leader answering. Understand vector 110. Listening out."

Now we knew where we were going. We'd been circling for altitude until we got the vector. I set the compass at 110, which would bring us over the North Sea. We knew we'd been assigned to one of two jobs, either to patrol or to get a bomber that was preying on a convoy. These are the usual North Sea assignments.

At 9,000 feet a cloud bank swallowed us. It took us two minutes to reach it. Luke and I were flying very tight, our wing tips three feet back of and inside B.'s ailerons. You've got to fly this way in the soup or you'll lose one another. And a lone Hurricane is just a piece of cake for Jerry. In the last war, air battles consisted of spectacular two-plane dogfights. Today these are the exception. Most modern fighting is done in teams, and the R.A.F. has developed flying and combat teamwork to the highest degree of efficiency the world has ever known.

I felt a bumping and scraping. It was my wing tip touching B.'s wing. The thought of a crumpled wing was most unpleasant. Three times I'd found paint from his wing on mine. I moved back into position and turned the oxygen on.

At 14,000 feet we burst through the clouds into the bright world of the upper air, a world with fantastic cloud landscapes of cottony valleys and billowy mountains. The scene dazzled me. This was the battleground of the second World War. At 20,000 feet we levelled off. I was a little light-headed from the quick climb, although I had kept the oxygen intake at 5,000 feet ahead of the actual altitude. A dial shows the amount of oxygen you are taking in. The higher the altitude, the more oxygen you turn on.

No enemy aircraft were visible, but B. ordered the section into line astern. You never could tell when Jerry would come swarming out of the clouds. Luke and I swung our Hurricanes in a line behind B., Luke being in the "rear man Charley" spot, protecting our tails. Then the radio crackled:

"Hello, Red Leader. Battle Control calling. Are you receiving me?"

B. reported he was.

"Hello, Red Leader. Angels one zero. Bandit."

An enemy aircraft at 10,000 feet; It must be a prowler over the North Sea. Down we shot into the clouds again. I boosted the throttle and the Hurricane jumped ahead, keeping close behind B. I turned the safety catch on the firing button, snapped on the gunsight and looked over the instruments quickly, my subconscious mind doing most of the work. The motor was heating a bit, but there was no time to do anything about it. Since I had my gunsight adjusted for the wing span of an Me. 109, I knew I would have to reset it before making an attack. Apparently there was only one bandit, and it must be a bomber whose wing span might be double that of a Messerschmitt fighter.

We came under the clouds at 11,000 feet and levelled off. Better stay near the stratus until we sized up the situation. Below was a great slab of sea, with a ragged, dark coastline to the west. England. About twelve miles offshore were black streaks which resembled a stream of ants. They were ships in a convoy.

There! About five miles ahead and 3,000 feet below scooted a black bug. I squinted to make out what it was. It looked like a Dornier 17 heavy bomber, one of the nastiest aircraft to tackle. Manned by four or five men, it was heavily gunned and armoured. I glanced up. There might be an escort of Messerschmitts just inside that sullen cloud curtain. No time for reconnoitering. We slanted toward the bomber—yes, it was a Dornier. We didn't want him to see us until we got closer. If only he took his time getting the range of the convoy, we could swoop down and nail him before he did any damage. I hoped none of the Spitfire boys were around to try and spoil our chase.

Suddenly the bomber dropped his nose in a steep dive toward the convoy. He must have spotted us and he wanted to get a vessel or two before going home. I saw the black cross on top of his starboard wing as he went into the plunge. His two big propellers glinted menacingly for a moment, like a wolf baring his teeth.

B. yelled, "Tallyho!" and dove after him. I followed pulling the teat, the auxilliary throttle that cut loose all 1,250 horsepower. We vaulted downstairs, our Merlins screaming. Just then the unhurried voice of operations reported over the radio : " Hello, Red Leader. Battle Control calling. You should be in vicinity of Tunbridge Wells and bandit." Tunbridge Wells, a small English town, was the code name for this convoy.

B. called, " Hello, Battle Control. Red Leader answering. We're chasing bandit!" Operations dropped his formal answer, merely saying, " Good luck."

It was a race now to see who got to the convoy first. The Dornier was away below us and was hard to see, being painted blue-grey, the colour of the sea. The Germans had a tricky habit of camouflaging their planes for every special job. We were gaining fast. Suddenly my Hurricane rocked violently. It steadied and started rocking again. I spotted a puff of smoke from a vessel in the convoy. He was shooting at the bomber, but his anti-aircraft shells were bursting somewhere near us.

The firing stopped as the Dornier and we approached the long line of ships. The Dornier cut loose a whole stick of four bombs. He wasn't wasting his time aiming and I knew the bombs would fall wide. We were about three-quarters of a mile from him now. B. veered off from the direct chase, diving for the first freighters in the convoy, trying to cut the Dornier off from his prey. Seeing that we were too close, the Jerry banked away toward home, dropping his other bomb stick and an aerial torpedo to lighten his load. The bombs sent up harmless geysers of water a mile from the nearest freighter. The torpedo, I knew, broke when it hit the water after being dropped from 2,000 feet. We had won the first round. Now to get the Dornier. We banked after him.

He had dropped so close to the sea that it looked as if he would ram into it. He levelled off a scant twenty feet above the choppy waves, his starboard wing tip almost cutting the water as he turned directly toward his base. These Dorniers could move fast. Quickly I set the gunsight for a fifty-nine-foot wing span.

Close to the water the Dornier was a tight target. We couldn't dive on him or we would ram into the sea. The only attack to make was directly astern, trying to pick off the top turret gunner before he blasted us. Then we could get at the pilot.

We were closing in fast. He was less than a mile away. B. began levelling off and I hauled back a little on the stick, to stay astern of him. It was hard to pull against the 400-plus-mile-an-hour wind velocity. I could see the Dornier's gunner now in his plastic glass blister, his hands on his twin cannon trigger.

As we came gradually out of the dive, centrifugal force dragged on my body. My hands grew heavy and my jaw sagged. Mustn't black out! I took a deep breath and yelled —anything to build up blood pressure so the blood wouldn't leave my brain. Another danger presented itself. We were much too close to the water. If we ever hit the propeller backwash of the bomber, it would bounce us into the sea.

The German opened fire, smoke from his tracers looping up at B., who threw his Hurricane into a criss-cross to throw off the Jerry's aim. B. started firing; his tracer bullets showed he was firing into the blister. Then B. was past the gunner and it was my turn.

I moved the stick right, then left, and alternated foot pressure on the rudder to keep the gunner in the sights. I could even see his tense face. His lips were parted, his teeth clenched as he sawed his fire-spouting cannons back and forth. I pressed the firing button with my thumb, hurling explosives, ball, incendiary, armour-piercing, and tracer bullets at him. The noise was like muffled high-pitched drums and the plane vibrated and slowed from the recoil. The tracers' chemical smoke trails showed the fire sweeping under the Dornier.

Abandoning caution to get a more accurate aim, I stopped the criss-cross and nosed the Hurricane right at him. He was only about 100 yards away now. There was a loud pow! And a splintering sound, like hailstones on a drum. He must have hit me. But I couldn't see where. My bullets were streaming into his blister, tearing great rents in the plastic glass.

Just as I swept over him, he fell back, arms upraised. I slipped up and to the side. A black curtain dropped over my eyes as I came around, almost in a vertical bank. I eased the stick forward to come to, knowing that Luke was giving the pilot the works.

I glanced back to see Luke almost cutting off the Dornier's tail with his prop, he was flying so close to him. The bomber was still flying. We didn't get him on the first attack.

As I followed B. down for another attack I heard Luke yell over the radio, "Red Leader. Red Three calling. Bandits over the French Coast!" I looked to the east. Nine planes in three vics were coming toward us, one vic far in advance of the others. The Dornier must have radioed for help. The planes still were several miles away but it wouldn't take a minute for them to get here. We had to work fast.

B.'s Hurricane thundered down on the Dornier's tail. I saw two Germans dragging the gunner's body from his seat. They were going to replace him. If they succeeded in doing this before we got the pilot, the Dornier was as good as safe on its home airdrome. The pilot would be protected by the new rear gunner until the Jerry fighter planes arrived. B. dove low over the Dornier's tail and gave the pilot's cockpit a long burst, sliding up and to the side again. Before I could start firing, the Dornier's wings wiggled slightly, the nose dropped slowly. He smacked the water, sheets of spray exploding up from his fuselage. He bounced twice and settled on the choppy sea. B. got him that time. Soon he would sink.

Heading upstairs in a hurry after B., I spotted the first

Jerry section of three aircraft slanting down to attack us. These aircraft were smaller than an Me. 109 and they were painted white. I had never seen them before. They must be the new, faster Heinkel 113 fighters we'd heard about.

I closed in behind B. and Luke was right on my tail. We were low on petrol and bullets and we had finished our job, so the better part of valour was to head for home quickly. Besides our planes had been damaged and might not be able to stand the terrific strain of combat. Below us the remainder of the Dornier crew launched a rubber life boat.

B. levelled off to gain speed and pointed for home. I followed, nearly deafened by the scream of air through the cowling where the cannon shell had penetrated, and by the shriek from the machine-gun mouths where the patches had been shot away.

The Jerries kept coming, so B. banked quickly and started circling. Now Jerry couldn't get on our tail because each one of us was protecting the other's tail. The three Heinkels veered away. They didn't like our circle.

" Red Two and Three, Red One calling. Maintain tight formation, line astern ! "

As one Heinkel got a little below us, B. suddenly straightened out and dove for it. Luke and I were right behind him. B. got in a long burst. The two other Heinkels immediately dove for B. I picked one Jerry and Luke the other. I got in one quick burst of fire on my Heinkel's tail. Then it power-dived out of range. In fact all three Heinkels veered off and hurried away. We quickly reformed behind B. Apparently they weren't too anxious to tangle.

B. called Battle Control, got the response and announced, " Hello, Battle Control. Red Leader calling. Dornier 17 down. See pilots in rubber boats. Bandits in vicinity." Operations might send a launch or flying boat after them.

Luke and I both reported that our petrol was running low. Luke added that his port wing had been badly ripped. I hoped everything would hold together until we landed.

We left the sea and the Jerries, vowing to be back for them later, and started flying over England. Operations was vectoring us home. Although the countryside was honeycombed with airdrome, we couldn't spot one from up here. Clever artists had blended buildings, airdromes, and gun emplacements with paint and secret camouflaging materials to look like a checkerboard of innocent farm plots, separated by hedges. Operations informed us we were above our airdrome and we circled down over what looked like a pasture, with hedges and haystacks. At 800 feet we made out the runway. Circling the field, we lowered our landing gear and flaps and came in at 100 miles an hour for a power landing. We slid across the field and my wheels rumbled pleasantly on the runway as the plane settled down. We were back! The clock showed we'd been gone only forty minutes!

We taxied to our camouflaged, sandbagged hangars, where the ground crews greeted us with cheers. They had heard the shriek of wind through the gun ports. I felt let down and tired from nervous exhaustion. My hands were clammy and the helmet seemed very heavy and tight. There was much conversation as we climbed out and inspected the damage. The crews swarmed over the aircraft and found that all three planes bore marks of the flight. The shell that had burst in my ship struck just ahead of the hatch and not six inches from where my forehead had been pressed against the gunsight rest. A close call. The floor was filled with glass fragments. Luke and I were assigned new planes until ours were repaired.

After checking the new aircraft, we made out combat reports and notified operations that we were in readiness again. Then we returned to the dispersal hut to wait for something else to happen.

One afternoon as the grey light over the airdrome was thickening into dusk, Luke and I had just settled down to a typical friendly argument with a British pilot over the merits of various fighter planes when our talk was cut short by the loud speaker:

"Squadron ——, Red and Blue sections. Squadron ——, Green and White sections. Scramble!"

The Britisher smiled hopefully as he jumped up with, "Twelve of us going up. It's a big flap this time!" It had to be or they wouldn't risk sending us aloft so late in the day.

A dozen of us, six Americans and six Britishers, ran out to our aircraft. The Britishers were the Spitfire boys. I climbed into a new Hurricane. The motor on mine was being overhauled. I was a little dubious about the new plane, not knowing its little habits. Each aircraft has its own.

Both sections of the Spitfire squadron roared down the runway and the six planes took off as one. Those boys were beautiful formation flyers.

M., the leader of our flight, taxied out, the two aircraft in his section coming into a vic behind him. They took off and

335

we followed immediately. In two tight vics one right behind the other, we thundered upward into a cloud canopy which was made almost as black as night by coal smoke from factories. M.'s tail was directly under my propeller. It was so dark I couldn't see his wings.

On the radio I heard him get vectored to 270, operations adding, "Buster!" This meant step on it. M.'s tail drew away. I pulled the teat a little and came up close. Our planes were just inches apart. I felt a vibration. Must be Luke's wing tip up against mine. Visibility was too poor now for him to see me motion him back. A quick glance showed Luke's wing edging back a little. He had felt the impact too.

Operations called again, reporting, "Angels two five. Many, many bandits!"

Many enemy aircraft at 25,000 feet! The altimeter read 12,000 feet. I turned on the oxygen, spinning the dial to 17,000 feet.

I fervently hoped operations was vectoring us right. There were two balloon barrages in this vicinity and it would be just too bad if we got snagged in one. I wondered if my guns were hot enough to fire, if the rest of the boys in the formation were getting the right information, and understood it, and if the motor, this new motor I'd never tried out before, would respond to the big job required of it in combat. You don't actually worry about these things, but you can't help their flashing through your mind.

Suddenly we burst through the black cloud bank into the brilliance of the evening sky. The sun was almost resting on a crimson mattress. Admiration of the beauty about us was cut off by operations:

"Hello, Red Leader. Locust Control calling. Are you receiving me?"

"Hello, Locust Control. Red Leader answering. Receiving you loud and clear. Over," M. answered.

"Hello, Red Leader. Locust Control calling. Bandits five miles to port at angels two zero. Buster!"

We were flying at 22,000 feet. We didn't see them. They must be under that big ragged hole in the clouds. M. called for echelon starboard. Our Hurricanes moved into single file, each plane to the right of the plane in front. M. banked to the left and one after the other we followed.

There were the Jerries! Three swarms of black specks several thousand feet above. They were the Messerschmitt fighter convoys. They were always above us. I could just make them out. There must be fifty of them. But we were not looking for them. I glanced below as we roared over the big cloud rift. There was our quarry. Fifteen big murky green bombers. Junker 88s, flying in three stepped-up, line-astern formations. It was the toughest formation to attack because the bombers were flying in three groups, one above the other. In our dive we had to run the gauntlet of cannon and machine-gun blasts from each level.

Far off in the golden mist I saw other clusters of planes. They must be over the English Channel. I couldn't tell whether they were German or British. Behind us were more planes. They were closer and camouflaged green and tan. They were Spitfires from some other airdrome, a welcome addition to the sky picture!

M. was angling for a beam attack. I set and turned on the gunsight, caught a glimpse of the reassuring glow and set the button in firing position. Striking down at the side of the bombers would give us the biggest target. Besides, the Ju.88s weren't armoured there. There was a cool feeling in my stomach and my mouth got very dry. The dryness may have been caused by the oxygen. I was taking in deep breaths of it. There was a swarm of Messerschmitt 109s directly overhead, and following us like hawks stalking their prey. They wouldn't dive until we did. Then they would be on our tail in a flash. I could see in the gathering dusk the black crosses on the underside of their square-cut wings.

Suddenly M. waggled his wings and peeled off, zooming down in a sixty-degree power dive with a "Tallyho!" Number two and number three followed screaming after him. I pulled the teat wide open and shoved the stick from me. The Hurricane jumped ahead and shrieked downstairs. The three Hurricanes on front broke formation and levelled off, each picking a separate target. I came out of my dive and got a bomber in the sights, the front Jerry in the middle formation. We must pick off the front bombers, for in one of them was the flight leader. If we got him, the rest of the formation would turn for home. But so long as he was still in action, they would keep right on to their objective.

Over the whining crescendo of airplane motors I heard in the earphones a "Yippee! Hi—Yoooo-oo!" It was one of our boys giving his cowboy battle yell. He had forgotten and left his radio on send, so we heard him.

As we roared in on them, the bombers didn't try to get out of the way. I was watching for some evasive action to throw our aim off. My target loomed larger and larger in the sights as I started rolling over. His murky camouflaging almost blended with the darkness. My thumb was itching to press the firing button. But he was still too far away. Smoke trails poured from the bomber as the gunner opened fire at me.

The stick vibrated in my hand. Bullets from somewhere were cutting into an aileron. I could tell this because the vibration was a sideways motion. It couldn't be from a bomber below. I wasn't in range yet. The rear-view mirror showed a Messerschmitt fighter on my tail. But he was too far off to hit me. The jerking stopped. The bullets must have come from the top formation of bombers. They were almost overhead.

No time to investigate. My target was only 350 yards away. My thumb squeezed down on the firing button. Tracer smoke showed the bullets falling short and too far ahead of the pilot's cabin. I tried to pull her nose in on the target. The Hurricane responded sluggishly. From the way her starboard wing dragged I knew it was the aileron on that wing that was damaged. Probably the fabric had been shot off. I tried to keep the gunsight just ahead of his nose so the pilot would run into the hail of death. I gave him another burst. There! The tracer smoke poured into the pilot's plastic cabin. I bore down on the trigger as if trying to force more bullets into him. As I pulled down and rocketed upside down across the bomber's belly, it started to roll over. That meant I had probably got him!

As the Hurricane started into the break-away, I caught sight of two Messerschmitts on my tail. I gazed a split second too long into the rear-vision mirror. The Hurricane was roaring directly at another bomber. I hadn't spotted it in the gloom. I gave it one quick, wicked burst at almost point-blank range as the Hurricane dropped away in a sickening dive.

Just as I felt the blood draining from my head I heard a "pow"! A cannon shell from the bomber ripped through the hatch just above my head, showering the cockpit with glass and miniature shrapnel fragments. Wind whistled in the cockpit and I had to drop my head far forward so that my helmet wouldn't get ripped off by the blast.

My head and shoulders were getting unbearably heavy. Centrifugal force pulled my jaw down. Even the chin strap couldn't keep it up. I groaned trying to take a deep breath. My eyelids became too heavy to keep open and consciousness faded away.

When I came to a few seconds later there were several screaming, diving planes around. There went a Spitfire in flames. The letters on the fuselage identified it as Hank, one of the English boys at our airdrome. Poor devil! No time for mourning now, though. It may be my turn next.

As I pulled gradually out of the dive, two streamers of fire whipped past the starboard wing. Tracers from a Messerschmitt! I had almost forgotten them. In fact, I thought my 7,000-foot dive would have carried me far away from their guns. Yes, one of them was right behind, his guns blinking like lights. There was just enough daylight left for him to see me if he was close. And he was much too close. I banked over in a tight turn. He was right after me. I twisted and writhed, but Jerry wouldn't shake loose. His bullets thrummed a tattoo somewhere on the fuselage. If an incendiary bullet started to work, it was all over. The Hurricane responded to the controls slowly because of the ruined aileron. That was why Jerry could follow me.

Only one thing was left to do—go into a spin. With the aileron damaged, the Hurricane might not come out of it, but it would be a lot better to take that chance than to sit still and be shot in the back. I gunned the throttle and jerked the stick toward me. Instantly the lift on the wings was gone. The Hurricane stalled at nearly 300 miles an hour and whipped over and down in a shrieking spin. Consciousness again left me, but I knew Jerry had zoomed past overhead.

As I began to come to it seemed as if a dozen huge propellers were spinning in my head. I shook my head to throw off the nauseating sensation and took a deep breath of oxygen. As my vision cleared, I realised that the ship was still spinning. The altimeter read 3,000 feet. I'd have to bring her out of it fast. Wondering if the bad aileron would let her come out, I shoved the stick forward and reversed the controls. Nothing happened. The altimeter showed 2,500 feet. The Hurricane was dropping at a little more than 200 miles an hour, the speedometer indicated, the spin having slowed her down.

Still holding the stick over, I grabbed for the hatch with my left hand and tried to jerk it back. It was time to jump. In an awful instant, I realised the cannon shell had jammed the hatch. Clenching my teeth and trying to swallow a panicky emotion that kept welling up in my throat, I shoved the throttle, opening it wide, and pulled the teat. It was kill or cure this time. The plane gathered speed.

Slowly—and I could hardly believe it—the controls grew firm and the spin slowed. Then it stopped as the speedometer needle climbed to 250 M.P.H.,—275—300. Quickly I eased the throttle and brought the stick back slowly on the left

339

side. I must keep the starboard wing up. If she dove again it would be my last ride. I didn't even know if I were coming out of this dive before ramming into the ground.

The altimeter read a scant 800 feet. I was flying entirely by instruments now as it was dark everywhere except for the glowing instrument panel.

At 300 feet the Hurricane levelled off and I gasped a deep breath, lifting my head a little to let the air blast cool it. snapping the radio switch to send, I called operations, asking for an emergency homing. I flipped the key to receive and listened, wondering whether the radio still worked. It did! The steady, unruffled voice of operations ordered:

" Talk for ten seconds."

This was to enable operations to get a bearing on me. I mumbled something into the mike, hardly aware of what it was. Then there was silence except for the roar of the motor and the wind screaming through the hatch and gun mouths.

It seemed hours, but in reality it was about fifty seconds when operations notified that I was over an airdrome. There was nothing but blackness below as I banked the Hurricane carefully in a descending turn. As the altimeter dropped below the 1,500-foot mark, a red-and-white Very rocket shot up from somewhere beneath. A welcome sight, these colours of the day! On a telegraph key I tapped out in Morse code " A " and " T ", the letters of the day. The dots and dashes blinked from the amber light under my plane—that is, if they hadn't been shot off.

Apparently they hadn't for almost immediately a row of dim lights flashed on, marking the runway of the airdrome. By their yellow colour I knew the lights were oil pots. This meant there was a ground haze, oil lights penetrating it better that electric lamps. Inexperienced pilots sometimes try to land on this haze—which hugs the ground to a depth of about four feet—because the top of it looks like the ground surface.

I lowered the landing wheels and flaps and nosed the Hurricane down, keeping the starboard wing up slightly. The plane slanted to the border of the runway and I edged her through the thick haze at 100 miles an hour. She hit the ground with the port wheel, bounced up, slid through the air a moment, then settled down on the runway. I shoved gently on the brakes and she eased to a stop. Suddenly I felt very much all in.

The duty pilot and a crew of mechanics and armourers raced

up to take the ship over. They pried open the badly damaged hatch and informed me that I was fifteen miles from the home airdrome. Her starboard aileron was more than half gone, part of the rudder had been shot away, three control wires were badly frayed, the cowling was smashed in near the hatch, and there were innumerable bullet holes through the fuselage and wings. Still she brought me in safely. That's a Hurricane for you!

After telephoning home, I climbed into a truck and spent a bumpy half-hour before reaching our officers' lounge. I arrived in time for a victory celebration. Pilots from our airdrome had brought down two bombers sure and one probable, as well as two fighters. The only one not there to help with the festivities was Hank. We drank a toast to his memory.

Later that night in our room Luke took Hank's photograph off the wall.

"Guess we'd better put him away until after the war," Luke said, placing the picture in his suitcase. Then he added, "This is one more casualty that is going to cost Jerry plenty!"

We solemnly shook hands on it.

A PERSONAL VIEW OF WATERLOO

Stendhal

That day the army, which had just won the battle of Ligny, was marching straight on Brussels. It was the eve of the battle of Waterloo. Towards midday, the rain still continuing to fall in torrents, Fabrizio heard the sound of the guns; this joy made him completely oblivious of the fearful moments of despair in which so unjust an imprisonment had plunged him. He rode on until late at night, and, as he was beginning to have a little common sense, went to seek shelter in a peasant's house a long way from the road. This peasant wept and pretended that everything had been taken from him; Fabrizio gave him a crown, and he found some barley. "My horse is no beauty," Fabrizio said to himself, "but that makes no difference, he may easily take the fancy of some *adjudant*," and he went to lie down in the stable by its side. An hour before dawn Fabrizio was on the road, and, by copious endearments, succeeded in making his horse trot. About five o'clock, he heard the cannonade: it was the preliminaries of Waterloo.

Fabrizio soon came upon some *vivandières,* and the extreme gratitude that he felt for the gaoler's wife of B—— impelled him to address them; he asked one of them where he would find the 4th Hussar Regiment, to which he belonged.

"You would do just as well not to be in such a hurry, young soldier," said the *cantinière,* touched by Fabrizio's pallor and glowing eyes. "Your wrist is not strong enough yet for the sabre-thrusts they'll be giving to-day. If you had a musket, I don't say, maybe you could let off your round as well as any of them."

This advice displeased Fabrizio; but however much he urged on his horse, he could go no faster than the *cantinière* in her cart. Every now and then the sound of the guns seemed to come nearer and prevented them from hearing each other speak, for Fabrizio was so beside himself with enthusiasm and delight that he had renewed the conversation. Every word uttered by the *cantinière* intensified his happiness by making him understand it. With the exception of his real name and his escape from prison, he ended by confiding every-

From: *Le Chartreuse de Parme.*

342

thing to this woman who seemed such a good soul. She was greatly surprised and understood nothing at all of what this handsome young soldier was telling her.

" I see what it is," she exclaimed at length with an air of triumph. " You're a young gentleman who has fallen in love with the wife of some captain in the 4th Hussars. Your mistress will have made you a present of the uniform you're wearing, and you're going after her. As sure as God's in heaven, you've never been a soldier; but, like the brave boy you are, seeing your regiment's under fire, you want to be there too, and not let them think you a chicken."

Fabrizio agreed with everything; it was his only way of procuring good advice. " I know nothing of the ways of these French people," he said to himself, " and if I am not guided by someone I shall find myself being put in prison again, and they'll steal my horse."

" First of all, my boy," said the *cantinière*, who was becoming more and more of a friend to him, " confess that you're not one-and-twenty: at the very most you might be seventeen."

This was the truth, and Fabrizio admitted as much with good grace.

" Then, you aren't even a conscript; it's simply because of Madame's pretty face that you're going to get your bones broken. Plague it, she can't be particular. If you've still got some of the *yellow-boys* she sent you, you must first of all buy yourself another horse; look how your screw pricks up his ears when the guns sound at all near; that's a peasant's horse, and will be the death of you as soon as you reach the line. That white smoke you see over there above the hedge, that's the infantry firing, my boy. So prepare for a fine fright when you hear the bullets whistling over you. You'll do as well to eat a bit while there's still time."

Fabrizio followed this advice and, presenting a napoleon to the *vivandière*, asked her to accept payment.

" It makes one weep to see him!" cried the woman; " the poor child doesn't even know how to spend his money! It would be no more than you deserve if I pocketed your napoleon and put Cocotte into a trot; damned if your screw could catch me up. What would you do, stupid, if you saw me go off? Bear in mind, when the *brute* growls, never to show your gold. Here," she went on, " here's 18 francs, 50 centimes, and your breakfast cost you 30 sous. Now, we shall soon have some horses for sale. If the beast is a small one, you'll give ten francs, and, in any case, never more than twenty, not if it was the horse of the Four Sons of Aymon."

The meal finished, the *vivandière*, who was still haranguing, was interrupted by a woman who had come across the fields and passed them on the road.

"Hallo there, hi!" this woman shouted. "Hallo, Margot! Your 6th Light are over there on the right."

"I must leave you, my boy," said the *vivandière* to our hero; "but really and truly I pity you; I've taken quite a fancy to you, upon my word I have. You don't know a thing about anything, you're going to get a wipe in the eye, as sure as God's in heaven! Come along to the 6th Light with me."

"I quite understand that I know nothing," Fabrizio told her, "but I want to fight, and I'm determined to go over there towards that white smoke."

"Look how your horse is twitching his ears! As soon as he gets over there, even if he's no strength left, he'll take the bit in his teeth and start galloping, and heaven only knows where he'll land you. Will you listen to me now? As soon as you get to the troops, pick up a musket and a cartridge pouch, get down among the men and copy what you see them do, exactly the same: But, good heavens, I'll bet you don't even know how to open a cartridge."

Fabrizio, stung to the quick, admitted nevertheless to his new friend that she had guessed aright.

"Poor boy! He'll be killed straight away; sure as God! It won't take long. You've got to come with me, absolutely," went on the *cantinière* in a tone of authority.

"But I want to fight."

"You shall fight too; why, the 6th Light are famous fighters, and there's fighting enough to-day for everyone."

"But shall we come soon to the regiment?"

"In a quarter of an hour at the most."

"With this honest woman's recommendations," Fabrizio told himself, "my ignorance of everything won't make them take me for a spy, and I shall have a chance of fighting." At this moment the noise of the guns redoubled, each explosion coming straight on top of the last. "It's like a Rosary," said Fabrizio.

"We're beginning to hear the infantry fire now," said the *vivandière*, whipping up her little horse, which seemed quite excited by the firing.

The *cantinière* turned to the right and took a side road that ran through the fields; there was a foot of mud in it; the little cart seemed about to be stuck fast: Fabrizio pushed the wheel. His horse fell twice; presently the road, though with less water on it, was nothing more than a bridle path through the grass. Fabrizio had not gone five hundred yards when his nag stopped short: it was a corpse, lying across the path, which terrified horse and rider alike.

Fabrizio's face, pale enough by nature, assumed a markedly green tinge; the *cantinière,* after looking at the dead man, said, as though speaking to herself: "That's not one of our Division." Then, raising her eyes to our hero, she burst out laughing.

"Aha, my boy! There's a titbit for you!" Fabrizio sat frozen. What struck him most of all was the dirtiness of the feet of this corpse which had already been stripped of its shoes and left with nothing but an old pair of trousers all clotted with blood.

"Come nearer," the *cantinière* ordered him, "get off your horse, you'll have to get accustomed to them; look," she cried, "he's stopped one in the head."

A bullet, entering on one side of the nose, had gone out at the opposite temple, and disfigured the corpse in a hideous fashion. It lay with one eye still open.

"Get off your horse then, lad," said the *cantinière,* "and give him a shake of the hand to see if he'll return it."

Without hesitation, although ready to yield up his soul with disgust, Fabrizio flung himself from his horse and took the hand of the corpse which he shook vigorously; then he stood still as though paralysed. He felt that he had not the strength to mount again. What horrified him more than anything was that open eye.

"The *vivandière* will think me a coward," he said to himself bitterly. But he felt the impossibility of making any movement; he would have fallen. It was a frightful moment; Fabrizio was on the point of being physically sick. The *vivandière* noticed this, jumped lightly down from her little carriage, and held out to him, without saying a word, a glass of brandy which he swallowed at a gulp; he was able to mount his screw, and continued on his way without speaking. The *vivandière* looked at him now and again from the corner of her eye.

"You shall fight to-morrow, my boy," she said at length; "to-day you're going to stop with me. You can see now that you've got to learn the business before you can become a soldier."

"On the contrary, I want to start fighting at once," exclaimed our hero with a sombre air which seemed to the *vivandière* to augur well. The noise of the guns grew twice as loud and seemed to be coming nearer. The explosions began to form a continuous bass; there was no interval between one and the next, and above this running bass, which suggested the roar of a torrent in the distance, they could make out quite plainly the rattle of musketry.

At this point the road dived down into a clump of trees. The *vivandière* saw three or four soldiers of our army who were coming towards her as fast as their legs would carry them; she jumped nimbly down from her cart and ran into cover fifteen or twenty paces from the road. She hid herself in a hole which had been left where a big tree had recently been uprooted. " Now," thought Fabrizio, " we shall see whether I am a coward!" He stopped by the side of the little cart which the woman had abandoned, and drew his sabre. The soldiers paid no attention to him and passed at a run along the wood, to the left of the road.

" They're ours," said the *vivandière* calmly, as she came back, quite breathless, to her little cart. . . . " If your horse was capable of galloping, I should say: push ahead as far as the end of the wood, and see if there's anyone on the plain." Fabrizio did not wait to be told twice, he tore off a branch from a poplar, stripped it and started to lash his horse with all his might; the animal broke into a gallop for a moment, then fell back into its regular slow trot. The *vivandière* had put her horse into a gallop. " Stop, will you, stop!" she called after Fabrizio. Presently both were clear of the wood. Coming to the edge of the plain, they heard a terrifying din, guns and muskets thundered on every side, right, left, behind them. And as the clump of trees from which they emerged grew on a mound rising nine or ten feet above the plain, they could see fairly well a corner of the battle; but still there was no one to be seen in the meadow beyond the wood. This meadow was bordered, half a mile away, by a long row of willows, very bushy; above the willows appeared a white smoke which now and again rose eddying into the sky.

" If I only knew where the regiment was," said the *cantinière*, in some embarrassment. " It won't do to go straight ahead over this big field. By the way," she said to Fabrizio, " if you see one of the enemy, stick him with the point of your sabre, don't play about with the blade."

At this moment, the *cantinière* caught sight of the four soldiers whom we mentioned a little way back; they were coming out of the wood on to the plain to the left of the road. One of them was on horseback.

"There you are," she said to Fabrizio. "Hallo there!" she called to the mounted men, "come over here and have a glass of brandy." The soldiers approached.

"Where are the 6th Light?" she shouted.

"Over there, five minutes away, across that canal that runs along by the willows; why, Colonel Macon has just been killed."

"Will you take five francs for your horse, you?"

"Five francs! That's not a bad one, *ma*! An officer's horse I can sell in ten minutes for five napoleons."

"Give me one of your napoleons," said the *vivandière* to Fabrizio. Then going up to the mounted soldier: "Get off, quickly," she said to him, "here's your napoleon."

The soldier dismounted, Fabrizio sprang gaily on to the saddle, the *vivandière* unstrapped the little portmanteau which was on his old horse.

"Come and help me, all of you!" she said to the soldiers, "is that the way you leave a lady to do the work?"

But no sooner had the captured horse felt the weight of the portmanteau than he began to rear, and Fabrizio, who was an excellent horseman, had to use all his strength to hold him.

"A good sign!" said the *vivandière*, "the gentleman is not accustomed to being tickled by portmanteaus."

"A general's horse," cried the man who had sold it, "a horse that's worth ten napoleons if it's worth a liard."

"Here are twenty francs," said Fabrizio, who could not contain himself for joy at feeling between his legs a horse that could really move.

At that moment a shot struck the line of willows, through which it passed obliquely, and Fabrizio had the curious spectacle of all those little branches flying this way and that as though mown down by a stroke of the scythe.

"Look, there's the *brute* advancing," the soldier said to him as he took the twenty francs. It was now about two o'clock.

Fabrizio was still under the spell of this strange spectacle when a party of generals, followed by a score of hussars, passed at a gallop across one corner of the huge field on the edge of which he had halted: his horse neighed, reared several times in succession, then began violently tugging the bridle that was holding him. "All right, then," Fabrizio said to himself.

The horse, left to his own devices, dashed off hell for leather to join the escort that was following the generals. Fabrizio counted four gold-laced hats. A quarter of an hour later, from a few words said by one hussar to the next, Fabrizio gathered that one of these generals was the famous Marshal Ney. His happiness knew no bounds; only he had no way of telling which of the four generals was Marshal Ney; he would have given everything in the world to know, but he remembered that he had been told not to speak. The escort halted, having to cross a wide ditch left full of water by the rain overnight; it was fringed with tall trees and formed the left-hand boundary of the field at the entrance to which Fabrizio had bought the horse. Almost all the hussars had dismounted; the bank of the ditch was steep and very slippery and the water lay quite three or four feet below the level of the field. Fabrizio, distracted with joy, was thinking more of Marshal Ney and of glory than of his horse, which, being highly excited, jumped into the canal; thus splashing the water up to a considerable height. One of the generals was soaked to the skin by the sheet of water, and cried with an oath: " Damn the f—— brute!" Fabrizio felt deeply hurt by this insult. "Can I ask him to apologise?" he wondered. Meanwhile, to prove that he was not so clumsy after all, he set his horse to climb the opposite bank of the ditch; but it rose straight up and was five or six feet high. He had to abandon the attempt; then he rode up stream, his horse being up to its head in water, and at last found a sort of drinking-place. By this gentle slope he was easily able to reach the field on the other side of the canal. He was the first man of the escort to appear there; he started to trot proudly down the bank; below him, in the canal, the hussars were splashing about, somewhat embarrassed by their position, for in many places the water was five feet deep. Two or three horses took fright and began to swim, making an appalling mess. A sergeant noticed the manœuvre that this youngster, who looked so very unlike a soldier, had just carried out.

"Up here! There is a watering-place on the left!" he shouted, and in time they all crossed.

On reaching the farther bank, Fabrizio had found the generals there by themselves; the noise of the guns seemed to him to have doubled; and it was all he could do to hear the general whom he had given such a good soaking and who now shouted in his ear:

"Where did you get that horse?"

Fabrizio was so much upset that he answered in Italian:

"*L'ho comprato poco fa.* (I bought it just now.)"

"What's that you say?" cried the general.

But the din at that moment became so terrific that Fabrizio

could not answer him. We must admit that our hero was very little of a hero at that moment. However, fear came to him only as a secondary consideration; he was principally shocked by the noise, which hurt his ears. The escort broke into a gallop; they crossed a large batch of tilled land which lay beyond the canal. And this field was strewn with dead.

"Red-coats! red-coats!" the hussars of the escort exclaimed joyfully, and at first Fabrizio did not understand; then he noticed that as a matter of fact almost all these bodies wore red uniforms. One detail made him shudder with horror; he observed that many of these unfortunate red-coats were still alive; they were calling out, evidently asking for help, and no one stopped to give it them. Our hero, being most humane, took every possible care that his horse should not tread upon any of the red-coats. The escort halted; Fabrizio, who was not paying sufficient attention to his military duty, galloped on, his eyes fixed on a wounded wretch in front of him.

"Will you halt, you young fool!" the sergeant shouted after him. Fabrizio discovered that he was twenty paces on the generals' right front, and precisely in the direction in which they were gazing through their glasses. As he came back to take his place behind the other hussars, who had halted a few paces in rear of them, he noticed the biggest of these generals who was speaking to his neighbour, a general also, in a tone of authority and almost of reprimand; he was swearing. Fabrizio could not contain his curiosity; and, in spite of the warning not to speak, given him by his friend the gaoler's wife, he composed a short sentence in good French, quite correct, and said to his neighbour:

"Who is that general who is *chewing up* the one next to him?"

"Gad, it's the Marshal!"

"What Marshal?"

"Marshal Ney, you fool! I say, where have you been serving?"

Fabrizio, although highly susceptible, had no thought of resenting this insult; he was studying, lost in childish admiration, the famous Prince de la Moskowa, the "Bravest of the Brave."

Suddenly they all moved off at full gallop. A few minutes later Fabrizio saw, twenty paces ahead of him, a ploughed field the surface of which was moving in a singular fashion. The furrows were full of water and the soil, very damp, which formed the ridges between these furrows kept flying off in little black lumps three or four feet into the air. Fabrizio noticed as he passed this curious effect; then his thoughts turned to dreaming of the Marshal and his glory. He heard a sharp cry close to him; two hussars fell struck by shot; and, when he looked back at them, they were already twenty paces behind the escort. What seemed to him horrible was a horse streaming with blood that was struggling on the ploughed land, its hooves caught in its own entrails; it was trying to follow the others: its blood ran down into the mire.

"Ah! So I am under fire at last!" he said to himself. "I have seen shots fired!" he repeated with a sense of satisfaction. "Now I am a real soldier." At that moment, the escort began to go hell for leather, and our hero realised that it was shot from the guns that was making the earth fly up all round him. He looked vainly in the direction from which the balls were coming, he saw the white smoke of the battery at an enormous distance, and, in the thick of the steady and continuous rumble produced by the artillery fire, he seemed to hear shots discharged much closer at hand: he could not understand in the least what was happening.

At that moment, the generals and their escort dropped into a little road filled with water which ran five feet below the level of the fields.

The Marshal halted and looked again through his glasses. Fabrizio, this time, could examine him at his leisure. He found him to be very fair, with a big red face. "We don't have any faces like that in Italy," he said to himself. "With my pale cheeks and chestnut hair, I shall never look like that," he added despondently. To him these words implied: "I shall never be a hero." He looked at the hussars; with a solitary exception, all of them had yellow moustaches. If Fabrizio was studying the hussars of the escort, they were all studying him as well. Their stare made him blush, and, to get rid of his embarrassment, he turned his head towards the enemy. They consisted of widely extended lines of men in red, but, what greatly surprised him, these men seemed to be quite minute. Their long files, which were regiments or divisions, appeared no taller than hedges. A line of red cavalry were trotting in the direction of the sunken road along which the Marshal and his escort had begun to move at a walk, splashing through the mud. The smoke made it impossible to distinguish anything in the direction in which they were advancing; now and then one saw men moving at a gallop against this background of white smoke.

Suddenly, from the direction of the enemy, Fabrizio saw four men approaching hell for leather. "Ah! We are attacked," he said to himself; then he saw two of these men speak to the Marshal. One of the generals on the latter's staff set off at a gallop towards the enemy, followed by two hussars of the escort and by the four men who had just come up. After a little canal which they all crossed, Fabrizio found himself riding beside a sergeant who seemed a good-natured fellow. "I must speak to this one," he said to himself, "then perhaps they'll stop staring at me." He thought for a long time.

"Sir, this is the first time that I have been present at a battle," he said at length to the sergeant. "But is this a real battle?"

"Something like. But who are you?"

"I am the brother of a captain's wife."

"And what is he called, your captain?"

Our hero was terribly embarrassed; he had never anticipated this question. Fortunately, the Marshal and his escort broke into a gallop. "What French name shall I say?" he wondered. At last he remembered the name of the inn-keeper with whom he had lodged in Paris; he brought his horse up to the sergeant's, and shouted to him at the top of his voice:

"Captain Meunier!" The other, not hearing properly in the roar of the guns, replied: "Oh, Captain Teulier? Well, he's been killed." "Splendid," thought Fabrizio. "Captain Teulier; I must look sad."

"Good God!" he cried; and assumed a piteous mien. They had left the sunken road and were crossing a small meadow, they were going hell for leather, shots were coming over again, the Marshal headed for a division of cavalry. The escort found themselves surrounded by dead and wounded men; but this sight had already ceased to make any impression on our hero; he had other things to think of.

While the escort was halted, he caught sight of the little cart of a *cantinière*, and his affection for this honourable corps sweeping aside every other consideration, set off at a gallop to join her.

"Stay where you are, curse you," the sergeant shouted after him.

"What can he do to me here?" thought Fabrizio, and he continued to gallop towards the *cantinière*. When he put spurs to his horse, he had had some hope that it might be his good *cantinière* of the morning; the horse and the little cart bore a strong resemblance, but their owner was quite

351

different, and our hero thought her appearance most forbidding. As he came up to her, Fabrizio heard her say: "And he was such a fine looking man, too!" A very ugly sight awaited the new recruit; they were sawing off a cuirassier's leg at the thigh, a handsome young fellow of five feet ten. Fabrizio shut his eyes and drank four glasses of brandy straight off.

"How you do go for it, you boozer!" cried the *cantinière*. The brandy gave him an idea: "I must buy the goodwill of my comrades, the hussars of the escort."

"Give me the rest of the bottle," he said to the *vivandière*.

"What do you mean," was her answer, "what's left there costs ten francs, on a day like this."

As he rejoined the escort at a gallop:

"Ah! You're bringing us a drop of drink," cried the sergeant. "That was why you deserted, was it? Hand it over."

The bottle went round, the last man to take it flung it in the air after drinking. "Thank you, chum!" he cried to Fabrizio. All eyes were fastened on him kindly. This friendly gaze lifted a hundredweight from Fabrizio's heart; it was one of those hearts of too delicate tissue which require the friendship of those around it. So at last he had ceased to be looked at askance by his comrades, there was a bond between them! Fabrizio breathed a deep sigh of relief, then in a bold voice said to the sergeant:

"And if Captain Teulier has been killed, where shall I find my sister?" He fancied himself a little Machiavelli to be saying Teulier so naturally instead of Meunier.

"That's what you'll find out to-night," was the sergeant's reply.

The escort moved on again and made for some divisions of infantry. Fabrizio felt quite drunk; he had taken too much brandy, he was rolling slightly in his saddle: he remembered most opportunely a favourite saying of his mother's coachman: "When you've been lifting your elbow, look straight between your horse's ears, and do what the man next you does." The Marshal stopped for some time beside a number of cavalry units which he ordered to charge; but for an hour or two our hero was barely conscious of what was going on round about him. He was feeling extremely tired, and when his horse galloped he fell back on the saddle like a lump of lead.

Suddenly the sergeant called out to his men: "Don't you see the Emperor, curse you!" Whereupon the escort shouted: "*Vive l'Empereur!*" at the top of their voices. It may be imagined that our hero stared till his eyes started out of his head, but all he saw was some generals galloping, also followed by an escort. The long floating plumes of horsehair which the dragoons of the bodyguard wore on their helmets prevented him from distinguishing their faces. "So I have missed seeing the Emperor on a field of battle, all because of those cursed glasses of brandy!" This reflection brought him back to his senses.

They went down into a road filled with water, the horses wished drink.

"So that was the Emperor who went past then?" he asked the man next to him.

"Why, surely, the one with no braid on his coat. How is it you didn't see him?" his comrade answered kindly. Fabrizio felt a strong desire to gallop after the Emperor's escort and embody himself in it. What a joy to go really to war in the train of that hero! It was for that that he had come to France. "I am quite at liberty to do it," he said to himself, "for after all I have no other reason for being where I am but the will of my horse, which started galloping after these generals."

What made Fabrizio decide to stay where he was that the hussars, his new comrades, seemed so friendly towards him; he began to imagine himself the intimate friend of all the troopers with whom he had been galloping for the last few hours. He saw arise between them and himself that noble friendship of the heroes of Tasso and Ariosto. If he were to attach himself to the Emperor's escort, there would be fresh acquaintances to be made, perhaps they would look at him askance, for these other horsemen were dragoons, and he was wearing the hussar uniform like all the rest that were following the Marshal. The way in which they now looked at him set our hero on a pinnacle of happiness; he would have done anything in the world for his comrades; his mind and soul were in the clouds. Everything seemed to have assumed a new aspect now that he was among friends, he was dying to ask them various questions. "But I am still a little drunk," he said to himself, "I must bear in mind what the gaoler's wife told me." He noticed on leaving the sunken road that the escort was no longer with Marshal Ney; the general whom they were following was tall and thin, with a dry face and an awe-inspiring eye.

This general was none other than Comte d'A——, the Lieutenant Robert of the 15th of May, 1796. How delighted he would have been to meet Fabrizio del Dongo!

It was already some time since Fabrizio had noticed the earth flying off in black crumbs on being struck by shot; they came in rear of a regiment of cuirassiers, he could hear distinctly the rattle of the grapeshot against their breastplates, and saw several men fall.

The sun was now very low and had begun to set when the escort, emerging from a sunken road, mounted a little bank three or four feet high to enter a ploughed field. Fabrizio heard an odd little sound quite close to him: he turned his head, four men had fallen with their horses; the general himself had been unseated, but picked himself up, covered in blood. Fabrizio looked at the hussars who were lying on the ground: three of them were still making convulsive movements, the fourth cried: "Pull me out!" The sergeant and two or three men had dismounted to assist the general who, leaning upon his aide-de-camp, was attempting to walk a few steps; he was trying to get away from his horse, which lay on the ground struggling and kicking out madly.

The sergeant came up to Fabrizio. At that moment our hero heard a voice say behind him and quite close to his ear: "This is the only one that can still gallop." He felt himself seized by the feet; they were taken out of the stirrups at the same time as someone caught him underneath the arms; he was lifted over his horse's tail and then allowed to slip to the ground here he landed sitting.

The aide-de-camp took Fabrizio's horse by the bridle; the general, with the help of the sergeant, mounted and rode off at a gallop; he was quickly followed by the six men who were left of the escort. Fabrizio rose up in a fury, and began to run after them shouting: "*Ladri! Ladri!* (Thieves! Thieves!)" It was an amusing experience to run after horse-stealers across a battlefield.

The escort and the general, Comte d'A——, disappeared presently behind a row of willows. Fabrizio, blind with rage, also arrived at this line of willows; he found himself brought to a halt by a canal of considerable depth which he crossed. Then, on reaching the other side, he began swearing again as he saw once more, but far away in the distance, the general and his escort vanishing among the trees. "Thieves! Thieves!" he cried, in French this time. In desperation, not so much at the loss of his horse as at the treachery to himself, he let himself sink down on the side of the ditch, tired out and dying of hunger. If his fine horse had been taken from him by the enemy, he would have thought no more about it; but to see himself betrayed and robbed by that sergeant whom he

354

liked so much and by those hussars whom he regarded as brothers! That was what broke his heart. He could find no consolation for so great an infamy, and, leaning his back against a willow, began to shed hot tears. He abandoned one by one all those beautiful dreams of a chivalrous and sublime friendship, like that of the heroes of the *Gerusalemme Liberata*. To see death come to one was nothing, surrounded by heroic and tender hearts, by noble friends who clasp one by the hand as one yields one's dying breath! But to retain one's enthusiasm surrounded by a pack of vile scoundrels! Like all angry men Fabrizio exaggerated. After a quarter of an hour of this melting mood, he noticed that the guns were beginning to range on the row of trees in the shade of which he sat meditating. He rose and tried to find his bearings. He scanned those fields bounded by a wide canal and the row of pollard willows: he thought he knew where he was. He saw a body of infantry crossing the ditch and marching over the fields, a quarter of a league in front of him. " I was just falling asleep," he said to himself; " I must see that I'm not taken prisoner." And he put his best foot foremost. As he advanced, his mind was set at rest; he recognised the uniforms, the regiments by which he had been afraid of being cut off were French. He made a right incline so as to join them.

After the moral anguish of having been so shamefully betrayed and robbed, there came another which, at every moment, made itself felt more keenly; he was dying of hunger. It was therefore with infinite joy that after having walked, or rather run for ten minutes, he saw that the column of infantry, which also had been moving very rapidly, was halting to take up a position. A few minutes later, he was among the nearest of the soldiers.

" Friends, could you sell me a mouthful of bread?"

" I say, here's a fellow who thinks we're bakers!"

This harsh utterance and the general guffaw that followed it had a crushing effect on Fabrizio. So war was no longer that noble and universal uplifting of souls athirst for glory which he had imagined it to be from Napoleon's proclamations! He sat down, or rather let himself fall on the grass; he turned very pale. The soldier who had spoken to him, and who had stopped ten paces off to clean the lock of his musket with his handkerchief, came nearer and flung him a lump of bread; then, seeing that he did not pick it up, broke off a piece which he put in our hero's mouth. Fabrizio opened his eyes, and ate the bread without having the strength to speak. When at length he looked round for the soldier to pay him, he found himself alone; the men nearest to him were a hundred yards off and were marching. Mechanically he rose and followed them. He entered a wood; he was dropping with exhaustion, and already had begun to look round for a comfortable resting-place; but what was his delight on recognising first of all the horse, then the cart, and finally the *cantinière* of that morning! She ran to him and was frightened by his appearance.

"Still going, my boy," she said to him; "you're wounded then? And where's your fine horse?" So saying she led him towards the cart, upon which she made him climb, supporting him under the arms. No sooner was he in the cart than our hero, utterly worn out, fell fast asleep.

Nothing could awaken him, neither the muskets fired close to the cart nor the trot of the horse which the *cantinière* was flogging with all her might. The regiment, attacked unexpectedly by swarms of Prussian cavalry, after imagining all day that they were winning the battle, was beating a retreat or rather fleeing in the direction of France.

The colonel, a handsome young man, well turned out, who had succeeded Macon, was sabred; the battalion commander who took his place, an old man with white hair, ordered the regiment to halt. "Damn you," he cried to his men, "in the days of the Republic we waited till we were forced by the enemy before running away. Defend every inch of ground, and get yourselves killed!" he shouted, and swore at them. "It is the soil of the Fatherland that these Prussians want to invade now!"

The little cart halted; Fabrizio awoke with a start. The sun had set some time back; he was quite astonished to see that it was almost night. The troops were running in all directions in a confusion which greatly surprised our hero; they looked shame-faced, he thought.

"What is happening?" he asked the *cantinière*.

"Nothing at all. Only that we're in the soup, my boy; it's the Prussian cavalry mowing us down, that's all. The idiot of a general thought at first they were our men. Come, quick, help me to mend Cocotte's trace; it's broken."

Several shots were fired ten yards off. Our hero, cool and composed, said to himself: "But really, I haven't fought at all, the whole day; I have only escorted a general.—I must go and fight," he said to the *cantinière*.

"Keep calm, you shall fight, and more than you want! We're done for.

"Aubry, my lad," she called out to a passing corporal, "keep an eye on the little cart now and then."

"Are you going to fight?" Fabrizio asked Aubry.

"Oh, no, I'm putting my pumps on to go to a dance!"

"I shall follow you."

"I tell you, he's all right, the little hussar," cried the *cantinière*. "The young gentleman has a stout heart." Corporal Aubry marched on without saying a word. Eight or nine soldiers ran up and joined him; he led them behind a big oak surrounded by brambles. On reaching it he posted them along the edge of the wood, still without uttering a word, on a widely extended front, each man being at least ten paces from the next.

"Now then, you men," said the corporal, opening his mouth for the first time, "don't fire till I give the order: remember you've only got three rounds each."

"Why, what is happening?" Fabrizio wondered. At length, when he found himself alone with the corporal, he said to him: "I have no musket."

"Will you hold your tongue? Go forward there: fifty paces in front of the wood you'll find one of the poor fellows of the Regiment who've been sabred; you will take his cartridge-pouch and his musket. Don't strip a wounded man, though; take the pouch and musket from one who's properly dead, and hurry up or you'll be shot in the back by our fellows." Fabrizio set off at a run and returned the next minute with a musket and a pouch.

"Load your musket and stick yourself behind this tree, and whatever you do don't fire till you get the order from me. . . . Great God in heaven!" the corporal broke off, "he doesn't even know how to load!" He helped Fabrizio to do this while going on with his instructions. "If one of the enemy's cavalry gallops at you to cut you down, dodge round your tree and don't fire till he's within three paces: wait till your bayonet's practically touching his uniform.

"Throw that great sabre away," cried the corporal. "Good God, do you want it to trip you up? Fine sort of soldiers they're sending us these days!" As he spoke he himself took hold of the sabre which he flung angrily away.

"You there, wipe the flint of your musket with your handkerchief. Have you never fired a musket?"

"I am a hunter."

357

"Thank God for that!" went on the corporal with a loud sigh. "Whatever you do, don't fire till I give the order." And he moved away.

Fabrizio was supremely happy. "Now I'm going to do some real fighting," he said to himself, "and kill one of the enemy. This morning they were sending cannon-balls over, and I did nothing but expose myself and risk getting killed; that's a fool's game." He gazed all round him with extreme curiosity. Presently he heard seven or eight shots fired quite close at hand. But receiving no order to fire he stood quietly behind his tree. It was almost night; he felt he was in a *look-out*, bear-shooting, on the mountain of Tramezzina, above Grianta. A hunter's idea came to him: he took a cartridge from his pouch and removed the ball. "If I see him," he said, "it won't do to miss him," and he slipped this second ball into the barrel of his musket. He heard shots fired close to his tree; at the same moment he saw a horseman in blue pass in front of him at a gallop, going from right to left. "It is more than three paces," he said to himself, "but at that range I am certain of my mark." He kept the trooper carefully sighted with his musket and finally pressed the trigger: the trooper fell with his horse. Our hero imagined he was stalking game: he ran joyfully out to collect his bag. He was actually touching the man, who appeared to him to be dying, when, with incredible speed, two Prussian troopers charged down on him to sabre him. Fabrizio dashed back as fast as he could go to the wood; to gain speed he flung his musket away. The Prussian troopers were not more than three paces from him when he reached another plantation of young oaks, as thick as his arm and quite upright, which fringed the wood. These little oaks delayed the horsemen for a moment, but they passed them and continued their pursuit of Fabrizio along a clearing. Once again they were just overtaking him when he slipped in among seven or eight big trees. At that moment his face was almost scorched by the flame of five or six musket shots fired from in front of him. He ducked his head; when he raised it again he found himself face to face with the corporal.

"Did you kill your man?" Corporal Aubry asked him.

"Yes; but I've lost my musket."

"It's not muskets we're short of. You're not a bad b——; though you do look as green as a cabbage you've won the day all right, and these men here have just missed the two who were chasing you and coming straight at them. I didn't see them myself. What we've got to do now is to get away at the double; the Regiment must be half a mile off, and there's a bit of a field to cross, too, where we may find ourselves surrounded."

As he spoke, the corporal marched off at a brisk pace at the head of his ten men. Two hundred yards farther on, as they entered the little field he had mentioned, they came upon a wounded general who was being carried by his aide-de-camp and an orderly.

"Give me four of your men," he said to the corporal in a faint voice, "I've got to be carried to the ambulance; my leg is shattered."

"Go and f—— yourself!" replied the corporal, "you and all your generals. You've all of you betrayed the Emperor to-day."

"What," said the general, furious, "you dispute my orders. Do you know that I am General Comte B——, commanding your Division," and so on. He waxed rhetorical. The aide-de-camp flung himself on the men. The corporal gave him a thrust in the arm with his bayonet, then made off with his party at the double. "I wish they were all in your boat," he repeated with an oath; "I'd shatter their arms and legs for them. A pack of puppies! All of them bought by the Bourbons, to betray the Emperor!" Fabrizio listened with a thrill of horror to this frightful accusation.

About ten o'clock that night the little party overtook their regiment on the outskirts of a large village which divided the road into several very narrow streets; but Fabrizio noticed that Corporal Aubry avoided speaking to any of the officers. "We can't get on," he called to his men. All these streets were blocked with infantry, cavalry, and, worst of all, by the limbers and wagons of the artillery. The corporal tried three of these streets in turn; after advancing twenty yards he was obliged to halt. Everyone was swearing and losing his temper.

"Some traitor in command here, too!" cried the corporal: "If the enemy has the sense to surround the village, we shall all be caught like rats in a trap. Follow me, you." Fabrizio looked round; there were only six men left with the corporal. Through a big gate which stood open they came into a huge courtyard; from this courtyard they passed into a stable, the back door of which let them into a garden. They lost their way for a moment and wandered blindly about. But finally, going through a hedge, they found themselves in a huge field of buckwheat. In less than half an hour, guided by the shouts and confused noises, they had regained the high road on the other side of the village. The ditches on either side of this road were filled with muskets that had been thrown away; Fabrizio selected one: but the road, although very broad, was so blocked with stragglers and transports that in the next half-hour the corporal and Fabrizio had not advanced more than five hundred yards at the most; they were told that this road led to Charleroi. As the village clock struck eleven:

"Let us cut across the field again," said the corporal. The little party was reduced now to three men, the corporal and Fabrizio. When they had gone a quarter of a league from the high road: "I'm done," said one of the soldiers.

"Me, too!" said another.

"That's good news! We're all in the same boat," said the corporal; "but do what I tell you and you'll get through all right." His eye fell on five or six trees marking the line of a little ditch in the middle of an immense cornfield. "Make for the trees!" he told his men; "lie down," he added when they had reached the trees, "and not a sound, remember. But before you go to sleep, who's got any bread?"

"I have," said one of the men.

"Give it here," said the corporal in a tone of authority. He divided the bread into five pieces and took the smallest himself.

"A quarter of an hour before dawn," he said as he ate it, "you'll have the enemy's cavalry on your backs. You've got to see you're not sabred. A man by himself is done for with cavalry after him on these big plains, but five can get away; keep in close touch with me, don't fire till they're at close range, and to-morrow evening I'll undertake to get you to Charleroi." The corporal roused his men an hour before daybreak and made them recharge their muskets. The noise on the high road still continued; it had gone on all night: it was like the sound of a torrent heard from a long way off.

"They're like a flock of sheep running away," said Fabrizio with a guileless air to the corporal.

"Will you shut your mouth, you young fool!" said the corporal, greatly indignant. And the three soldiers who with Fabrizio composed his whole force scowled angrily at our hero as though he had uttered blasphemy. He had insulted the nation.

"That is where their strength lies!" thought our hero. "I noticed it before with the Viceroy at Milan; they are not running away, oh, no! With these Frenchmen you must

360

never speak the truth if it shocks their vanity. But as for their savage scowls, they don't trouble me, and I must let them understand as much." They kept on their way, always at an interval of five hundred yards from the torrent of fugitives that covered the high road. A league farther on, the corporal and his party crossed a road running into the high road in which a number of soldiers were lying. Fabrizio purchased a fairly good horse which cost him forty francs, and among all the sabres that had been thrown down everywhere made a careful choice of one that was long and straight. "Since I'm told I've got to stick them," he thought, "this is the best." Thus equipped, he put his horse into a gallop and soon overtook the corporal who had gone on ahead. He sat up in his stirrups, took hold with his left hand of the scabbard of his straight sabre, and said to the four Frenchmen:

"Those people going along the high road look like a flock of sheep . . . they are running like frightened sheep. . . ."

In spite of his dwelling upon the word *sheep,* his companions had completely forgotten that it had annoyed them an hour earlier. Here we see one of the contrasts between the Italian character and the French; the Frenchman is no doubt the happier of the two; he glides lightly over the events of life and bears no malice afterwards.

We shall not attempt to conceal the fact that Fabrizio was highly pleased with himself after using the word *sheep.* They marched on, talking about nothing in particular. After covering two leagues more, the corporal, still greatly astonished to see no sign of the enemy's cavalry, said to Fabrizio:

"You are our cavalry; gallop over to that farm on the little hill; ask the farmer if he will *sell* us breakfast: mind you tell him there are only five of us. If he hesitates, put down five francs of your money in advance; but don't be frightened, we'll take the dollar back from him after we've eaten."

Fabrizio looked at the corporal; he saw in his face an imperturbable gravity and really an air of moral superiority; he obeyed. Everything fell out as the commander in chief had anticipated; only, Fabrizio insisted on their not taking back by force the five francs he had given to the farmer.

"The money is mine," he said to his friends; "I'm not paying for you, I'm paying for the oats he's given my horse."

Fabrizio's French accent was so bad that his companions thought they detected in his words a note of superiority; they were keenly annoyed, and from that moment a duel began to take shape in their minds for the end of the day. They found him very different from themselves, which shocked them; Fabrizio, on the contrary, was beginning to feel a warm friendship towards them.

They had marched without saying a word for a couple of hours when the corporal, looking across at the high road, exclaimed in a transport of joy: "There's the Regiment!" They were soon on the road; but, alas, round the eagle were mustered not more than two hundred men. Fabrizio's eye soon caught sight of the *vivandière*: she was going on foot, her eyes were red and every now and again she burst into tears. Fabrizio looked in vain for the little cart and Cocotte.

"Stripped, ruined, robbed!" cried the *vivandière,* in answer to our hero's inquiring glance. He, without a word, got down from his horse, took hold of the bridle and said to the *vivandière*: "Mount!" She did not have to be told twice.

"Shorten the stirrups for me," was her only remark.

As soon as she was comfortably in the saddle she began to tell Fabrizio all the disasters of the night. After a narrative of endless length but eagerly drunk in by our hero who, to tell the truth, understood nothing at all of what she said but had a tender feeling for the *vivandière,* she went on:

"And to think that they were Frenchmen who robbed me, beat me, destroyed me. . . ."

"What! It wasn't the enemy?" said Fabrizio with an air of innocence which made his grave, pale face look charming.

"What a fool you are, you poor boy!" said the *vivandière,* smiling through her tears; "but you're very nice, for all that."

"And such as he is, he brought down his Prussian properly," said Corporal Aubry, who, in the general confusion round them, happened to be on the other side of the horse on which the *cantinière* was sitting. "But he's proud," the corporal went on. . . . Fabrizio made an impulsive movement. "And what's your name?" asked the corporal; "for if there's a report going in I should like to mention you."

"I'm called Vasi," replied Fabrizio, with a curious expression on his face. "Boulot, I mean," he added, quickly correcting himself.

Boulot was the name of the late possessor of the marching orders which the gaoler's wife at B—— had given him; on his way from B—— he had studied them carefully, for he was beginning to think a little and was no longer so easily surprised. In addition to the marching orders of Trooper Boulot, he had stowed away in a safe place the precious

Italian passport according to which he was entitled to the noble appellation of Vasi, dealer in barometers. When the corporal had charged him with being proud, it had been on the tip of his tongue to retort: "I proud! I, Fabrizio Volterra, Marchesino del Dongo, who consent to go by the name of a Vasi, dealer in barometers!"

While he was making these reflections and saying to himself: "I must not forget that I am called Boulot, or look out for the prison fate threatens me with," the corporal and the *cantinière* had been exchanging a few words with regard to him.

"Don't say I'm inquisitive," said the *cantinière*, ceasing to address him in the second person singular, "it's for your good I ask these questions. Who are you, now, really?"

Fabrizio did not reply at first. He was considering that never again would he find more devoted friends to ask for advice, and he was in urgent need of advice from someone. "We are coming into a fortified place, the governor will want to know who I am, and ware prison if I let him see by my answers that I know nobody in the 4th Hussar Regiment whose uniform I am wearing!" In his capacity as an Austrian subject, Fabrizio knew all about the importance to be attached to a passport. Various members of his family, although noble and devout, although supporters of the winning side, had been in trouble a score of times over their passports; he was therefore not in the least put out by the question which the *cantinière* had addressed to him. But as, before answering, he had to think of the French words which would express his meaning most clearly, the *cantinière*, pricked by a keen curiosity, added, to induce him to speak: "Corporal Aubry and I are going to give you some good advice."

"I have no doubt you are," replied Fabrizio. "My name is Vasi and I come from Genoa; my sister, who is famous for her beauty, is married to a captain. As I am only seventeen, she made me come to her to let me see something of France, and form my character a little; not finding her in Paris, and knowing that she was with this army, I came on here. I've searched for her everywhere and haven't found her. The soldiers, who were puzzled by my accent, had me arrested. I had money then, I gave some to the *gendarme*, who let me have some marching orders and a uniform, and said to me: 'Get away with you, and swear you'll never mention my name.'"

"What was he called?" asked the *cantinière*.

"I've given my word," said Fabrizio.

"He's right," put in the corporal, "the *gendarme* is a sweep, but our friend ought not to give his name. And what is the other one called, this captain, your sister's husband? If we knew his name, we would try to find him."

"Teulier, Captain in the 4th Hussars," replied our hero.

"And so," said the corporal, with a certain subtlety, "from your foreign accent the soldiers took you for a spy?"

"That's the abominable word!" cried Fabrizio, his eyes blazing. "I who love the Emperor so and the French people! And it was that insult that annoyed me more than anything."

"There's no insult about it; that's where you're wrong; the soldiers' mistake was quite natural," replied Corporal Aubry gravely.

And he went on to explain in the most pedantic manner that in the army one must belong to some corps and wear a uniform, failing which it was quite simple that people should take one for a spy. "The enemy sends us any number of them; everybody's a traitor in this war." The scales fell from Fabrizio's eyes; he realised for the first time that he had been in the wrong in everything that had happened to him during the last two months.

"But make the boy tell us the whole story," said the *cantinière*, her curiosity more and more excited. Fabrizio obeyed. When he had finished:

"It comes to this," said the *cantinière*, speaking in a serious tone to the corporal, "this child is not a soldier at all; we're going to have a bloody war now that we've been beaten and betrayed. Why should he go and get his bones broken free, gratis and for nothing?"

"Especially," put in the corporal, "as he doesn't even know how to load his musket, neither by numbers, nor in his own time. It was I put in the shot that brought down the Prussian."

"Besides, he lets everyone see the colour of his money," added the *cantinière*; "he will be robbed of all he has as soon as he hasn't got us to look after him."

"The first cavalry non-com. he comes across," said the corporal, "will take it from him to pay for his drink, and perhaps they'll enlist him for the enemy; they're all traitors. The first man he meets will order him to follow, and he'll follow him; he would do better to join our Regiment."

"No, please, if you don't mind, corporal!" Fabrizio exclaimed with animation; "I am more comfortable on a horse. And, besides, I don't know how to load a musket, and you have seen that I can manage a horse."

Fabrizio was extremely proud of this little speech. We need

not report the long discussion that followed between the corporal and the *cantinière* as to his future destiny. Fabrizio noticed that in discussing him these people repeated three or four times all the circumstances of his story: the soldiers' suspicions, the *gendarme* selling him marching orders and a uniform, the accident by which, the day before, he had found himself forming part of the marshal's escort, the glimpse of the Emperor as he galloped past, the horse that had been *scoffed* from him, and so on indefinitely.

With feminine curiosity the *cantinière* kept harking back incessantly to the way in which he had been dispossessed of the good horse which she had made him buy.

"You felt yourself seized by the feet, they lifted you gently over your horse's tail, and sat you down on the ground!" "Why repeat so often," Fabrizio said to himself, "what all three of us know perfectly well?" He had not yet discovered that this is how, in France, the lower orders proceed in quest of ideas.

"How much money have you?" the *cantinière* asked him suddenly. Fabrizio had no hesitation in answering. He was sure of the nobility of the woman's nature; that is the fine side of France.

"Altogether, I may have got left thirty napoleons in gold, and eight or nine five-franc pieces."

"In that case, you have a clear field!" exclaimed the *cantinière*. "Get right away from this rout of an army; clear out, take the first road with ruts on it that you come to on the right; keep your horse moving and your back to the army. At the first opportunity, buy some civilian clothes. When you've gone nine or ten leagues and there are no more soldiers in sight, take the mail-coach, and go and rest for a week and eat beefsteaks in some nice town. Never let anyone know that you've been in the army, or the police will take you up as a deserter; and, nice as you are, my boy, you're not quite clever enough yet to stand up to the police. As soon as you've got civilian clothes on your back, tear up your marching orders into a thousand pieces and go back to your real name: say that you're Vasi. And where ought he to say he comes from?" she asked the corporal.

"From Cambrai on the Scheldt: it's a good town and quite small, if you know what I mean. There's a cathedral there, and Fénelon."

"That's right," said the *cantinière*. "Never let on to anyone that you've been in battle, don't breathe a word about B——, or the *gendarme* who sold you the marching orders. When you're ready to go back to Paris, make first for Versailles, and pass the Paris barrier from that side in a leisurely way, on foot, as if you were taking a stroll. Sew up your napoleons inside your breeches, and remember, when you have to pay for anything, shew only the exact sum that you want to spend. What makes me sad is that they'll take you and rob you and strip you of everything you have. And whatever will you do without money, you that don't know how to look after yourself . . ." and so on.

The good woman went on talking for some time still; the corporal indicated his support by nodding his head, not being able to get a word in himself. Suddenly the crowd that was packing the road first of all doubled its pace, then, in the twinkling of an eye, crossed the little ditch that bounded the road on the left and fled helter-skelter across country. Cries of "The Cossacks! The Cossacks!" rose from every side.

"Take back your horse!" the *cantinière* shouted.

"God forbid!" said Fabrizio. "Gallop! Away with you! I give him to you. Do you want something to buy another cart with? Half of what I have is yours."

"Take back your horse, I tell you!" cried the *cantinière* angrily; and she prepared to dismount. Fabrizio drew his sabre. "Hold on tight!" he shouted to her; and gave two or three strokes with the flat of his sabre to the horse, which broke into a gallop and followed the fugitives.

Our hero stood looking at the road; a moment ago, two or three thousand people had been jostling along it, packed together like peasants at the tail of a procession. After the shout of: "Cossacks!" he saw not a soul on it; the fugitives had cast away shakoes, muskets, sabres, everything. Fabrizio, quite bewildered, climbed up into a field on the right of the road and twenty or thirty feet above it; he scanned the line of the road in both directions, and the plain, but saw no trace of the Cossacks. "Funny people, these French!" he said to himself. "Since I have got to go to the right," he thought, "I may as well start off at once; it is possible that these people have a reason for running away that I don't know." He picked up a musket, saw that it was charged, shook up the powder in the priming, cleaned the flint, then chose a cartridge-pouch that was well filled and looked round him again in all directions; he was absolutely alone in the middle of this plain which just now had been so crowded with people. In the far distance he could see the fugitives who were beginning to disappear behind the trees, and were still running.

" That's a very odd thing," he said to himself, and remembering the tactics employed by the corporal the night before, he went and sat down in the middle of a field of corn. He did not go farther because he was anxious to see again his good friends the *cantinière* and Corporal Aubry.

In this cornfield, he made the discovery that he had no more than eighteen napoleons, instead of thirty as he had supposed; but he still had some small diamonds which he had stowed away in the lining of the hussar's boots, before dawn, in the gaoler's wife's room at B——. He concealed his napoleons as best he could, pondering deeply the while on the sudden disappearance of the others. " Is that a bad omen for me?" he asked himself. What distressed him most was that he had not asked Corporal Aubry the question: " Have I really taken part in a battle?" It seemed to him that he had, and his happiness would have known no bounds could he have been certain of this.

" But even if I have," he said to himself, " I took part in it bearing the name of a prisoner, I had a prisoner's marching orders in my pocket, and, worse still, his coat on my back! That is the fatal threat to my future: what would the Priore Blanès say to it? And that wretched Boulot died in prison. It is all of the most sinister augury; fate will lead me to prison." Fabrizio would have given anything in the world to know whether Trooper Boulot had really been guilty; when he searched his memory, he seemed to recollect that the gaoler's wife had told him that the hussar had been taken up not only for the theft of silver plate but also for stealing a cow from a peasant and nearly beating the peasant to death: Fabrizio had no doubt that he himself would be sent to prison some day for a crime which would bear some relation to that of Trooper Boulot. He thought of his friend the *parroco* Blanès: what would he not have given for an opportunity of consulting him! Then he remembered that he had not written to his aunt since leaving Paris. " Poor Gina!" he said to himself. And tears stood in his eyes, when suddenly he heard a slight sound quite close to him: a soldier was feeding three horses on the standing corn; he had taken the bits out of their mouths and they seemed half dead with hunger; he was holding them by the snaffle. Fabrizio got up like a partridge; the soldier seemed frightened. Our hero noticed this, and yielded to the pleasure of playing the hussar for a moment.

" One of these horses belongs to me, f—— you, but I don't mind giving you five francs for the trouble you've taken in bringing it here."

"What are you playing at?" said the soldier. Fabrizio took aim at him from a distance of six paces.

"Let go the horse, or I'll blow your head off."

The soldier had his musket slung on his back; he reached over his shoulder to seize it.

"If you move an inch, you're a dead man!" cried Fabrizio, rushing upon him.

"All right, give me the five francs and take one of the horses," said the embarrassed soldier, after casting a rueful glance at the high road, on which there was absolutely no one to be seen. Fabrizio, keeping his musket raised in his left hand, with the right flung him three five franc pieces.

"Dismount, or you're a dead man. Bridle the black, and go farther off with the other two. . . . If you move, I fire."

The soldier looked savage but obeyed. Fabrizio went up to the horse and passed the rein over his left arm, without losing sight of the soldier, who was moving slowly away; when our hero saw that he had gone fifty paces, he jumped nimbly on to the horse. He had barely mounted and was feeling with his foot for the off stirrup when he heard a bullet whistle past close to his head: it was the soldier who had fired at him. Fabrizio, beside himself with rage, started galloping after the soldier who ran off as fast as his legs could carry him, and presently Fabrizio saw him mount one of his two horses and gallop away. "Good, he's out of range now," he said to himself. The horse he had just bought was a magnificent animal, but seemed half starved. Fabrizio returned to the high road, where there was still not a living soul; he crossed it and put his horse into a trot to reach a little fold in the ground on the left, where he hoped to find the *cantinière*; but when he was at the top of the little rise he could see nothing save, more than a league away, a few scattered troops. "It is written that I shall not see her again," he said to himself with a sigh, "the good, brave woman!" He came to a farm which he had seen in the distance on the right of the road. Without dismounting, and after paying for it in advance, he made the farmer produce some oats for his poor horse, which was so famished that it began to gnaw the manger. An hour later, Fabrizio was trotting along the high road, still in the hope of meeting the *cantinière,* or at any rate Corporal Aubry. Moving all the time and keeping a look-out all round him, he came to a marshy river crossed by a fairly narrow wooden bridge. Between him and the bridge, on the right of the road, was a solitary house bearing the sign of the White Horse. "There I shall get some dinner," thought

Fabrizio. A cavalry officer with his arm in a sling was guarding the approach to the bridge; he was on horseback and looked very melancholy; ten paces away from him, three dismounted troopers were filling their pipes.

"There are some people," Fabrizio said to himself, "who look to me very much as though they would like to buy my horse for even less than he cost me." The wounded officer and the three men on foot watched him approach and seemed to be waiting for him. "It would be better not to cross by this bridge, but to follow the river bank to the right; that was the way the *cantinière* advised me to take to get clear of difficulties. . . . Yes," thought our hero, "but if I take to my heels now, to-morrow I shall be thoroughly ashamed of myself; besides, my horse has good legs, the officer's is probably tied; if he tries to make me dismount I shall gallop." Reasoning thus with himself, Fabrizio pulled up his horse and moved forward at the slowest possible pace.

"Advance, you, hussar!" the officer called to him with an air of authority.

Fabrizio went on a few paces and then halted.

"Do you want to take my horse?" he shouted.

"Not in the least; advance."

Fabrizio examined the officer; he had a white moustache, and looked the best fellow in the world; the handkerchief that held up his left arm was drenched with blood, and his right hand also was bound up in a piece of bloodstained linen. "It is the men on foot who are going to snatch my bridle," thought Fabrizio; but, on looking at them from nearer, he saw that they too were wounded.

"On your honour as a soldier," said the officer, who wore the epaulettes of a colonel, "stay here on picket, and tell all the dragoons, chasseurs and hussars that you see that Colonel Le Baron is in the inn over there, and that I order them to come and report to me." The old colonel had the air of a man broken by suffering; with his first words he had made a conquest of our hero, who replied with great good sense:

"I am very young, sir, to make them listen to me; I ought to have a written order from you."

"He is right," said the colonel, studying him closely; "make out the order, La Rose, you've got the use of your right hand."

Without saying a word, La Rose took from his pocket a little parchment book, wrote a few lines, and, tearing out a leaf, handed it to Fabrizio; the colonel repeated the order to him, adding that after two hours on duty he would be relieved, as was right and proper, by one of the three wounded troopers he had with him. So saying he went into the inn with his men. Fabrizio watched them go and sat without moving at the end of his wooden bridge, so deeply impressed had he been by the sombre, silent grief of these three persons. " One would think they were under a spell," he said to himself. At length he unfolded the paper and read the order, which ran as follows:

" Colonel Le Baron, 6th Dragoons, Commanding the 2nd Brigade of the 1st Cavalry Division of the XIV Corps, orders all cavalrymen, dragoons, chasseurs and hussars, on no account to cross the bridge, and to report to him at the White Horse Inn, by the bridge, which is his headquarters.

" Headquarters, by the bridge of La Sainte, June 19, 1815.
" For Colonel Le Baron, wounded in the right
arm and by his orders,
" LA ROSE, *Sergeant*."

Fabrizio had been on guard at the bridge for barely half an hour when he saw six chasseurs approaching him mounted, and three on foot; he communicated the colonel's order to them. " We're coming back," said four of the mounted men, and crossed the bridge at a fast trot. Fabrizio then spoke to the other two. During the discussion, which grew heated, the three men on foot crossed the bridge. Finally, one of the two mounted troopers who had stayed behind asked to see the order again, and carried it off, with:
" I am taking it to the others, who will come back without fail; wait for them here." And off he went at a gallop; his companion followed him. All this had happened in the twinkling of an eye.
Fabrizio was furious, and called to one of the wounded soldiers, who appeared at a window of the White Horse. This soldier, on whose arm Fabrizio saw the stripes of a cavalry sergeant, came down and shouted to him: " Draw your sabre, man, you're on picket." Fabrizio obeyed, then said: " They've carried off the order."
" They're out of hand after yesterday's affair," replied the other in a melancholy tone. " I'll let you have one of my pistols; if they force past you again, fire it in the air; I shall come, or the colonel himself will appear."
Fabrizio had not failed to observe the sergeant's start of surprise on hearing of the theft of the order. He realised that

it was a personal insult to himself, and promised himself that he would not allow such a trick to be played on him again.

Armed with the sergeant's horse-pistol, Fabrizio had proudly resumed his guard when he saw coming towards him seven hussars, mounted. He had taken up a position that barred the bridge; he read them the colonel's order, which seemed greatly to annoy them; the most venturesome of them tried to pass. Fabrizio, following the wise counsel of his friend the *vivandière,* who, the morning before, had told him that he must thrust and not slash, lowered the point of his long, straight sabre and made as though to stab with it the man who was trying to pass him.

" Oh, so he wants to kill us, the baby! " cried the hussars, " as if we hadn't been killed quite enough yesterday! " They all drew their sabres at once and fell on Fabrizio: he gave himself up for dead; but he thought of the sergeant's surprise, and was not anxious to earn his contempt again. Drawing back on to his bridge, he tried to reach them with his sabre-point. He looked so absurd when he tried to wield this huge, straight heavy-dragoon sabre, a great deal too heavy for him, that the hussars soon saw with what sort of soldier they had to deal; they then endeavoured not to wound him but to slash his clothing. In this way Fabrizio received three or four slight sabre-cuts on his arms. For his own part, still faithful to the *cantinière's* precept, he kept thrusting the point of his sabre at them with all his might. As ill luck would have it, one of these thrusts wounded a hussar in the hand: highly indignant at being touched by so raw a recruit, he replied with a downward thrust which caught Fabrizio in the upper part of the thigh. What made this blow effective was that our hero's horse, so far from avoiding the fray, seemed to take pleasure in it and to be flinging himself on the assailants. These, seeing Fabrizio's blood streaming along his right arm, were afraid that they might have carried the game too far, and, pushing him against the left-hand parapet of the bridge, crossed at a gallop. As soon as Fabrizio had a moment to himself he fired his pistol in the air to warn the colonel.

Four mounted hussars and two on foot, of the same regiment as the others, were coming towards the bridge and were still two hundred yards away from it when the pistol went off. They had been paying close attention to what was happening on the bridge, and, imagining that Fabrizio had fired at their comrades, the four mounted men galloped upon him with raised sabres: it was a regular cavalry charge. Colonel Le Baron, summoned by the pistol-shot, opened the door of the inn and rushed on to the bridge just as the galloping hussars reached it, and himself gave them the order to halt.

" There's no colonel here now!" cried one of them, and pressed on his horse. The colonel in exasperation broke off the reprimand he was giving them, and with his wounded right hand seized the rein of this horse on the off side.

" Halt! You bad soldier," he said to the hussar; " I know you, you're in Captain Henriot's squadron."

" Very well, then! The captain can give me the order himself! Captain Henriot was killed yesterday," he added with a snigger, " and you can go and f—— yourself!"

So saying, he tried to force a passage, and pushed the old colonel who fell in a sitting position on the roadway of the bridge. Fabrizio, who was a couple of yards farther along upon the bridge, but facing the inn, pressed his horse, and, while the breast-piece of the assailant's harness threw down the old colonel who never let go the off rein, Fabrizio, indignant, bore down upon the hussar with a driving thrusts. Fortunately the hussar's horse, feeling itself pulled towards the ground by the rein which the colonel still held, made a movement sideways, with the result that the long blade of Fabrizio's heavy-cavalry sabre slid along the hussar's jacket, and the whole length of it passed beneath his eyes. Furious, the hussar turned round and, using all his strength, dealt Fabrizio a blow which cut his sleeve and went deep into his arm: our hero fell.

One of the dismounted hussars, seeing the two defenders of the bridge on the ground, seized the opportunity, jumped on to Fabrizio's horse and tried to make off with it by starting at a gallop across the bridge.

The sergeant, as he hurried from the inn, had seen his colonel fall, and supposed him to be seriously wounded. He ran after Fabrizio's horse and plunged the point of his sabre into the thief's entrails; he fell. The hussars, seeing no one now on the bridge but the sergeant, who was on foot, crossed at a gallop and rapidly disappeared. The one on foot bolted into the fields.

The sergeant came up to the wounded men. Fabrizio was already on his feet; he was not in great pain, but was bleeding profusely. The colonel got up more slowly; he was quite stunned by his fall, but had received no injury. " I feel nothing," he said to the sergeant, " except the old wound in my hand."

The hussar whom the sergeant had wounded was dying. " The devil take him!" exclaimed the colonel. " But," he said to the sergeant and the two troopers who came running out, "look after this young man whose life I have risked, most improperly. I shall stay on the bridge myself and try to stop these madmen. Take the young man to the inn and tie up his arm. Use one of my shirts."

The whole of this adventure had not lasted a minute. Fabrizio's wounds were nothing; they tied up his arm with bandages torn from the colonel's shirt. They wanted to make up a bed for him upstairs in the inn.

"But while I am tucked up here in the stable floor," said Fabrizio to the sergeant, "my horse, who is down in the stable, will get bored with being left alone and will go off with another master."

"Not bad for a conscript!" said the sergeant. And they deposited Fabrizio on a litter of clean straw in the same stall as his horse.

Then, as he was feeling very weak, the sergeant brought him a bowl of mulled wine and talked to him for a little. Several compliments included in this conversation carried our hero to the seventh heaven.

Fabrizio did not wake until dawn on the following day; the horses were neighing continuously and making a frightful din; the stable was filled with smoke. At first Fabrizio could make nothing of all this noise, and did not even know where he was: finally, half-stifled by the smoke, it occurred to him that the house was on fire; in the twinkling of an eye he was out of the stable and in the saddle. He raised his head; smoke was belching violently from the two windows over the stable; and the roof was covered by a black smoke which rose curling into the air. A hundred fugitives had arrived during the night at the White Horse; they were all shouting and swearing. The five or six whom Fabrizio could see close at hand seemed to him to be completely drunk; one of them tried to stop him and called out to him: "Where are you taking my horse?"

When Fabrizio had gone a quarter of a league, he turned his head. There was no one following him; the building was in flames. Fabrizio caught sight of the bridge; he remembered his wound, and felt his arm compressed by bandages and very hot. "And the old colonel, what has become of him? He gave his shirt to tie up my arm." Our hero was this morning the coolest man in the world; the amount of blood he had shed had liberated him from all the romantic element in his character.

"To the right!" he said to himself, "and no time to lose."

373

He began quietly following the course of the river which, after passing under the bridge, ran to the right of the road. He remembered the good *cantinière*'s advice. "What friendship!" he said to himself, "what an open nature!"

After riding for an hour he felt very weak. "Oho! Am I going to faint?" he wondered. "If I faint, someone will steal my horse, and my clothes, perhaps, and my money and jewels with them." He had no longer the strength to hold the reins, and was trying to keep his balance in the saddle when a peasant who was digging in a field by the side of the high road noticed his pallor and came up to offer him a glass of beer and some bread.

"When I saw you look so pale, I thought you must be one of the wounded from the great battle," the peasant told him. Never did help come more opportunely. As Fabrizio was munching the piece of bread his eyes began to hurt him when he looked straight ahead. When he felt a little better he thanked the man. "And where am I?" he asked. The peasant told him that three quarters of a league farther on he would come to the township of Zonders, where he would be very well looked after. Fabrizio reached the town, not knowing quite what he was doing and thinking only at every step of not falling off his horse. He saw a big door standing open; he entered. It was the Woolcomb Inn. At once there ran out to him the good lady of the house, an enormous woman; she called for help in a voice that throbbed with pity. Two girls came and helped Fabrizio to dismount; no sooner had his feet touched the ground than he fainted completely. A surgeon was fetched, who bled him. For the rest of that day and the days that followed Fabrizio scarcely knew what was being done to him, he slept almost without interruption.

The sabre wound in his thigh threatened to form a serious abscess. When his mind was clear again, he asked them to look after his horse, and kept on repeating that he would pay them well, which shocked the good hostess and her daughters. For a fortnight he was admirably looked after and he was beginning to be himself again when he noticed one evening that his hostess seemed greatly upset. Presently a German officer came into his room: in answering his questions they used a language which Fabrizio did not understand, but he could see that they were speaking about him; he pretended to be asleep. A little later, when he thought that the officer must have gone, he called his hostesses.

"That officer came to put my name on a list, and make

me a prisoner, didn't he?" The landlady assented with tears in her eyes.

"Very well, there is money in my dolman!" he cried, sitting up in bed; "buy me some civilian clothes and to-night I shall go away on my horse. You have already saved my life once by taking me in just as I was going to drop down dead in the street; save it again by giving me the means of going back to my mother."

At this point the landlady's daughters began to dissolve in tears; they trembled for Fabrizio; and, as they barely understood French, they came to his bedside to question him. They talked with their mother in Flemish; but at every moment pitying eyes were turned on our hero; he thought he could make out that his escape might compromise them seriously, but that they would gladly incur the risk. A Jew in the town supplied a complete outfit, but when he brought it to the inn about ten o'clock that night, the girls saw, on comparing it with Fabrizio's dolman, that it would require an endless amount of alteration. At once they set to work; there was no time to lose. Fabrizio showed them where several napoleons were hidden in his uniform, and begged his hostess to stitch them into the new garments. With these had come a fine pair of new boots. Fabrizio had no hesitation in asking these kind girls to slit open the hussar's boots at the place which he showed them, and they hid the little diamonds in the lining of the new pair.

One curious result of his loss of blood and the weakness that followed from it was that Fabrizio had almost completely forgotten his French; he used Italian to address his hostesses, who themselves spoke a Flemish dialect, so that their conversation had to be conducted almost entirely in signs. When the girls, who for that matter were entirely disinterested, saw the diamonds, their enthusiasm for Fabrizio knew no bounds; they imagined him to be a prince in disguise. Aniken, the younger and less sophisticated, kissed him without ceremony. Fabrizio, for his part, found them charming, and towards midnight, when the surgeon had allowed him a little wine in view of the journey he had to take, he felt himself almost inclined not to go. "Where could I be better off than here?" he asked himself. However, about two o'clock in the morning, he rose and dressed. As he was leaving the room, his good hostess informed him that his horse had been taken by the officer who had come to search the house that afternoon.

"Ah! The swine!" cried Fabrizio with an oath, "robbing

a wounded man!" He was not enough of a philosopher, this young Italian, to bear in mind the price at which he himself had acquired the horse.

Aniken told him with tears that they had hired a horse for him. She would have liked him not to go. Their farewells were tender. Two big lads, cousins of the good landlady, helped Fabrizio into the saddle: during the journey they supported him on his horse, while a third, who walked a few hundred yards in advance of the little convoy, searched the roads for any suspicious patrol. After going for a couple of hours, they stopped at the house of a cousin of the landlady of the Woolcomb. In spite of anything that Fabrizio might say, the young men who accompanied him refused absolutely to leave him; they claimed that they knew better than anyone the hidden paths through the woods.

"But to-morrow morning, when my flight becomes known, and they don't see you anywhere in the town, your absence will make things awkward for you," said Fabrizio.

They proceeded on their way. Fortunately, when day broke at last, the plain was covered by a thick fog. About eight o'clock in the morning they came in sight of a little town. One of the young men went on ahead to see if the post-horses there had been stolen. The postmaster had had time to make them vanish and to raise a team of wretched screws with which he had filled his stables. Grooms were sent to find a pair of horses in the marshes where they were hidden, and three hours later Fabrizio climbed into a little cabriolet which was quite dilapidated but had harnessed to it a pair of good post-horses. He had regained his strength. The moment of parting with the young men, his hostess's cousins, was pathetic in the extreme; on no account, whatever friendly pretext Fabrizio might find would they consent to take any money.

"In your condition, sir, you need it more than we do," was the invariable reply of these worthy young fellows. Finally they set off with letters in which Fabrizio, somewhat embolden by the agitation of the journey, had tried to convey to his hostesses all that he felt for them. Fabrizio wrote with tears in his eyes, and there was certainly love in the letter addressed to little Aniken.

In the rest of the journey there was nothing out of the common. He reached Amiens in great pain from the cut he had received in his thigh; it had not occurred to the country doctor to lance the wound, and in spite of the bleedings an abscess had formed. During the fortnight that Fabrizio spent in the inn at Amiens, kept by an obsequious and avaricious family, the Allies were invading France, and Fabrizio became another man, so many and profound were his reflections on the things that had happened to him. He had remained a child upon one point only: what he had seen, was it a battle; and, if so, was that battle Waterloo? For the first time in his life he found pleasure in reading; he was always hoping to find in the newspapers, or in the published accounts of the battle, some description which would enable him to identify the ground he had covered with Marshal Ney's escort, and afterwards with the other general. During his stay at Amiens he wrote almost every day to his good friends at the Woolcomb. As soon as his wound was healed, he came to Paris.

FALLING THROUGH SPACE

Richard Hillary

September 3rd dawned dark and overcast, with a slight breeze ruffling the waters of the Estuary. Hornchurch airdrome, twelve miles east of London, wore its usual morning pallor of yellow fog, lending an air of added grimness to the dim shapes of the Spitfires around the boundary. From time to time a balloon would poke its head grotesquely through the mist, as though looking for possible victims, before falling back like some tired monster.

We came out onto the tarmac at about eight o'clock. During the night our machines had been moved from the Dispersal Point over to the hangars. All the machine tools, oil, and general equipment had been left on the far side of the airdrome. I was worried. We had been bombed a short time before, and my plane had been fitted out with a brand-new cockpit hood. This hood unfortunately would not slide open along its groove; and with a depleted ground staff and no tools, I began to fear it never would. Unless it did open, I shouldn't be able to bail out in a hurry if I had to. Miraculously, "Uncle George" Denholm, our Squadron Leader, produced three men with a heavy file and lubricating oil, and the corporal-fitter and I set upon the hood in a fury of haste. We took it turn by turn, filing and oiling, oiling and filing, until at last the hood began to move. But agonisingly slowly: by ten o'clock, when the mist had cleared and the sun was blazing out of a clear sky, the hood was still sticking firmly half-way along the groove; at ten-fifteen, what I had feared for the last hour happened. Down the loud-speaker came the emotionless voice of the controller: "603 Squadron take off and patrol base; you will receive further orders in the air: 603 Squadron take off as quickly as you can, please." As I pressed the starter and the engine roared into life, the corporal stepped back and crossed his fingers significantly. I felt the usual sick feeing in the pit of the stomach, as though I were about to row a race, and then I was too busy getting into position to feel anything.

Uncle George and the leading section took off in a cloud of dust; Brian Carberry looked across and put up his thumbs.

From: *Falling Through Space*. Copyright 1942. By permission of Reynal & Hitchcock.

I nodded and opened up, to take off for the last time from Hornchurch. I was flying No. 3 in Brian's section, with Stapme Stapleton on the right: the third section consisted of only two machines, so that our Squadron strength was eight. We headed southeast, climbing all out on a steady course. At about 12,000 feet we came up through the clouds: I looked down and saw them spread out below me like layers of whipped cream. The sun was brilliant and made it difficult to see even the next plane when turning. I was peering anxiously ahead, for the controller had given us warning of at least fifty enemy fighters approaching very high. When we did first sight them, nobody shouted, as if we had all seen them at the same moment. They must have been 500 to 1,000 feet above us and coming straight on like a swarm of locusts. I remember cursing and going automatically into line astern: the next moment we were in among them and it was each man for himself. As soon as they saw us they spread out and dived, and the next ten minutes was a blur of twisting machines and tracer bullets. One Messerschmitt went down in a sheet of flame on my right, and a Spitfire hurtled past in a half-roll; I was weaving and turning in a desperate attempt to gain height, with the machine practically hanging on the airscrew. Then, just below me and to my left, I saw what I had been praying for—a Messerschmitt climbing and away from the sun. I closed in to 200 yards, and from slightly to one side gave him a two-second burst: fabric ripped off the wing and black smoke poured from the engine, but he did not go down. Like a fool, I did not break away, but put in another three-second burst. Red flames shot upwards and he spiralled out of sight. At that moment, I felt a terrific explosion which knocked the control stick from my hand, and the whole machine quivered like a stricken animal. In a second, the cockpit was a mass of flames: instinctively, I reached up to open the hood. It would not move. I tore off my straps and managed to force it back; but this took time, and when I dropped back into the seat and reached for the stick in an effort to turn the plane on its back, the heat was so intense that I could feel myself going. I remember a second of sharp agony, remember thinking, "So this is it!" and putting both my hands up to my eyes. Then I passed out.

When I regained consciousness I was free of the machine and falling rapidly. I pulled the rip-cord of my parachute and checked my descent with a jerk. Looking down, I saw that my left trouser leg was burnt off, that I was going to fall into the sea, and that the English coast was far away. About twenty feet above the water, I attempted to undo my parachute, failed, and flopped into the sea with it billowing round me. I was told later that the machine went into a spin at about 25,000 feet and that at 10,000 feet I fell out—unconscious. This may well have been so, for I discovered later a large cut on the top of my head, presumably collected while bumping round inside.

The water was not unwarm and I was pleasantly surprised to find that my life-jacket, my "Mae West" kept me afloat. I looked at my watch: it was not there. Then, for the first time, I noticed how burnt my hands were: down to the wrist, the skin was dead white and hung in shreds: I felt faintly sick from the smell of burnt flesh. By closing my eye, I could see my lips, jutting out like motor tyres. The side of my parachute harness was cutting into me particularly painfully, so that I guess my right hip was burnt. I made a further attempt to undo the harness, but owing to the pain of my hands, soon desisted. Instead, I lay back and reviewed my position. I was a long way from land; my hands were burnt, and so, judging from the pain of the sun, was my face; it was unlikely that a ship would come by; I could float for possibly four hours in my Mae West. I began to feel that I had perhaps been premature in considering myself lucky to have escaped from the machine. After about half an hour my teeth started chattering, and to quiet them I kept up a regular tuneless chant, varying it from time to time with calls for help. There can be few more futile pastimes than yelling for help alone in the North Sea, with a solitary seagull for company, yet it gave me a certain melancholy satisfaction, for I had once written a short story in which the hero, falling from a liner, had done just this. (It was rejected.)

The water now seemed much colder and I noticed with surprise that the sun had gone in though my face was still burning. I looked down at my hands, and not seeing them, realised that I had gone blind. So I was going to die. It came to me like that —I was going to die, and I was not afraid. This realisation came as a surprise. The manner of my approaching death appalled and horrified me, but the actual vision of death left me unafraid: I felt only a profound curiosity and a sense of satisfaction that within a few minutes or a few hours I was to learn the great answer. I decided that it should be in a few minutes. I had no qualms about hastening my end and reaching up, I managed to unscrew the valve of my Mae West. The air escaped in a rush and my head went under water. It is said by people who have all but died in the sea that drowning is a pleasant death. I did not find it so. I swallowed a large quantity of water before my head came up again, but derived little satisfaction from it. I tried again, to find that I could not move. For the next ten minutes, I tore my hands to ribbons on the spring-release catch. It was stuck fast. I lay back exhausted, and then I started to laugh. By this time I was probably not entirely normal and I doubt if my laughter was wholly sane, but there was something irresistibly comical in my grand gesture of suicide being so simply thwarted.

Goethe once wrote that no one, unless he had led the full life and realised himself, completely, had the right to take his own life. Providence seemed determined that I should not incur the great man's displeasure.

Another thing often said is that a dying man relives his whole life in one rapid kaleidoscope. I merely thought gloomily of the Squadron returning, of my mother at home, and of the few people who would miss me. Outside my family, I could count them on the fingers of one hand. What did gratify me enormously was to find that I indulged in no frantic abasements or prayers to the Almighty. It is an old jibe of God-fearing people that the irreligious always change their tune when about to die: I was pleased to think that I was proving them wrong. Because I seemed to be in for an indeterminate period of waiting, I began to feel a terrible loneliness and sought for some means to take my mind off my plight. I took it for granted that I must soon become delirious, and I attempted to hasten the process: I encouraged my mind to wander vaguely and aimlessly, with the result that I did experience a certain peace. But when I forced myself to think of something concrete, I found that I was still only too lucid. I went on shuttling between the two with varying success until I was picked up. I remember as in a dream hearing somebody shout: it seemed as far away and quite unconnected with me. . . .

Then willing arms were dragging me over the side; my parachute was taken off (and with such ease!); a brandy flask was pushed between my lips; a voice said, "O.K., Joe, it's one of ours and still kicking"; and I was safe. I was neither relieved nor angry: I was past caring.

It was to the Margate lifeboat that I owed my rescue. Watchers on the coast had seen me come down, and for three hours they had been searching for me. Owing to wrong directions, they were just giving up and turning back for land when ironically enough one of them saw my parachute. They were then fifteen miles east of Margate.

While in the water I had been numb and had felt little pain. Now that I began to thaw out, the agony was such that I could have cried out. The good fellows made me as comfortable as possible, put up some sort of awning to keep the sun from my face, and phoned through for a doctor. It seemed to me to take an eternity to reach shore. I was put into an ambulance and driven rapidly to a hospital. Through all this I was quite conscious, though unable to see. At the hospital they cut off my uniform, I gave the requisite information to a nurse about my next of kin, and then to my infinite relief, felt a hypodermic syringe pushed into my arm.

I can't help feeling that a good epitaph for me at that moment would have been four lines of Verlaine:

> *Quoique sans patrie et sans roi,*
> *Et très brave ne l'étant guère,*
> *J'ai voulu mourir à la guerre.*
> *La mort n'a pas voulu de moi.*

A man who has been rejected by death is easily tempted to take up the pen.

THE END

ACKNOWLEDGEMENTS

The Editor gratefully acknowledges permission to reprint copyright material to the following:

The Executors of the late Winston S. Churchill and Odhams Books Ltd. for THE CAVALRY CHARGE AT OMDURMAN from *My Early Life*.

The Executors of the late Richard Hillary and Macmillan & Co. Ltd. for THE INVADERS and FALLING THROUGH SPACE from *The Last Enemy*.

The Executors of the late Ernest Hemingway and Jonathan Cape Ltd. for THE FIGHT ON THE HILLTOP and THE RETREAT FROM CAPORETTO from *For Whom the Bell Tolls* and *A Farewell to Arms*.

Madame Catherine Guillaume for AT ALL COSTS from *Roads to Glory* by Richard Aldington.

Leonard Ehrlich and Simon & Schuster for HARPER'S FERRY from *God's Angry Man*.

The executors of the late C. S. Forester and A. D. Peters & Co. for AN EGG FOR THE MAJOR.

Alan Moorehead and The Daily Express for TANK FIGHTING IN LIBYA.

T. E. Lawrence and Jonathan Cape Ltd. for BLOWING UP A TRAIN from *The Seven Pillars of Wisdom*.

Marquis James and The Bobbs-Merrill Co. Inc. for THE STOLEN RAILROAD TRAIN from *They Had Their Hour*.

The Executors of the late William Faulkner and Chatto & Windus Ltd. for TURN ABOUT from *Collected Stories*.

The Executors of the late Charles Nordhoff and of the late James Norman Hall for AIR BATTLE from *Falcons of France*.

David Divine and The Reader's Digest Association, Pleasantville, New York, for MIRACLE AT DUNKIRK.

Peter Davies Ltd. for HER PRIVATES WE by Frederic Manning.

Mrs. Frank Richards and Faber & Faber Ltd. for THE BATTLE OF YPRES from *Old Soldiers Never Die*.

Mrs. George Bambridge and Macmillan & Co. Ltd. for THE TAKING OF LUNGTUNGPEN from *Soldiers Three*, by Rudyard Kipling.

Byron Kennerly for SQUADRON SCRAMBLE! from *The Eagle's Roar*.

Famous War Books in Fontana

The Battle of Britain   Basil Collier
'A clear, authoritative, round-by-round account of this desperate, chancy slogging match' *Spectator*. 'Basil Collier describes it all with fluent enthusiasm and a keen eye for the shape of the battle.' *Tribune*

The First and the Last   Adolf Galland
The rise and fall of the Luftwaffe—by Germany's greatest fighter pilot. 'Some of his air-battles read almost as fast as the Messerschmitts he flew, and his staff-battle accounts give the clearest picture yet of how the Germans lost their war in the air.' *Time Magazine*

Winged Dagger   Roy Farran
The thrilling account of Captain Farran's amazing career in the Special Air Service during World War II. 'Strongly recommended.' *Evening Standard*

Malta Convoy   Peter Shankland and Anthony Hunter
The story of the *Ohio*—the only tanker fast enough to run the murderous Nazi blockades. Malta's sole hope of survival, she carried in her straining holds the fate of the war itself.

Sinister Twilight   Noel Barber
The fall of Singapore. 'A penetrating account of one of the most momentous turning points of our century.' *Sunday Express* 'An entirely fresh light on what was regarded as a scandalous betrayal . . . so freshly and readably different.' *Evening News*

Escape Alone   David Howarth
Occupied Norway 1943—and eighty miles of unmapped mountain peaks lay between Jan Baalsrud and safety. 'One of the most remarkable survival stories ever.' *Guardian*

Dawn of D-Day   David Howarth
The invasion of Normandy—and the men who were there. 'The shocks, the mistakes, the courage and glory . . . brilliantly put across.' *Punch*

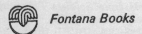 *Fontana Books*